Project Maths

Text & Tests **1**

Common Introductory Course for First-Year Maths

O. D. Morris · Paul Cooke · Paul Behan

 The Celtic Press

Acknowledgements
We would like to express our deep gratitude to the UK Mathematics Trust (www.ukmt.org.uk) for permission to reproduce Junior Maths Challenge questions.

First published in 2011 by
The Celtic Press
Educational Publishers,
Goldenbridge, Dublin 8.

ISBN: 978-1-907705-12-0

Design: Identikit Design
Layout and artwork: Tech-Set Limited

Printed and bound in Ireland by
Colour Books Limited,
Baldoyle,
Dublin 13.

Contents

Preface

Text and Tests 1 was compiled and written for **Project Maths – Common Introductory Course** for first-year students. It provides a comprehensive and solid basis for the further study of mathematics at second-level. The book incorporates the recommendations made in the **Bridging Framework for Mathematics** for the continuation of the teaching methods pupils experienced in sixth class of primary school. The book reflects the overall approach to the teaching of mathematics as envisaged in **Project Maths**. It encourages not only the development of the students' mathematical knowledge and skills but also the understanding needed for continuing their learning of mathematics.

There is an excellent range of imaginatively-written and probing questions on each topic which will help students to understand what they are doing and to develop their problem-solving skills. A sufficient number of questions in varying degrees of difficulty have been provided to satisfy the needs of almost all first-year students. Students are introduced to new topics in a way that is appropriate for mixed-ability first-year classes. This avoids the difficulties involved in taking any topic all the way to Junior Certificate examination standard in first-year.

The motivating and stimulating full-colour design, together with the large number of well-constructed diagrams, should help the student's understanding of the topic being studied. At the beginning of each chapter there is a list of **Key Words** that students are expected to know and understand when the chapter is completed. Each chapter includes a blue-coloured **Test Yourself** section which provides comprehensive consolidation and revision. At the end of each chapter there is a **For the problem-solver** page where students encounter the type of question that will introduce them to problem-solving. These questions are particularly suitable for the student who likes a challenge and enjoys the exploration of numbers.

Finally we would like to wish all first-year students a happy experience in their learning of mathematics at second-level.

O.D. Morris
Paul Cooke
Paul Behan

March 2011

Chapter 1

Natural Numbers

Key words

natural numbers   odd   even   consecutive   number line   place-value
numerals   factor   divisor   prime number   highest common factor (HCF)
lowest common multiple (LCM)   squares   square root   commutative
associative   rounding   significant figures   distributive

Section 1.1 Natural numbers

The counting numbers 1, 2, 3, 4, 5, … are generally called **natural numbers**.

We use the capital letter **N** to represent these numbers.

Thus N = 1, 2, 3, 4, 5, 6, …

> Zero is not a natural number.

These numbers go on and on …; there is no end number.

Natural numbers can be divided into two groups, namely **even** numbers and **odd** numbers.

2, 4, 6, 8, 10, …   are the **even** natural numbers because they can be divided by 2 with no remainder.

1, 3, 5, 7, 9, …   are the **odd** natural numbers.

Tuesday, Wednesday and Thursday are **consecutive** days of the week.

Similarly 6, 7, 8, 9 are consecutive natural numbers,
while 2, 4, 6, 8, … are consecutive even natural numbers.

The Number Line

A very useful and simple way of depicting natural numbers is to place them at equal distances apart on a horizontal line as illustrated below:

The dots on the line represent the numbers 1, 2, 3, 4, …, while the arrow to the right indicates that the line continues on without ending.

Place value

The symbols 2, 3, 5, 8 etc, that we use to represent numbers, are called **numerals**.

In our number system we can write any number, large or small, using the ten numerals 0, 1, 2, 3, 4, 5, 6, 7, 8, 9.

The big advantage of the system is that the same numeral may have different values depending on the place it occupies in the number.

The place-value diagram below shows the numbers 368 and 26 427.

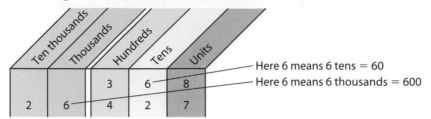

Here 6 means 6 tens = 60
Here 6 means 6 thousands = 600

The numeral 6 has a different value in each of the numbers as shown above.

Example 1

Find the difference between the largest and smallest numbers that can be made from the digits, 3, 7, 4, 9 if each is used once only in the number.

The largest number is 9743.
The smallest number is 3479.

The difference is
$$\begin{array}{r} 9\ 7\ 4\ 3 \\ -\ 3\ 4\ 7\ 9 \\ \hline 6\ 2\ 6\ 4 \end{array}$$

∴ the difference is 6264.

Exercise 1.1

1. Say whether each of the following is true or false.
   (i) 3 is a natural number   (ii) $4\frac{1}{2}$ is a natural number
   (iii) -2 is a natural number   (iv) 101 is a natural number
   (v) The smallest natural number is 2.

2. List the numbers in each of the following:
   (i) the even natural numbers between 7 and 15
   (ii) the odd natural numbers less than 12
   (iii) the first four natural numbers
   (iv) four consecutive natural numbers beginning with 7
   (v) five consecutive odd natural numbers beginning with 5.

3. Describe in words each of the following arrays of numbers:
   (i) 1, 2, 3, 4, 5   (ii) 1, 3, 5, 7, 9, ...   (iii) 2, 4, 6
   (iv) 6, 8, 10, 12, ...   (v) 9, 11, 13, 15, ...   (vi) 101, 102, 103, ...

4. Write down the value of the red digit in each of these numbers:
   (i) 38**4**   (ii) **4**96   (iii) 6**2**49   (iv) **4**792   (v) 134**9**

5. Write down the three numbers shown in the diagram below.

Start at the top.

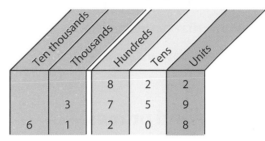

6. Write down
   (i)   a four-digit number with a 4 in the thousands column.
   (ii) a two-digit number with a 3 in the tens column.
   (iii) a five-digit number with a 1 in the hundreds column.
   (iv) a three-digit number with a 9 in the units column.
   (v)   a four-digit number with a 0 in the tens column.
   (vi) a five-digit number with a 4 in the hundreds column.
   (vii) a four-digit number with a 7 in every column except the tens column.
   (viii) a five-digit number with a 6 in the thousands column and the units column.

7. Using all the digits 4, 3, 1, 7 what is
   (i)   the largest   (ii)   the smallest four-digit number that can be formed from them?

8. What is the difference between the values of the two fours in the number 34746?

9. What is the sum of the values of the threes in the number 34353?

10. What is the difference between the largest and smallest four-digit numbers that can be formed using the digits 2, 9, 3, 5?

11. Write down each of these numbers:
   (i)   seven hundred and nine
   (ii) two thousand, three hundred and nine
   (iii) six thousand and four
   (iv) twenty thousand, four hundred and two
   (v)   ninety thousand and ninety
   (vi) three hundred and two thousand and forty five
   (vii) one million and thirty thousand

12. Write these numbers in order, starting with the smallest:
     3297   2988   3079   3190   931   3098

13. Write the next car registration number for each of these:

    (i) 10 D 799   (ii) 11 KE 1019   (iii) 12 KY 7999

14. By placing all these cards in a line, ⌷3⌷ ⌷8⌷ ⌷2⌷ ⌷2⌷ ⌷1⌷ ⌷6⌷ , write down

    (i) the largest number that can be made

    (ii) the smallest number that can be made.

Section 1.2 Factors and primes

Discovery

There are 20 sweets in a jar.

    (i) Can the sweets be shared equally between three people?

    (ii) Write down all the numbers of people between whom the sweets can be shared equally.

         How many do they each receive?

In the problem above you were looking for the numbers that divide evenly into 20.

These numbers are 1, 2, 4, 5, 10, 20.

Each of these numbers is a **factor** or **divisor** of 20.

By this we mean that each number divides into 20 with no remainder.

When asked for the factors of 24 we can give more than one answer.
For example, 24 = 24 × 1 or 12 × 2 or 8 × 3 or 6 × 4.

Each of these is called a **pair of factors** of 24.
Thus all the numbers 1, 2, 3, 4, 6, 8, 12 and 24 are *factors* or *divisors* of 24.

Similarly, the divisors of 18 are 1, 2, 3, 6, 9, 18.

Notice that 1 is a factor of every number and every number is a factor of itself.

Highest common factor

The factors of 16 are: 1, 2, 4, **8**, 16.

The factors of 24 are: 1, 2, 3, 4, 6, **8**, 12, 24.

In the above lists, the highest factor common to both is 8.
8 is called the **highest common factor** (or divisor) and is denoted by **HCF**.

Example 1

Find the highest common factor of 36 and 54.

The factors of 36 = {1, 2, 3, 4, 6, 9, 12, **18**, 36}

The factors of 54 = {1, 2, 3, 6, 9, **18**, 27, 54}

The highest common factor = 18.

Prime numbers

The factors of 4 are 1, 2, 4.

The factors of 5 are 1, 5.

The factors of 7 are 1, 7.

Notice that the numbers 5 and 7 have two factors only, i.e., the number itself and 1. Numbers which have 2 factors only are called **prime** numbers.

The first five prime numbers are

   2, 3, 5, 7, 11

> A prime number is a number with 2 factors only.

Note that 1 is not a prime number and that 2 is the only even prime number.

Expressing a number as a product of prime factors

$12 = 4 \times 3$	$18 = 9 \times 2$	$36 = 9 \times 4$
$= 2 \times 2 \times 3$	$= 3 \times 3 \times 2$	$= 3 \times 3 \times 2 \times 2$

Each of the numbers above is expressed as a product of prime numbers.

Thus $12 = 2 \times 2 \times 3$ is expressed as a product of its **prime factors**.

Example 2

Find the prime factors of
(i) 28   (ii) 60

$28 = 4 \times 7$
    $= 2 \times 2 \times 7$

$60 = 30 \times 2$
    $= 15 \times 2 \times 2$
    $= 3 \times 5 \times 2 \times 2$
    $= 2 \times 2 \times 3 \times 5$

Exercise 1.2

1. Say whether each of the following statements is true or false.
   If the statement is true, write the result as a multiplication.
   The first one is done for you.
   (i)   4 is a factor of 20   True, $4 \times 5 = 20$ (ii)   8 is a factor of 12
   (iii)   9 is a factor of 18   (iv)   5 is a factor of 35
   (v)   11 is a factor of 34   (vi)   12 is a factor of 60
   (vii) 16 is a factor of 30   (viii) 16 is a factor of 48

2. 3×4, 6×2 and 12×1 are pairs of factors of 12.
   Write out all the pairs of factors of these numbers.
   (i) 18   (ii) 30   (iii) 36   (iv) 40

3. Which of the numbers 1, 2, 4, 5, 7 is not a factor of 28?

4. List all the factors of each of these numbers:
   (i) 6   (ii) 8   (iii) 15   (iv) 24
   (v) 28   (vi) 35   (vii) 84   (viii) 108

5. Show that the factors of 28 (excluding 28 itself) add up to 28.

6. Is 3 a factor of these numbers?
   (i) 36   (ii) 56   (iii) 141   (iv) 285

   Notice that the sum of the digits in each number that has 3 as a factor is also divisible by 3.
   Investigate if this applies to other numbers that have 3 as a factor.

7. Is 7 a factor of these numbers?
   (i) 49   (ii) 63   (iii) 74   (iv) 252

8. (i) Write down all the factors of 18.
   (ii) Write down all the factors of 24.
   (iii) Write down the factors that are common to 18 and 24.
   (iv) What is the highest common factor of 18 and 24.

9. Find the highest common factor of each of these sets of numbers.
   (i)   15, 25   (ii) 14, 49   (iii) 28, 42
   (iv) 42, 70   (v) 36, 63   (vi) 45, 72

10. Find the highest common factor of each of these sets of numbers.
    (i) 18, 27, 36   (ii) 14, 28, 42   (iii) 39, 52, 78

11. (i) Write down the first eight prime numbers.
    (ii) Explain why there is only one even prime number.

12. Write 26 as the sum of two primes in three different ways.

13. Which of these numbers are prime?
(i) 7   (ii) 19   (iii) 26   (iv) 31   (v) 39

14. Continue the sequence 6, 12, 18, … as far as 48.
Now write down the numbers which are one smaller and one larger than this sequence, i.e., 5, 7, 11, … 49.
Which of these numbers are **not** prime?

15. Write down the number 30 as
(i) the sum of 3 prime numbers
(ii) the product of 3 prime numbers.

16. Are the following statements true or false? If false, say why.
(i) All prime numbers are odd numbers.
(ii) The only even prime number is 2.
(iii) All odd numbers are prime numbers.
(iv) There are only three prime numbers between 10 and 20.

17. Write down all the factors of 48.
How many of these factors are prime?

18. Write three 2-digit prime numbers which, when their digits are reversed, are also prime. (exclude 11.)

19. Write down the prime factors of each of these numbers:
(i) 12   (ii) 30   (iii) 45   (iv) 84   (v) 108

20. Find a pair of prime numbers that total each of these numbers:
(i) 12   (ii) 16   (iii) 24   (iv) 32

21. Twin primes are prime numbers with a difference of 2. The first pair of twin primes is 3 and 5. What are the next three pairs of twin primes?

22. Think of a number between 1 and 13.
Multiply it by one less than the number you have chosen and then add 41.
Do this a few times. Comment on your answers.

23. Find two prime numbers with a sum of 46 and a difference of 12.

24. Look at the numbers 3, 4, 5, 9, 10, 12, 15, 18, 30.
(i) Which numbers are prime?
(ii) Which numbers are factors of 30?
(iii) Which numbers have 6 as a factor?
(iv) How many of the numbers are divisible by 5?

Section 1.3 Multiples – Lowest common multiple

The multiples of 3 are 3, 6, 9, 12, 15, 18, **21**, 24, …

The multiples of 7 are 7, 14, **21**, 28, 35, …

Notice that **21** is the smallest number common to both sets of multiples.

21 is called the lowest common multiple (LCM) of 3 and 7.

Lowest Common Multiple

> The lowest common multiple (LCM) of two or more numbers is the smallest number into which each of the numbers divide.

Example 1

Find the lowest common multiple of 8, 12, 18.

The multiples of 8 are: 8, 16, 24, 32, 40, 48, 56, 64, **72**, …

The multiples of 12 are: 12, 24, 36, 48, 60, **72**, 84, …

The multiples of 18 are: 18, 36, 54, **72**, …

The lowest common multiple (LCM) = 72.

Exercise 1.3

1. The red dots on the number line show the first six multiples of 3.

   ```
   0  1  2  3  4  5  6  7  8  9  10 11 12 13 14 15 16 17 18 19 20 21 22 23 24 25
   ```

   (i)   What is the difference between any multiple of 3 and the next multiple?

   (ii) What are the next two multiples of 3 after 18?

   (iii) What is the 9th multiple of 3?

   (iv) What is the hundredth multiple of 3?

2. (i)   Write out the first six multiples of 7.

   (ii) Is 98 a multiple of 7?

   (iii) 140 is a multiple of 7. Work out the next two multiples of 7.

3. Write out all the multiples of 9 that are less than 80.

4. (i)   Write out the first six multiples of 4.

   (ii) Write out the first six multiples of 6.

   (iii) Which of the numbers are common multiples of 4 and 6?

   (iv) What is the lowest common multiple of 4 and 6?

5. Find the lowest common multiple of each of these pairs of numbers.
   (i) 2, 5   (ii) 6, 8   (iii) 4, 7   (iv) 10, 12   (v) 7, 8

6. Find the LCM of each set of numbers.
   (i) 2, 4, 8   (ii) 3, 4, 6   (iii) 3, 5, 10   (iv) 6, 8, 12

7. (i) The lowest common multiple of two numbers is 24.
       What could these numbers be?
   (ii) Find three numbers whose lowest common multiple is 24.

8. Find three numbers whose lowest common multiple is
   (i) 36   (ii) 45.

9. Jenny is buying food for a barbecue. Burgers are sold in packs of 6 and buns are sold in packs of 8. What is the least number of packs of burgers and buns Jenny should buy so that there is one bun for each burger?

10. The machine below accepts two different inputs. It compares the multiples of each number and outputs the LCM.

   (i)   Copy and complete this machine with inputs of 12 and 15.
   (ii) What are the possible inputs if the output is 12?
   (iii) What are the possible inputs if the output is 42?

11. Describe each of the following statements as *true* or *false*.
    (i)   Any multiple of 6 is also a multiple of 3.
    (ii) Any multiple of 5 is also a multiple of 10.
    (iii) The LCM of 6 and 8 is 48.
    (iv) You always get a common multiple of a pair of numbers by multiplying them together.

12. (i) Copy the diagram.
        Write down the first nine multiples of 9 in line 1 and the first nine multiples of 5 in line 2.
    (ii) Line 3 is the difference between each term in lines 1 and 2, and line 4 is the sum. Complete lines 3 and 4 and describe them in words.

line 1	9								81
line 2	5								45
line 3	4								36
line 4	14								126

    (iii) Line 5 is the difference between line 4 and line 3. Describe line 5.

13. One light flashes every 25 seconds. Another light flashes every 30 seconds.
At a certain time they flash together.
How many seconds will it be before they flash together again?

Section 1.4 Squares and square roots

A short way of writing 3×3 is 3^2. It is pronounced *three squared*.
The small 2 is called the **index** or **power**.

Similarly   (i) $2 \times 2 \times 2 = 2^3$ ... pronounced *two cubed*.
          (ii) $3 \times 3 \times 3 \times 3 = 3^4$

The number 3^4 is said to be written in *index form*.

To find the value of 2×5^2, we square the 5 first and then multiply the result by 2.
     i.e. $2 \times 5^2 = 2 \times 25 = 50$

Similarly   (i) $3 \times 4^2 = 3 \times 16 = 48$
          (ii) $3^2 \times 5 = 9 \times 5 = 45$
          (iii) $2^2 + 3^3 = (2 \times 2) + (3 \times 3 \times 3)$
                 $= 4 + 27 = 31$

> Always work out
> the powers first.

> ### Example 1
>
> Find the value of each of the following:
>   (i) 4^3 (ii) $4^2 - 3^2$ (iii) 3×4^2 (iv) half of 8^2
>
>   (i) $4^3 = 4 \times 4 \times 4$ (ii) $4^2 - 3^2 = 16 - 9$
> $= 64$ $= 7$
>
>   (iii) $3 \times 4^2 = 3 \times 16$ (iv) half of $8^2 = \frac{1}{2}$ of 64
> $= 48$ $= 32$

The square root

$\sqrt{16}$ is read as 'the square root of 16'.

To find $\sqrt{16}$ we look for the number which, when multiplied by itself, gives 16.

This number is 4, i.e., $\sqrt{16} = 4$.

Similarly, $\sqrt{25} = 5$, since $5 \times 5 = 25$.

For harder square roots you will need your calculator.

Look for $\boxed{\sqrt{}}$ button to find the square root of a number.

To find $\sqrt{289}$, key in $\boxed{\sqrt{}}$ $\boxed{2}$ $\boxed{8}$ $\boxed{9}$ $\boxed{=}$.

The answer is 17.

Example 2

Find the value of each of these:

(i) $\sqrt{64} + 2^3$ (ii) $3 \times 2^2 +$ twice $\sqrt{81}$

(i) $\sqrt{64} + 2^3 = 8 + 8$ (ii) $3 \times 2^2 +$ twice $\sqrt{81}$
$\qquad\qquad = 16$ $\qquad\qquad = 3 \times 4 +$ twice 9
$\qquad\qquad\qquad\qquad\qquad\qquad\qquad\qquad = 12 + 18$
$\qquad\qquad\qquad\qquad\qquad\qquad\qquad\qquad = 30$

Exercise 1.4

1. Work out each of these:

(i) 4^2 (ii) 6^2 (iii) 12^2 (iv) 14^2
(v) $3^2 + 4^2$ (vi) $2^2 + 7^2$ (vii) $9^2 + 5^2$ (viii) $10^2 - 8^2$

2. Find the value of each of these:

(i) 4×2^2 (ii) 8×3^2 (iii) $10^2 \times 4$ (iv) twice 7^2
(v) half of 8^2 (vi) $6^2 \div 4$ (vii) $9^2 \div 3$ (viii) $12^2 - 6^2 - 4^2$

3. Work out each of these:

(i) $2^2 \times 3^2$ (ii) $5^2 + 4^2$ (iii) $8^2 - 7^2$ (iv) half $10^2 - 4^2$

4. The numbers 1, 4, 9, 16, 25, ... are called **square numbers**.
Write down the next four square numbers after 25.

5. Find a square number between each of these pairs of numbers:
   (i) 12, 17   (ii) 30, 40   (iii) 75, 84   (iv) 105 and 130

6. (i) Write two consecutive odd numbers, multiply them together, then add 1.
         Repeat the process several times.
         What do you notice about your final answers?
     (ii) What happens if you use consecutive even numbers instead?

7. Write each of the following as a single number to a power, e.g., 3^4:
   (i) $2 \times 2 \times 2$ (ii) $3 \times 3 \times 3$
   (iii) $6 \times 6 \times 6 \times 6$ (iv) 2×2^4

8. Investigate if each of these is true or false:
   (i) $3^2 \times 4^2 = 12^2$ (ii) $(2 \times 5)^2 = 2^2 \times 5^2$ (iii) $3^2 + 4^2 = (3 + 4)^2$.

9. Express each of these as a single number to a power:
   (i) 16   (ii) 8   (iii) 27   (iv) 1000   (v) 125   (vi) 121

10. Write down the answer to each of these square roots:
   (i) $\sqrt{9}$ (ii) $\sqrt{25}$ (iii) $\sqrt{64}$ (iv) $\sqrt{144}$ (v) $\sqrt{400}$.

11. Find the missing number in each of the following:
   (i) The square root of 49 is $\square$.   (ii) The square root of $\square$ is 9.
   (iii) 12 is the square root of $\square$.   (iv) The square of 9 is $\square$.
   (v) $\square$ is the square of 8.   (vi) $\square$ is the square root of 1.

12. Write as a single number each of these:
   (i) $\dfrac{10^3}{\sqrt{100}}$ (ii) $\sqrt{81} + 3^2$ (iii) $\dfrac{\sqrt{100}}{5}$ (iv) $\dfrac{3^2 \times \sqrt{81}}{3^3}$.

13. Which is bigger   (i) the sum of the squares of 3 and 5
       or   (ii) the square of the sum of 3 and 5?

14. Which is bigger   (i) the square root of the sum of 9 and 16
       or   (ii) the sum of the square roots of 9 and 16?

15. $2^2 = 4$. This can be written as the sum of two prime numbers: $2 + 2 = 4$
     $3^2 = 9$. This can be written as the sum of two prime numbers: $2 + 7 = 9$
     Now write (i) 4^2 (ii) 6^2 (iii) 7^2 (iv) 10^2
     as the sum of two prime numbers.

16. Copy and complete using consecutive whole numbers:

    (i) $\square < \sqrt{5} < \square$ (ii) $\square < \sqrt{30} < \square$ (iii) $\square < \sqrt{46} < \square$

17. Use the $\boxed{\sqrt{}}$ button on your calculator to find each of these:

    (i) $\sqrt{169}$ (ii) $\sqrt{225}$ (iii) $\sqrt{441}$ (iv) $\sqrt{676}$ (v) $\sqrt{961}$

18. Find the value of n such that each of the following is true:

    (i) $4^n = 16$ (ii) $2^n = 8$ (iii) $8^n = 64$ (iv) $2^n = 16$

19. Copy and complete these.

    (i) Describe the pattern in the numbers in the left-hand column.

    (ii) What happens to the powers of 10 as the starting numbers increase?

$$10 = 10^1$$
$$100 = 10 \times 10 = 10^2$$
$$1000 = \square \times \square \times \square = 10^{\square}$$
$$10\,000 = \square \times \square \times \square \times \square = \square^{\square}$$
$$100\,000 = \square \times \square \times \square \times \square \times \square = \square^{\square}$$
$$1\,000\,000 = \square^{\square}$$

Section 1.5 Order of operations

When a calculation involves addition and subtraction, you can work from left to right to find the answer.

For example,   (i) $3 + 4 + 8 = 7 + 8$ (ii) $14 - 5 - 3 = 9 - 3$
                             $= 15$ $= 6$

Multiplication and division are equally important operations.

When calculations involve just $\times$ or $\div$, you work from left to right to find the answers.

    (i) $3 \times 4 \times 6 = 12 \times 6$ (ii) $36 \div 6 \div 3 = 6 \div 3$
                 $= 72$ $= 2$

    (iii) $18 \times 4 \div 6 = 72 \div 6$ (iv) $54 \div 9 \times 3 = 6 \times 3$
                 $= 12$ $= 18$

Multiplication and division are more important operations than addition and subtraction, so you must do these first.

Work out $\left(\;\times\;\;\div\;\right)$ before $\left(\;+\;\;-\;\right)$

    (i) $4 + 5 \times 6 = 4 + 30$ (ii) $18 - 14 \div 2 = 18 - 7$
                 $= 34$ $= 11$

    (iii) $10 + 6 - 4 \times 2 = 10 + 6 - 8$ (iv) $7 \times 4 + 35 \div 7 = 28 + 5$
                      $= 16 - 8$ $= 33$
                      $= 8$

Powers and roots are more important operations than multiplication and division. They must be done first.

Work out before (× ÷) and then do (+ −)

(i) $24 - \sqrt{25} + 3^2$

$= 24 - 5 + 9$

$= 19 + 9$

$= 28$

(ii) $63 \div 9 + \sqrt{36}$

$= 63 \div 9 + 6$

$= 7 + 6$

$= 13$

If there are **brackets** in a calculation, do the calculation inside them first.

When a calculation involves brackets as well as other operations, this is the correct order to work out the answers.

First	Second	Third	Fourth
( )	$\Box^2$ or $\boxed{\sqrt{}}$	× or ÷	+ or −

B – brackets
I – indices (powers)
M – multiplication
D – division
A – addition
S – subtraction

Example 1

Work out   (i) $12 + 8 \div 2 + 4 \times 3$ (ii) $7 \times 8 - 3 - (72 \div 8)$

(i) $12 + 8 \div 2 + 4 \times 3$

$= 12 + 4 + 12$

$= 28$

(ii) $7 \times 8 - 3 - (72 \div 8)$

$= 7 \times 8 - 3 - (9)$

$= 56 - 3 - 9$

$= 53 - 9$

$= 44$

Note: A horizontal line is the same as the ÷ symbol.

For example,   (i) $\dfrac{15}{3} = 15 \div 3 = 5$ (ii) $\dfrac{20 \div 5}{2} = \dfrac{4}{2} = 2$

Exercise 1.5

Work out numbers (1–15).

1. $5 + 3 \times 4$

2. $6 \times 2 + 5$

3. $9 \times 4 - 8$

4. $22 - 5 \times 4$

5. $18 \div 3 + 7$

6. $16 - 4 + 3 \times 9$

7. $5 + 16 \times 2 - 8$

8. $25 - 16 \div 4$

9. $5 \times 7 - 27 \div 3$

10. $6 \times 3 + 36 \div 4$

11. $5 \times 8 - 6 + 36 \div 3$

12. $15 - 10 \div 2 + 8$

13. $9 - 6 \div 2 + 5 \times 4$

14. $9 \times 6 - 27 \div 3$

15. $34 - 8 + 54 \div 9$

16. Copy and complete these calculations.
Each ☐ stands for an operation $(+, -, \times, \text{ or } \div)$.
(i) $5 \boxed{} 7 \times 2 = 19$
(ii) $21 \boxed{} 3 + 11 = 18$
(iii) $18 + 6 \boxed{} 2 = 21$
(iv) $12 \boxed{} 2 \times 5 = 22$
(v) $15 \boxed{} 2 - 11 = 19$
(vi) $24 \boxed{} 8 \boxed{} 5 = 15$

17. Work out each of these:
(i) $4 \times (5 + 6)$
(ii) $7 \times (12 - 8)$
(iii) $9 \times (7 - 1)$
(iv) $(14 - 3) \times 2$
(v) $(6 - 3) \times 4$
(vi) $48 - 3 \times (9 - 3)$
(vii) $(36 - 12) \div 3 + 9$
(viii) $25 \div (8 - 3) - 2$
(ix) $5 \times 4 + 3 \times (10 - 4)$

18. Find the value of each of these:
(i) $15 - 10 \div 2 + 6 \times 4$
(ii) $5 \times 8 - 3 \times (7 - 4)$
(iii) $15 \div (7 - 4) + 12$
(iv) $(16 + 4) \div 5 + 14 \times 2$
(v) $2 \times (7 - 4) + 28 \div 7$
(vi) $(10 \times 3 - 20) \times 5$

19. Work out each of these:
(i) $\dfrac{22 + 13}{7}$
(ii) $\dfrac{5 + 9 - 2}{6}$
(iii) $\dfrac{100}{2 \times 5}$
(iv) $\dfrac{7 + 9}{10 - 6}$
(v) $26 - \dfrac{15}{3}$
(vi) $\dfrac{6 + 8 \times 3}{5}$

20. Find the value of each of these:
(i) $4 + 5^2$
(ii) $128 - 8^2$
(iii) $4 + 2 \times 3^2$
(iv) $2 \times \sqrt{25} + 4^2$
(v) $6 \times 3^2 - \sqrt{16}$
(vi) $2 \times 5^2 \div 10$

21. Work out each of these:
(i) $(3 + 5) \times 2 - 3^2$
(ii) $\sqrt{16} + 5 \times 2^2$
(iii) $4 \times \sqrt{9} + 6^2$
(iv) $4 \times 3^2 + 8 \div 4$
(v) $5^2 \times 2^2 - 8$
(vi) $2^2 + \sqrt{16} + 5^2$

22. Find the value of each of these:
(i) $\dfrac{8^2}{\sqrt{64}}$
(ii) $\dfrac{\sqrt{81} + 5}{4 \times 4 - 2}$
(iii) $\dfrac{2^2 \times \sqrt{100}}{4 \times (6 - 1)}$

23. Work out each of these:
(i) $3 + 5 \times 2^2 - 6 \times 3$
(ii) $(3 + 4)^2 - 2 \times 3^2$

24. Copy these statements and write in brackets to make them true.
(i) $5 \times 4 + 3 = 35$
(ii) $20 - 3 + 8 = 9$
(iii) $8 + 10 \div 2 = 9$
(iv) $48 \div 16 - 4 = 4$
(v) $11 - 6 \times 2 = 10$
(vi) $5 + 3 \times 4 - 2 = 30$

25. Which of the following has the greatest value? Find this value.
A: $(1 \times 2) \times (3 \times 4)$
B: $(1 \times 2) + (3 \times 4)$
C: $(1 \times 2) \times (3 + 4)$
D: $(1 + 2) \times (3 \times 4)$
E: $(1 + 2) \times (3 + 4)$

26. Which **one** of these calculations is **incorrect**?

A: $4 \times 5 + 67 = 45 + 6 \times 7$

B: $3 \times 7 + 48 = 37 + 4 \times 8$

C: $6 \times 3 + 85 = 63 + 8 \times 5$

D: $2 \times 5 + 69 = 25 + 6 \times 9$

E: $9 \times 6 + 73 = 96 + 7 \times 3.$

27. Which one of these calculations is incorrect?

(i) $(20 - 15)^2 - 10 \div 5 = 3$ (ii) $(20 - 15)^2 - 10 \div 5 = 23$

Section 1.6 Working with natural numbers ─────────

While calculators are now widely used, it is still important to be able to perform the basic operations on numbers without their use.

Here are examples of long multiplication and division.

(i) 134×29

$$
\begin{array}{r}
134 \times 29 \\
29 \\
\hline
1206 \dots (134 \times 9) \\
2680 \dots (134 \times 20) \\
\hline
3886
\end{array}
$$

Answer $= 3886$

(ii) $3672 \div 27$

$$
\begin{array}{r}
136 \\
27\overline{)3672} \\
\underline{27} \\
97 \\
\underline{81} \\
162 \\
\underline{162}
\end{array}
$$

Answer $= 136$

Properties of natural numbers ─────────────────

1. **Commutative property**

   $3 + 5 = 5 + 3$ shows that we can change the order in which two numbers are added without changing the result.

   Similarly, $7 \times 8 = 8 \times 7$.

   The examples above illustrate a very important property in mathematics, namely, addition and multiplication are **commutative**.

   However subtraction and division are not commutative as illustrated by the following examples.

   (i) $12 - 8 = 4$ but $8 - 12 = -4$

       $\therefore$ $12 - 8 \neq 8 - 12$

   (ii) $6 \div 2 = 3$ but $2 \div 6 = \frac{2}{6} = \frac{1}{3}$

       $\therefore$ $6 \div 2 \neq 2 \div 6$

   > Addition and multiplication are commutative but subtraction and division are not.

2. **Brackets**

   Consider this problem $5 \times (3 + 4)$.

   Now $5 \times (3 + 4) = 5 \times 7 \dots$ do what is inside the brackets first
   $$= 35$$

   We would get the same result by multiplying each number inside the brackets by 5 and adding the results.

   Thus $5 \times (3 + 4) = 5 \times 3 + 5 \times 4$
   $$= 15 + 20$$
   $$= 35 \dots \text{as found above.}$$

   $5 \times (3 + 4)$ may be written more neatly as $5(3 + 4)$.

   The statement $5(3 + 4) = 5 \times 3 + 5 \times 4$ illustrates that **multiplication is distributive over addition**.

3. **The associative property**

   To perform the operation $6 + 8 + 10$, we could do it in either of these ways:

   (i) $6 + 8 + 10 = (6 + 8) + 10 = 14 + 10 = 24$

   (ii) $6 + 8 + 10 = 6 + (8 + 10) = 6 + 18 = 24$

   Similarly, $3 \times 4 \times 5 = (3 \times 4) \times 5 = 12 \times 5 = 60$

   or $3 \times 4 \times 5 = 3 \times (4 \times 5) = 3 \times 20 = 60$

   These examples illustrate the **associative property** of addition and multiplication which states that the way in which the numbers are grouped does not change the result.

   However $(12 \div 6) \div 2 = 2 \div 2 = 1$ but $12 \div (6 \div 2) = 12 \div 3 = 4$

   and $(12 - 6) - 3 = 6 - 3 = 3$ but $12 - (6 - 3) = 12 - 3 = 9$

   These examples illustrate that division and subtraction are not associative.

   Remember   Addition and multiplication are associative but subtraction and division are not.

Example 1

State whether each of the following is true or false:

(i) $9 \times 5 = 5 \times 9$ ii) $10 \div 5 = 5 \div 10$ (iii) $(4 \times 5) \times 6 = 4 \times (5 \times 6)$

(i) $9 \times 5 = 45$ and $5 \times 9 = 45 \dots$ true

(ii) $10 \div 5 = 2$ and $5 \div 10 = \frac{5}{10} = \frac{1}{2} \dots$ false

(iii) $(4 \times 5) \times 6 = 20 \times 6 = 120$ and $4 \times (5 \times 6) = 4 \times 30 = 120 \dots$ true

Exercise 1.6

(Do not use a calculator for these exercises.)

1. Work out each of the following:
   (i) 125 + 38 + 9 + 450   (ii) 27 + 1037 + 326 + 9
   (iii) 2017 + 151 + 39 + 6216   (iv) 168 + 2167 + 17 + 1076

2. Copy and complete these subtractions:
   (i)   908   (ii)   673   (iii)   738   (iv)   580   (v)   611
         − 304   − 187   − 354   − 364   − 87

3. Complete each of these subtractions:
   (i) 506 − 328   (ii) 1296 − 377   (iii) 1094 − 29
   (iv) 7002 − 946   (v) 629 − 380   (vi) 6200 − 5177

4. Do these calculations mentally and write down the answers:
   (i) 30 + 10 + 10   (ii) 80 − 20 − 10   (iii) 80 + 40 − 30
   (iv) 80 + 30 + 20   (v) 60 + 50 − 30   (vi) 130 + 70 − 40

5. Work out each of these mentally:
   (i) 60 × 2   (ii) 50 × 9   (iii) 300 × 5   (iv) 400 × 6   (v) 40 × 10
   (vi) 8 × 100   (vii) 40 × 50   (viii) 240 × 10   (ix) 120 × 40   (x) 90 × 90

6. Write down the answers to these questions:
   (i) 18 ÷ 3   (ii) 180 ÷ 3   (iii) 240 ÷ 6   (iv) 630 ÷ 9   (v) 560 ÷ 8

7. Work out each of these multiplications:
   (i) 47 × 9   (ii) 426 × 11   (iii) 89 × 29   (iv) 168 × 50
   (v) 186 × 28   (vi) 765 × 18   (vii) 186 × 47   (viii) 316 × 31

8. Five people shared a prize-draw win of €3200 equally.
   How much did each person receive?

9. A bus company owns twelve 48-seater coaches.
   Every Saturday all the coaches are used for trips.
   (i) How many people can be carried at the same time in the twelve coaches?

   One Saturday, seven of the coaches each carried 39 people.
   The other coaches each had 11 empty seats.
   (ii) How many people went on trips altogether that Saturday?

10. This table shows the numbers of students in each year group at Corbett College.

Year 1	Year 2	Year 3	Year 4	Year 5
112	121	104	98	126

   (i) How many students are at the school altogether?
   (ii) How many fewer students are in Year 4 than in Year 2?

   (iii) Each class in Year 5 has 21 students.
How many classes are there in Year 5?

   (iv) There are 3 times as many students in St. David's as in Corbett College.
How many students are in St. David's?

11. The number in the square is found by multiplying the two numbers in the circles on either side of it.

Copy and complete each of the following:

(i)   (ii)   (iii)

12. The digits of the year 2000 A.D. add up to 2.
There are nine other years since 1 A.D. that this has happened.
Name these nine years.

13. Jason bought three boxes of toffees. There were 30 toffees in each box. Jason ate 14 toffees himself and then shared all the rest equally between himself and his three sisters.

   (i) How many toffees did Jason have to start with?

  (ii) When they were shared out, how many toffees did each person get?

14. State whether each of the following is true or false:

    (i) $21 \times 6 = 6 \times 21$ (ii) $10 - 3 = 3 - 10$ (iii) $8 \div 4 = 4 \div 8$

  (iv) $34 \times 5 = 35 \times 4$ (v) $3(4 + 5) = 17$ (vi) $5(6 - 4) = 10$

15. Here are four statements:

A Addition is commutative   C Multiplication is commutative

B Subtraction is not commutative   D Division is not commutative

Which of the statements A, B, C or D does each of the following operations illustrate?

    (i) $12 \times 8 = 8 \times 12$ (ii) $14 - 10 \neq 10 - 14$

  (iii) $14 \div 7 \neq 7 \div 14$ (iv) $16 + 8 = 8 + 16$

16. State whether each of the following is true or false. Justify your answers.
  (i) $(6 + 8) + 10 = 6 + (8 + 10)$ (ii) $(24 - 8) - 6 = 24 - (8 - 6)$
  (iii) $(7 \times 4) \times 5 = 7 \times (4 \times 5)$ (iv) $(36 \div 6) \div 3 = 36 \div (6 \div 3)$

17. Which of the statements in the boxes below do each of these operations illustrate?
  (i) $(5 + 8) + 10 = 5 + (8 + 10)$ (ii) $15 - (10 - 2) \neq (15 - 10) - 2$
  (iii) $(7 \times 4) \times 3 = 7 \times (4 \times 3)$ (iv) $(20 - 10) - 4 \neq 20 - (10 - 4)$

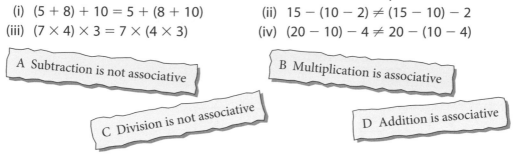

A Subtraction is not associative

B Multiplication is associative

C Division is not associative

D Addition is associative

18. Two different whole numbers are each greater than 0 and less than 10.
These two numbers are (i) multiplied and (ii) added.
Work out the greatest possible difference between (i) and (ii).

Section 1.7 Rounding off numbers – Estimating

When dealing with numbers, calculators can save a lot of time. However, when using calculators it is very important to have some estimate of the answer you expect. Then you will know if the answer shown on the calculator is reasonable or not.

When making a rough estimate we generally round whole numbers off to the nearest 10 or 100. If we wish to round off a number to the nearest 10, we examine the units only.

This number line is divided into coloured regions.

You can use it to round numbers to the nearest 10.

Numbers inside a coloured region round to the value at its centre.

44 is in a yellow region. It is nearer to 40 than 50.

44 rounds down to 40 to the nearest 10.

47 is in the green region and rounds up to 50 to the nearest 10.

85 is on the boundary between two regions.

When a number ends in 5, we round up.

So 85 rounds up to 90 to the nearest 10.

When rounding to the nearest 100, your answer will be one of these numbers:
     0, 100, 200, 300, 400, 500, …

When rounding to the nearest 1000, your answer will be one of these numbers:
     0, 1000, 2000, 3000, 4000, …

Significant figures

If the attendance at a football match was 34 176, it would be reasonable to write down 34 200 or 34 000.

     34 200 is written correct to 3 significant figures.

     34 000 is written correct to 2 significant figures.

To round a whole number to a given number of significant figures, you start at the left of the number.

In the number 2834, 2 is the first significant figure and 8 is the second significant figure.

Thus 2834 = 2800, correct to two significant figures.

Notice that the zeros at the end of the number are not counted but they must be included in the final result.

Thus 52 764 = 52 760 correct to 4 significant figures

            = 52 800 correct to 3 significant figures

            = 53 000 correct to 2 significant figures

            = 50 000 correct to 1 significant figure

The number 70 425 = 70 400 correct to 3 significant figures.
Notice here that the zero between the 7 and 4 is significant, but the two final zeros are not.

When rounding a number to 1 significant figure

> Start at the left and find the first two digits.
> If the second digit is 5 or more, add 1 to the first digit.
> If the second digit is 4 or less, leave the first digit as it is.
> Replace all the other digits with zeros.

Here are more examples:

  (i) 5210 = 5200 correct to two significant figures

 (ii) 75 462 = 80 000 correct to one significant figure

(iii) 80 483 = 80 500 correct to three significant figures.

Exercise 1.7

1. Use the number line below to help you write each of these numbers to the nearest 10.
  (i) 634   (ii) 622   (iii) 644   (iv) 598
  (v) 604   (vi) 647   (vii) 605   (viii) 645

```
|‖‖‖‖‖‖‖‖|‖‖‖‖‖‖‖‖|‖‖‖‖‖‖‖‖|‖‖‖‖‖‖‖‖|‖‖‖‖‖‖‖‖|‖‖‖‖‖‖‖‖|
     600       610       620       630       640       650
```

2. Use the number line above to write the numbers where the yellow and green regions meet.

3. Round off each of the following numbers to the nearest 10:
  (i) 137   (ii) 84   (iii) 677   (iv) 1764   (v) 3785

4. Round off these numbers to the nearest 100:
  (i) 823   (ii) 276   (iii) 2184   (iv) 3099   (v) 3708

5. Round off these numbers to the nearest 1000:
  (i) 2864   (ii) 5726   (iii) 8416   (iv) 9650   (v) 10 890

6. The attendance at an All-Ireland Final in Croke Park was 82 379.
  Write this number   (i) to the nearest 100
                        (ii) to the nearest 1000.

7. Round 28 460   (i) to three significant figures
                        (ii) to two significant figures
                       (iii) to one significant figure.

8. Rounded off to the nearest 100 people, the number of workers at a factory is 800.
  What is (i) the largest, (ii) the smallest number that could work at the factory?

9. The attendance at a rugby match, correct to the nearest 1000, was 38 000.
  Find (i) the largest and (ii) the smallest number that could have attended.

10. 62 680 people went to a concert.
  (i) The local newspaper reported that about 63 000 people went to the concert.
      Was this given to the nearest 100, nearest 1000 or nearest 10 000?
  (ii) Another newspaper reported that about 60 000 people went to the concert.
      Was this given to the nearest 1000 or nearest 10 000?

11. By rounding each number to the nearest 10, find a rough estimate for each of these:
  (i) 38×51 (ii) 48×32 (iii) 69×28 (iv) 288×12

12. By rounding off each number to the nearest 10, calculate a rough estimate of the value of each of the following:

(i) $\dfrac{124 \times 231}{458}$ (ii) $\dfrac{709 \times 118}{236}$ (iii) $\dfrac{268 \times 147}{176}$

13. The size of a crowd at a concert was given as 23 700, to the nearest hundred.
   (i) What is the smallest number the crowd could be?
  (ii) What is the largest number the crowd could be?

14. The table gives the areas of five European Union states and their populations in 2004.

Country	Area (km²)	Population
Greece	131 944	10 645 343
Italy	301 225	57 436 280
Netherlands	33 812	16 318 199
Germany	356 733	83 251 851
Ireland	70 283	3 883 159

   (i) Round off the areas correct to three significant figures.
  (ii) Round off the populations correct to two significant figures.
 (iii) When the populations are rounded to one significant figure, which country has three times the population of another country?

Test yourself 1

1. Find the value of each of these:
   (i) $634 + 95 - 237$
   (ii) $2 \times (3 + 5) - 3^2$

2. Write down
   (i) the highest common factor of 16 and 40
   (ii) the lowest common multiple of 6 and 9.

3. (i) List all the prime numbers in this array:
   $$2, 4, 5, 9, 11, 16, 19, 21$$
   (ii) List all the factors of 28.
   Now write 28 as a product of its prime factors.

4. Write down the values of the numbers A, B, C and D which are marked with arrows in the following diagrams:

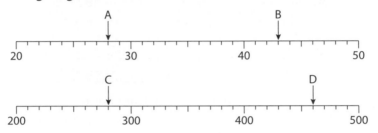

5. Evaluate each of these:
   (i) $2 \times 8 - 5$
   (ii) $14 - 3 \times 3$
   (iii) $3 \times (7 + 3)$
   (iv) $4 \times 12 \div (8 - 6)$
   (v) $44 \div 4 + 3 \times 7$
   (vi) $(7 - 3) \times 4 + 16 \div 8$

6. An aeroplane lands at Rome on its way to Cairo.
   183 people got off and 42 got on.
   If there were then 235 people on the plane, how many people were on the plane before it landed?

7. Fiona has four cards.
   Each card has a number written on it.
   Fiona puts all four cards on the table to make a number.

   $\boxed{4}\ \boxed{9}\ \boxed{1}\ \boxed{5}$

   (i) Write the smallest number Fiona can make using all four cards.
   (ii) Write the largest number Fiona can make using all four cards.

   Fiona uses the cards to make a true statement.

   (iii) Write this calculation.
   Use each of the numbers on Fiona's cards **once**.

8. Choosing numbers from 3, 4, 9, 13, 15, 23, 25, 28, 64, write down
    (i)   three prime numbers
    (ii) a multiple of 7
    (iii) three numbers which are factors of 60
    (iv) four numbers whose square roots are whole numbers.

9. Round each number to the nearest 10 and make an estimate of the answer to each of these:

    (i) $\dfrac{63 \times 57}{31}$
    (ii) $\dfrac{204 \times 96}{53}$
    (iii) $\dfrac{396 \times 304}{154}$

10. Evaluate each of these:

    (i) $6 \times (5 + 3) - 8 \div 2$
    (ii) $\dfrac{30 - (3 \times 2)}{4 \times 2 - 2}$

11. There are 576 pupils in a school.
    If there are 48 more boys than girls, how many girls are there in the school?

12. Write these numbers in order, starting with the smallest:

    $9 \qquad \sqrt{49} \qquad 2^3 \qquad 2^2 \times 3 \qquad \sqrt{64} \div 2 \qquad \sqrt{(100 - 64)}$

13. The table on the right gives the areas, in square kilometres, of five member states of the European Union.
    (i)   Write each of these areas to the nearest 1000.
    (ii) Which country has the smallest area?
    (iii) One country has about six times the area of another country.
          Name these two countries.
    (iv) One country is about one third the size of another country.
          Name these two countries.

Country	Area
Belgium	30 513
Luxembourg	2576
Spain	504 782
Portugal	92 082
France	547 026

14. Find the value of each of these:
    (i) $15 - 10 \div 2 + 7 \times 4$
    (ii) $3 \times 4^2 + 36 \div 2^2$

15. State whether each of the following is true or false.
    If a statement is false give an example to show that it is false.
    (i)   All multiples of 8 are also multiples of 4.
    (ii) All factors of 8 are also factors of 4.
    (iii) All numbers have an even number of different factors.
    (iv) $\sqrt{9} + \sqrt{16} = \sqrt{25}$
    (v)   There are only three prime numbers which are less than 10.

For the problem solver...

1. Here is a subtraction using the digits
   2, 3, 4, 5, 6.

   465 – 23

   Which subtraction using all the digits
   2, 3, 4, 5, 6 has the smallest positive answer?

2. Use the clues to find the mystery number.
   > the sum of the digits is 8
   > the number reads the same forwards as backwards
   > the number is less than 2000
   > the number has four digits

   ?

3. Mr Bigg has a lot of tables and chairs in his house. Each rectangular table seats eight people and each round table seats five people. What is the smallest number of tables he will need to use to seat 35 guests and himself, without any of the seating around these tables remaining unoccupied?

4. Write all the whole numbers from 1 to 10 using the digit 4 exactly four times for each number. All the usual mathematical symbols such as $+, -, \times, \div$, and brackets may be used.
   The first two numbers are done for you.
   $1 = (4 + 4) \div (4 + 4)$ or $1 = \frac{4}{4} \times \frac{4}{4}$
   $2 = \frac{4}{4} + \frac{4}{4}$ or $2 = (4 \times 4) \div (4 + 4)$

5. The pages of a book are numbered 1, 2, 3, …
   In total, it takes 852 digits to number all the pages of the book.
   What is the number of the last page?

6. Each block shown in this tower is to have a number displayed on it. Some are already done. For each block above the bottom row, the number on it should be the sum of the numbers on the two blocks it stands upon. What number should replace *n*?

7. Water lilies double in area every 24 hours. There is one water lily in the middle of a lake. If it takes 40 days for the lake to be completely covered in water lilies, how many days does it take to cover half the lake?

Integers

chapter 2

Key words

positive	**negative**	**zero**	**integers**	**increasing**
decreasing	**number line**	**temperature**	**brackets**	

Section 2.1 Negative numbers

This thermometer is showing a temperature
of −10°C or 10°C below zero.

Numbers greater than zero are called **positive numbers.**
   1, 2, 3, 4, … are positive.

Number less than zero are called **negative numbers**.
   −1, −2, −3, … are negative.

The set of positive and negative whole numbers,
together with zero, is called the set of **integers**.
We use the letter **Z** to represent the set of integers.
These integers can be represented on a number line as shown below.

Decreasing   Increasing

−10 −9 −8 −7 −6 −5 −4 −3 −2 −1 0 1 2 3 4 5 6 7 8 9 10

Negative numbers are always written with the negative sign, −, before them, e.g.,
−3, −5, −8.
However it is not necessary to write the plus sign, +, before positive numbers.

Using the number line to compare numbers.

On the number line the smaller number will appear to the left of the bigger one.

−5 −4 −3 −2 −1 0 1 2 3 4 5

From the number line above
   (i) $-3 < -1$ as −3 is to the left of −1
   (ii) $-2 > -4$ as −2 is to the right of −4.

$<$ means 'is less than'
$>$ means 'is greater than'

Exercise 2.1

1. Use the number line to help you find the missing terms in these sequences.

(i) 6, 4, 2, ☐, ☐, ☐

(ii) 5, 3, 1, ☐, ☐, ☐

(iii) 8, 4, 0, ☐, ☐, ☐

(iv) −3, −1, 1, ☐, ☐, ☐

(v) −4, −2, 0, ☐, ☐, ☐

(vi) 8, 5, ☐, ☐, −4, ☐

2. Which is the higher temperature in each of the following?

(i) 8°C or 10°C

(ii) −2°C or 5°C

(iii) 0°C or −5°C

(iv) −8°C or −5°C

(v) −12°C or −6°C

(vi) −8°C or −14°C

3. What temperature is

(i) 3°C warmer than 7°C

(ii) 5°C colder than 8°C

(iii) 6°C colder than 3°C

(iv) 3°C colder than −4°C

(v) 4°C warmer than −10°C

(vi) 8°C warmer than −8°C?

4. Write these numbers in order, starting with the smallest:

(i) 3, 6, −3, 0, −4, 1

(ii) 6, −5, −8, −2, 0, 4

(iii) −5, 3, 1, −2, −8, 9

(iv) −3, 5, −7, 0, −1, 3, −4

5. How many degrees difference is there between

(i) −1°C and 10°C

(ii) 13°C and −5°C

(iii) −3°C and −14°C?

6. The temperature in a freezer is −15°C and the temperature in the room is 17°C. How many degrees difference is this?

7. List the next four integers:

(i) greater than 2

(ii) less than −1

(iii) greater than −7.

8. Say if each of the following is true or false:

(i) 9 > 0

(ii) −1 < 4

(iii) 2 < −3

(iv) −4 > −1

(v) 0 > −4

(vi) −12 > 6

(vii) −1 < −7

(viii) 6 > −7.

9. The temperature of the fridge compartment of a fridge-freezer is set at 5°C.
The freezer compartment is set at −18°C.
What is the difference between these temperature settings?

10. The table gives the highest and lowest temperatures recorded in several cities during one year.

	New York	Paris	Rome	Moscow	Sydney
Highest temperature	27°C	32°C	34°C	28°C	34°C
Lowest temperature	−9°C	−6°C	8°C	−21°C	7°C

  (i) Which city recorded the lowest temperature?

  (ii) Which city recorded the biggest difference between its highest and lowest temperatures?

  (iii) Which city recorded the smallest difference between its highest and lowest temperatures?

11. Copy and complete the following by putting the symbols $>$ or $<$ in the box.

  (i) 2 ☐ 5   (ii) 2 ☐ −3   (iii) 0 ☐ 4   (iv) 0 ☐ −2

  (v) −3 ☐ 4   (vi) −3 ☐ −4   (vii) −5 ☐ −1   (viii) −3 ☐ 0

Section 2.2 Adding and subtracting integers

If the temperature is 2°C and drops 6°C, it is then −4°C.

That is $2 - 6 = -4$.

When combining negative and positive numbers such as $2 - 6$, it can be very helpful to use the number line.

To find $2 - 6$ on the number line, start at 2 and move 6 places to the left.

You finish at −4.

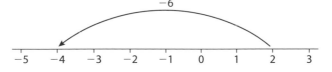

To find the value of $-1 - 4$, start at −1 and move 4 places to the left.

The result is −5, as shown below.

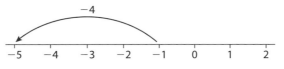

Rules for adding integers

When there are too many numbers it may be no longer convenient to use a number line to add integers.

Take these numbers: $4 - 6 + 8 - 3$

Write the positive numbers first: $4 + 8 - 6 - 3$

Now combine the positive numbers and negative numbers separately.

$4 + 8 - 6 - 3 = 12 - 9$
$= 3$

Rules for adding integers

1. When the signs are the same, add the numbers and retain the sign.

2. When the signs are different, retain the sign of the numerically bigger number and take the smaller number from the bigger number.

Example 1

Express each of these as a single integer:
  (i) $-4 - 8$ (ii) $-7 + 2$ (iii) $-2 + 5 - 13 + 6$

  (i) $-4 - 8 = -12$ ... retain the sign and add the numbers
  (ii) $-7 + 2 = -5$ ... retain sign of bigger number and take 2 from 7
  (iii) $-2 + 5 - 13 + 6$

We rewrite this as $-2 - 13 + 5 + 6$
$= -15 + 11$
$= -4$

Exercise 2.2

1. Work out the following calculations using the number line.

  (i) $3 - 5$ (ii) $2 - 6$ (iii) $0 - 3$ (iv) $1 - 4$
  (v) $-1 + 4$ (vi) $-2 + 7$ (vii) $-1 - 3$ (viii) $-2 - 4$

2. Write down the calculation represented by each diagram:

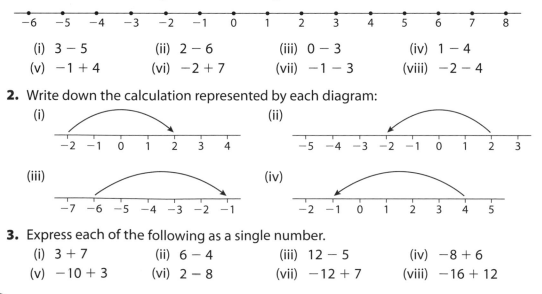

3. Express each of the following as a single number.
  (i) $3 + 7$ (ii) $6 - 4$ (iii) $12 - 5$ (iv) $-8 + 6$
  (v) $-10 + 3$ (vi) $2 - 8$ (vii) $-12 + 7$ (viii) $-16 + 12$

4. Simplify each of these:
   (i) $-1 - 2$ (ii) $-9 + 3$ (iii) $-4 - 2$ (iv) $1 - 8$
   (v) $-7 - 4$ (vi) $-2 + 12$ (vii) $-12 - 3$ (viii) $-20 - 30$

Express numbers 5 to 16 as a single number.

5. $6 + 7 - 5$

6. $12 + 4 - 8$

7. $14 - 3 - 2$

8. $16 - 5 - 3$

9. $20 - 5 - 8$

10. $3 - 7 + 9$

11. $6 - 2 - 9$

12. $-3 + 7 - 1$

13. $6 - 9 + 12$

14. $12 - 9 + 4 - 3$

15. $12 - 8 + 9 - 4$

16. $-7 - 3 + 4 + 8$

17. Copy and complete these calculations:
   (I) $\boxed{} + 6 = 9$ (ii) $-7 + \boxed{} = 4$ (iii) $\boxed{} + 3 = -6$
   (iv) $-9 + \boxed{} = -6$ (v) $-6 - \boxed{} = 14$ (vi) $\boxed{} + 5 = -4$

18. Copy and complete these addition squares:
   (i)

+	7	−1		−4
	6			
−3			−8	
2				
−4				

   (ii)

+	−5	3		
−1		2		0
			10	
4				
			6	−1

19. Copy and complete these addition pyramids.
   (i)

−2	3	−7	2

   (ii)

   (with −7 and) | 6 | −4 | | −2 |

20. In a magic square each row, each column and each diagonal adds up to the same number.

   Now copy and complete each of these magic squares.

   (i)

−8	−1	−6
	−5	

   (ii)

2	1	−3
	0	

   (iii)

−6	−5	−4
		−10

21. At 7 p.m. the temperature in Berlin was 2°C. By midnight it had dropped by 5°C. By 4 a.m. it had dropped a further 5°C. What was the temperature at 4 a.m.?

22. John had €180 in his bank account. He lodged a further €135 to his account and then withdrew €115. How much was then in his account?

Section 2.3: Multiplying and dividing integers

$$-2 - 2 - 2 - 2 = -8$$

4 lots of $-2 = -8$ $\qquad\qquad$ -2 multiplied by $4 = -8$

$4 \times -2 = -8$ $\qquad\qquad\qquad$ $-2 \times 4 = -8$

The example above illustrates that a positive number multiplied by a negative number results in a negative number.

Now look at the multiplication grid opposite.

From the grid we can see that two minus numbers multiplied together give a positive number.

×	−3	−2	−1	1	2	3
3	−9	−6	−3	3	6	9
2	−6	−4	−2	2	4	6
1	−3	−2	−1	1	2	3
−1	3	2	1	−1	−2	−3
−2	6	4	2	−2	−4	−6
−3	9	6	3	−3	−6	−9

The same rules apply to division as apply to multiplication.

Remember

When multiplying or dividing integers
- ❯ like signs give plus
- ❯ unlike signs give minus

Example 1

Write as a single integer
- (i) -3×5
- (ii) -3×-7
- (iii) $-2 \times 3 \times -4$

- (i) $-3 \times 5 = -15$ ... unlike signs give minus
- (ii) $-3 \times -7 = 21$ ... like signs give plus
- (iii) $-2 \times 3 \times -4 = -6 \times -4$ ... take two at a time
  $\qquad\qquad\qquad\qquad = 24$

Example 2

Find the value of
(i) $-14 \div 2$ (ii) $-26 \div (-2)$ (iii) $\dfrac{-5 \times (-8)}{4}$

(i) $-14 \div 2 = -7$
(ii) $-26 \div (-2) = 13$
(iii) $\dfrac{-5 \times (-8)}{4} = \dfrac{40}{4} = 40 \div 4 = 10$

Removing brackets

$-4(-2)$ is the same as $-4 \times (-2) = 8$.

Now consider $-(-4)$.

$-(-4)$ is the same as $-1(-4) = -1 \times -4$ $-(-4) = 4$
$\qquad\qquad\qquad\qquad\qquad = 4$

Example 3

Find the value of
(i) $6 - (-5)$ (ii) $-7 - (-3 + 2)$ (iii) $-7 \times 4 - (-5)$

(i) $6 - (-5) = 6 + 5 = 11$
(ii) $-7 - (-3 + 2) = -7 - (-1) = -7 + 1$
$\qquad\qquad\qquad\qquad\qquad\qquad = -6$
(iii) $-7 \times 4 - (-5) = -28 - (-5)$
$\qquad\qquad\qquad\qquad = -28 + 5$
$\qquad\qquad\qquad\qquad = -23$

Exercise 2.3

1. Write down the answer to each of the following:
(i) 6×4 (ii) -5×4 (iii) $7 \times (-8)$
(iv) $5 \times (-9)$ (v) -6×9 (vi) $(-9) \times (-4)$
(vii) $(-8) \times (-6)$ (viii) $10 \times (-7)$ (ix) -9×8
(x) $(-6) \times (-11)$ (xi) $4 \times (-20)$ (xii) $(-18) \times 3$

2. Work out each of these:
(i) $-12 \div 2$ (ii) $36 \div (-4)$ (iii) $-20 \div 5$
(iv) $-15 \div (-5)$ (v) $-30 \div (-10)$ (vi) $-24 \div 8$

3. Write down the answer to each of these:

(i) $\dfrac{16}{2}$ (ii) $\dfrac{-8}{4}$ (iii) $\dfrac{-27}{3}$ (iv) $\dfrac{15}{-3}$ (v) $\dfrac{-42}{-7}$

(vi) $\dfrac{-35}{7}$ (vii) $\dfrac{54}{-6}$ (viii) $\dfrac{-54}{-9}$ (ix) $\dfrac{-63}{7}$ (x) $\dfrac{55}{-11}$

4. Find the missing number in each of the following:

(i) $6 \times \square = -48$ (ii) $-4 \times \square = 24$ (iii) $-5 \times \square = -40$

(iv) $-20 \div \square = -4$ (v) $36 \div \square = -9$ (vi) $\square \div (-7) = -3$

5. This is a 'multiplication wall'.
The number on each brick is found by multiplying the two numbers on the bricks below.
What will be the number on the top brick of this wall?

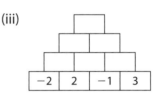

6. Copy and complete these multiplication walls.

(i)   (ii)   (iii)

7. Express as a single integer:

(i) $6 \times 2 \times (-3)$ (ii) $4 \times (-3) \times (-2)$ (iii) $(-6) \times 5 \times (-3)$

(iv) $(-4) \times (-3) \times 5$ (v) $(-2) \times 6 \times (-8)$ (vi) $(-3) \times (-2) \times (-7)$

8. Express each of the following as a single integer:

(i) $\dfrac{3 \times (-6)}{9}$ (ii) $\dfrac{(-5) \times (-10)}{-10}$ (iii) $\dfrac{(-12) \times 4}{8}$

(iv) $\dfrac{(-8) \times (-9)}{-12}$ (v) $\dfrac{9 \times (-6)}{-2}$ (vi) $\dfrac{(-8) \times 3 \times (-6)}{-12}$

9. Choose pairs of numbers from the loop to make these calculations correct.

(i) $\square \div \square = -3$ (ii) $\square \times \square = 14$

(iii) $\square \times \square = -6$ (iv) $\square \div \square = -5$

(v) $\square \div \square = 5$ (vi) $\square \times \square = -63$

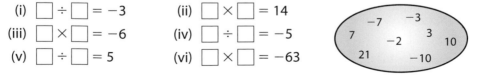

10. Given that $(-4)^2 = -4 \times (-4) = 16$, work out each of these:

(i) $(-3)^2$ (ii) $(-6)^2$ (iii) $(-7)^2$ (iv) $(-2)^3$

11. Noting that you multiply and divide before you add and subtract, simplify each of the following:

(i) $3 - 8 + 8 \times (-2)$

(ii) $15 + 6 \div 2 + 12 \times (-2)$

(iii) $(16 - 4) \div 2 + 5 \times (-4)$

(iv) $(15 - 10) \times -3 + 5 \times (-6)$

(v) $14 + 4 \times (-2) - (7 - 15)$

(vi) $100 \div (13 - 3) + (-4) \times (-7)$.

12. Since $3 \times 4 = 12$, we call 12 the product of the two numbers 3 and 4.

Now copy and complete the table shown below.

	Sum	Product	Two numbers
(i)	−7	10	
(ii)	−13	30	
(iii)	−5	6	
(iv)	5	−6	
(v)	−8	12	
(vi)	−2	−15	

13. In a quiz there are ten questions.

Each correct answer gains five points.

Each wrong answer loses two points.

(i) Jane gave ten correct answers.
How many points did she get altogether?

(ii) Shane gave seven correct answers and three wrong answers.
How many points did he get altogether?

(iii) Elena answered all ten questions.
Explain how Elena could get 43 points altogether.

Test yourself 2

1. Express each of the following as a single integer:
   - (i) $6 - 4$
   - (ii) $-6 + 4$
   - (iii) $-3 - 7$
   - (iv) $2 - 4 - 5$
   - (v) -3×5
   - (vi) $-6 \times (-3)$
   - (vii) $-18 \div 6$
   - (viii) $-24 \div (-12)$

2. List these numbers in order of size, starting with the smallest:
   - (i) $4, -3, 9, 0, -12, -1, 6$
   - (ii) $-3, 2, 14, -9, -4, 7$

3.

   - (i) What is the temperature reading marked A?
   - (ii) What temperature is 4°C warmer than the temperature at A?
   - (iii) What temperature is 12°C colder than the temperature at B?
   - (iv) What is the difference between the temperatures at A and B?

4. Copy each of the following and insert the symbols $>$ (greater than) or $<$ (less than) between each pair of numbers:
   - (i) $3 \, \square \, -2$
   - (ii) $-5 \, \square \, -4$
   - (iii) $0 \, \square \, -7$
   - (iv) $-1 \, \square \, -8$

5. Choose pairs of numbers from the loop to make these calculations correct.
   - (i) $\square + \square = -6$
   - (ii) $\square \times \square = -15$
   - (iii) $\square \times \square = 40$
   - (iv) $\square + \square = -13$

   $-7 \quad 3 \quad -5 \quad -8 \quad 2 \quad 5$

6. Copy and complete this multiplication pyramid.

	2		
-2	-1	3	-1

7. Simplify each of these:
   - (i) $6 - 8 + 5 - 10$
   - (ii) $6 - (-4) + 3$
   - (iii) $4 \times (-3) \times (-5)$

8. Copy and complete these multiplication grids.

   (i)

×	5	-3
	10	
-3	-15	

   (ii)

×		5	
		-15	
-1	5		-6
	-20	20	

   (iii)

×			
1			-2
-4	12	0	
			-10

9. On a cold day, wind chill can make it *feel* even colder.
   If the wind chill is −10°C, then a temperature of 4°C would feel like −6°C.
   What does each of these temperatures feel like with a wind chill of −10°C?
       (i)   1°C   (ii)   3°C   (iii)   −2°C   (iv)   −15°C

10. In this grid each letter corresponds to a number.
    For example, K corresponds to 20
    because 5 × 4 = 20.
       (i)   What number corresponds to the letter J?
       (ii)   What letter corresponds to the number −10?
       (iii)   For each set of numbers, work out the
             corresponding letters to spell a word.
       (a)   9, 10, 15, 12   (b)   30, −30, −4, 15   (c)   −10, 10, −30, 20

×	2	−3	4	−6
−2	A	B	C	D
−3	E	F	G	H
5	I	J	K	L
−5	M	N	O	P

11. Copy and complete the addition grid shown on the right.

+	−7	3	0	
	−11			
−2				−6
0				
		−2		

12. The top of Mount Kenya, in Africa, is about 5000 metres above sea level.
    When you climb a mountain the temperature drops by 6 degrees Celsius for every
    1000 metres climbed.
    When the temperature at sea level is 26°C, what will the temperature be on the top
    of Mount Kenya?

13. Work out the answers and write them in order, lowest first.
    The letters will spell the name of a city.

K	A	L	C	U	N	D	A
−2 × 3	3 × (−4)	−7 + 2	1 − 9	−8 − 2	5 − 5	−3 + 7	−1 − 3

14. In a certain test there are 10 questions. Candidates score
    3 for every question answered correctly,
    −2 for every question answered incorrectly and
    −1 for every question they do not answer.
    Declan answered 5 questions correctly, answered 3 questions incorrectly and did
    not answer 2 questions.
    Calculate his total score.

For the problem solver...

1. I have some strange dice: the faces show the numbers 1 to 6 as usual, except that the odd numbers are negative (i.e. $-1, -3, -5$ in place of 1, 3, 5).

   If I throw two such dice, which total cannot be achieved?

   A 3   B 4   C 5   D 7   E 8

2. The sum of ten consecutive integers is 5.
   What is the largest of these integers?

3. The number in the square is the product of the two integers on either side of it. Copy and complete:

   (i)   (ii)   (iii)

4. Which is smallest?

   A $\dfrac{(2 + 3)}{(4 + 6)}$ B $\dfrac{(2 \div 3)}{(4 \div 6)}$ C $\dfrac{23}{46}$

   D $\dfrac{(2 - 3)}{(4 - 6)}$ E $\dfrac{(2 \times 3)}{(4 \times 6)}$

5. Four of these give the same answer. Which one is different?

   A $1 - (2 \times 3) + 4$ B $1 + (2 - 3 \times 4) \div 5$
   C $((1 \times 2 - 3) - 4) \div 5$ D $(1 \times 2) - 3$
   E $(1 - 2) - 3 \div 4$

6. Write down the number 78 using three nines and any of the usual mathematical symbols.

7. Arrange all the other integers from -1 to -9 so that each line of three numbers adds up to the same number.

   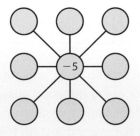

   Does the puzzle work if you put a different number in the middle circle?

Fractions

Key words

simplify   equivalent fraction   proper fraction   improper fraction
numerator   simplest form   denominator   lowest common multiple (LCM)
mixed number   magic square   cancelling

Section 3.1 Recognising fractions – Equivalent fractions

The circle on the right is divided into 4 equal parts.

The shaded part is $\frac{1}{4}$.

The unshaded part is $\frac{3}{4}$.

$\frac{1}{4}$ and $\frac{3}{4}$ are examples of **fractions**.

$\dfrac{3}{4}$
The top number is called the **numerator**.
The bottom number is called the **denominator**.

Equivalent Fractions

The diagrams below show that the fractions $\frac{1}{2}$, $\frac{2}{4}$, $\frac{3}{6}$ and $\frac{4}{8}$ are all equal.

Each fraction represents half of the circle.

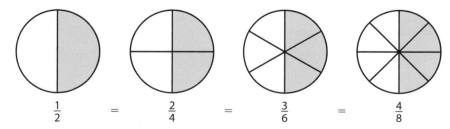

$$\frac{1}{2} \quad = \quad \frac{2}{4} \quad = \quad \frac{3}{6} \quad = \quad \frac{4}{8}$$

These fractions are said to be **equivalent** as they all have the same value.

Simplifying fractions

Fractions can be **simplified** if the top and bottom can be divided by a common factor.

Take $\frac{4}{8}$ for example.

The top and bottom can both be divided by 4.

So $\frac{4}{8}$ can be simplified to $\frac{1}{2}$. $\frac{1}{2}$

Similarly $\qquad \dfrac{12}{15} = \dfrac{12 \div 3}{15 \div 3} = \dfrac{4}{5}.$

Since $\frac{4}{5}$ cannot be reduced any more, it is said to be expressed in its **simplest form**.

Example 1

Express the following fractions in their simplest form:

(i) $\frac{18}{27}$ 　　　　 (ii) $\frac{21}{35}$ 　　　 (iii) $\frac{22}{77}$ 　　　　 (iv) $\frac{48}{72}$

(i) $\dfrac{18}{27} = \dfrac{18 \div 9}{27 \div 9} = \dfrac{2}{3}$ 　　　 (ii) $\dfrac{21}{35} = \dfrac{21 \div 7}{35 \div 7} = \dfrac{3}{5}$

(iii) $\dfrac{22}{77} = \dfrac{22 \div 11}{77 \div 11} = \dfrac{2}{7}$ 　　 (iv) $\dfrac{48}{72} = \dfrac{48 \div 8}{72 \div 8} = \dfrac{6}{9}$

　　　　　　　　　　　　　　　 Now $\dfrac{6}{9} = \dfrac{6 \div 3}{9 \div 3} = \dfrac{2}{3}$

Exercise 3.1

1. What fraction of each of these diagrams is shaded?

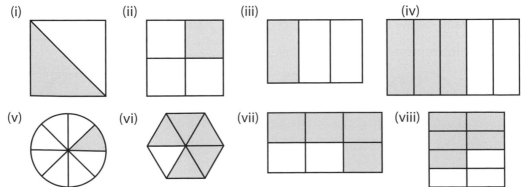

(i)　　　　　　(ii)　　　　　(iii)　　　　　　　(iv)

(v)　　　　　(vi)　　　　(vii)　　　　　(viii)

2. What fraction of each of the diagrams above is unshaded?

3. Write down the shaded part of this figure as a fraction in two different ways.
What are these two fractions known as?

4. (i) What fraction of a week is 1 day?
(ii) What fraction of a year is 3 months?
(iii) What fraction of a year is 9 months?
(iv) What fraction of an hour is 20 minutes?

5. A cake is cut into eighths.
(i) How many people can have 1 piece each?
(ii) How many people can have 2 pieces each?

6. Fill in the missing numbers in each of the following:

(i) $\frac{4}{8} = \frac{\square}{2}$ (ii) $\frac{6}{8} = \frac{\square}{4}$ (iii) $\frac{4}{6} = \frac{\square}{3}$ (iv) $\frac{10}{15} = \frac{\square}{3}$

(v) $\frac{9}{12} = \frac{3}{\square}$ (vi) $\frac{9}{15} = \frac{3}{\square}$ (vii) $\frac{18}{27} = \frac{2}{\square}$ (viii) $\frac{\square}{21} = \frac{2}{3}$

7. Write each of the following fractions in its lowest terms:

(i) $\frac{2}{4}$ (ii) $\frac{3}{9}$ (iii) $\frac{4}{12}$ (iv) $\frac{8}{24}$ (v) $\frac{5}{30}$

(vi) $\frac{6}{18}$ (vii) $\frac{16}{24}$ (viii) $\frac{15}{25}$ (ix) $\frac{18}{27}$ (x) $\frac{21}{35}$

8. What fraction of this rectangle is shaded?
Write it in its simplest form.

9. Write, in its simplest form, the fraction of each rectangle that is shaded.

(i) (ii) (iii)

(iv) (v) (vi)

(vii) (viii)

10. Write each of the following fractions as an equivalent fraction with denominator 24:

(i) $\frac{1}{2}$ (ii) $\frac{3}{4}$ (iii) $\frac{2}{3}$ (iv) $\frac{5}{8}$ (v) $\frac{11}{12}$

Use your answers to find which is the bigger fraction in each of the following:

(a) $\frac{2}{3}$ or $\frac{5}{8}$ (b) $\frac{3}{4}$ or $\frac{2}{3}$ (c) $\frac{5}{8}$ or $\frac{11}{12}$

11. To what fraction is each of the following arrows pointing?

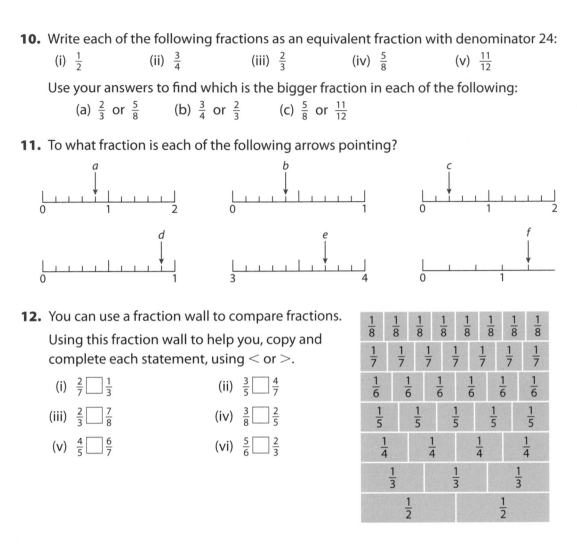

12. You can use a fraction wall to compare fractions.

Using this fraction wall to help you, copy and complete each statement, using $<$ or $>$.

(i) $\frac{2}{7} \square \frac{1}{3}$ (ii) $\frac{3}{5} \square \frac{4}{7}$

(iii) $\frac{2}{3} \square \frac{7}{8}$ (iv) $\frac{3}{8} \square \frac{2}{5}$

(v) $\frac{4}{5} \square \frac{6}{7}$ (vi) $\frac{5}{6} \square \frac{2}{3}$

Section 3.2 Types of fractions – Fraction of a number ____

Fractions such as $\frac{2}{3}$ and $\frac{3}{4}$ are less than 1 since the numerator is less than the denominator.

Fractions which are less than 1 are called **proper fractions**.

Take the fraction $2\frac{1}{2}$.

$2\frac{1}{2}$ is five halves or $\frac{5}{2}$.

Fractions such as $\frac{5}{2}$ or $\frac{8}{3}$ are all greater than 1.

These are called **improper fractions**.

The number $4\frac{2}{3}$ consists of a whole number and a fraction.

It is called a **mixed number**.

> Fractions less than 1 are **proper fractions**.
> Fractions greater than 1 are **improper fractions**.

Example 1

Change (i) $4\frac{2}{3}$ to an improper fraction

(ii) $\frac{15}{4}$ to a mixed number.

(i) $4\frac{2}{3} = 4 + \frac{2}{3}$

$= \frac{12}{3} + \frac{2}{3} = \frac{14}{3}$

> You will get the same result if you multiply 3 by 4 and then add 2, i.e., $(3 \times 4) + 2 = \frac{14}{3}$.

(ii) To change an improper fraction to a mixed number, divide the numerator (top) by the denominator (bottom) as follows:

$\frac{15}{4} = 3 + \frac{3}{4} = 3\frac{3}{4}$

Comparing fractions

It is much easier to compare fractions if they are written with the same denominator. Take the fractions $\frac{4}{5}$ and $\frac{3}{4}$.

The smallest number into which both 5 and 4 divide evenly is 20.

Thus $\frac{4}{5} = \frac{4 \times 4}{5 \times 4} = \frac{16}{20}$

$\frac{3}{4} = \frac{3 \times 5}{4 \times 5} = \frac{15}{20}$

> 20 is the LCM of 5 and 4.

It is now clear that $\frac{16}{20} > \frac{15}{20}$, i.e., $\frac{4}{5} > \frac{3}{4}$.

Finding a fraction of a number

$\frac{1}{4}$ of $60 = 60 \div 4 = 15$

$\frac{3}{4}$ of $60 = 3$ times $\frac{1}{4}$ of $60 = 3 \times 15 = 45$.

Example 2

Find $\frac{7}{8}$ of 120.

$\frac{1}{8}$ of $120 = 120 \div 8 = 8\overline{|120} \div 8$ i.e. 15

$\frac{7}{8}$ of $120 = 15 \times 7 = 105$

Exercise 3.2

1. State whether each of the following is a proper or improper fraction:

    (i) $\frac{3}{5}$ (ii) $\frac{7}{4}$ (iii) $\frac{1}{8}$ (iv) $\frac{9}{5}$ (v) $\frac{15}{12}$

2. Write these improper fractions as mixed numbers:

    (i) $\frac{6}{5}$ (ii) $\frac{8}{3}$ (iii) $\frac{11}{2}$ (iv) $\frac{11}{4}$ (v) $\frac{16}{3}$

    (vi) $\frac{25}{6}$ (vii) $\frac{29}{3}$ (viii) $\frac{47}{11}$ (ix) $\frac{63}{10}$ (x) $\frac{43}{8}$

3. Express each of these mixed numbers as an improper fraction:

    (i) $1\frac{2}{3}$ (ii) $2\frac{2}{5}$ (iii) $2\frac{3}{8}$ (iv) $3\frac{3}{4}$ (v) $3\frac{4}{5}$

    (vi) $4\frac{2}{3}$ (vii) $6\frac{2}{3}$ (viii) $5\frac{2}{9}$ (ix) $3\frac{7}{10}$ (x) $5\frac{4}{9}$

4. By writing each pair of fractions with the same denominator, find which is the bigger fraction in each case:

    (i) $\frac{3}{5}$ or $\frac{2}{3}$ (ii) $\frac{2}{3}$ or $\frac{3}{4}$ (iii) $\frac{2}{5}$ or $\frac{3}{7}$ (iv) $\frac{3}{4}$ or $\frac{4}{7}$

    (v) $\frac{4}{7}$ or $\frac{3}{5}$ (vi) $\frac{5}{8}$ or $\frac{4}{5}$ (vii) $\frac{2}{9}$ or $\frac{1}{5}$ (viii) $\frac{7}{10}$ or $\frac{3}{4}$

5. Work out each of these:

    (i) $\frac{1}{4}$ of 24   (ii) $\frac{3}{4}$ of 36   (iii) $\frac{2}{5}$ of 65

    (iv) $\frac{3}{10}$ of 80   (v) $\frac{4}{9}$ of 63   (vi) $\frac{4}{7}$ of 490

6. Find these amounts:

    (i) $\frac{5}{6}$ of 36 km   (ii) $\frac{3}{8}$ of €192   (iii) $\frac{7}{8}$ of 72 litres

    (iv) $\frac{5}{9}$ of 207 cm   (v) $\frac{5}{11}$ of €165   (vi) $\frac{6}{7}$ of 161 metres

7. Find the missing number in each of these:

    (i) $\frac{1}{3}$ of $\square$ = 8   (ii) $\frac{1}{\square}$ of 40 = 5   (iii) $\frac{1}{\square}$ of 12 = 3

    (iv) $\frac{2}{\square}$ of 18 = 12   (v) $\frac{\square}{5}$ of 30 = 18   (vi) $\frac{\square}{10}$ of 80 = 24

8. Put the digits in the boxes to make the calculation correct:

    (i) $\frac{\square}{\square}$ of $\square$ = $\square$ (ii) $\frac{\square}{\square}$ of $\square$ = $\square$ (iii) $\frac{\square}{\square}$ of $\square$ = $\square$

    　　3　4　6　8　　　　　9　2　6　3　　　　15　25　3　5

9. A store employs 115 people and $\frac{2}{5}$ of these are men.
   How many women does the store employ?

10. Darina sold 560 sandwiches today.
    $\frac{1}{4}$ were ham sandwiches, $\frac{2}{5}$ were salad, $\frac{1}{8}$ were tuna and the rest were cheese.
    How many of each type did Darina sell?

11. What words do these make?
  (i) The first $\frac{1}{3}$ of CAMERA and the second $\frac{1}{2}$ of LIVE
  (ii) The last $\frac{2}{5}$ of HIPPO, the first $\frac{1}{2}$ of LITTER and the last $\frac{3}{11}$ of MATHEMATICS.

12. A diagram of Jim's garden is shown.
  (i) Copy the diagram and shade $\frac{3}{4}$ of it.
  (ii) How many sixteenths are there in $\frac{3}{4}$?

Section 3.3 Adding and subtracting fractions

It is easy to add (or subtract) fractions which have the same denominator.
For example $\frac{4}{7} + \frac{5}{7} = \frac{9}{7} = 1\frac{2}{7}$

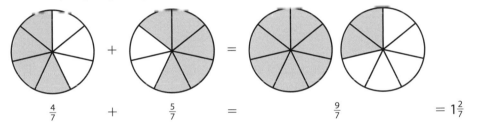

$$\frac{4}{7} \quad + \quad \frac{5}{7} \quad = \quad \frac{9}{7} \quad = 1\frac{2}{7}$$

The diagrams above show that when adding fractions with the same denominator, you add the numerators and keep the **same** denominator.

Thus $\frac{2}{9} + \frac{3}{9} = \frac{5}{9}$ and $\frac{6}{11} - \frac{2}{11} = \frac{4}{11}$

Fractions with different denominators

How do we add $\frac{2}{3} + \frac{4}{5}$?

We must first write each fraction so that they have the same denominator.

The smallest number into which both 3 and 5 divide is 15.

$$\frac{2}{3} = \frac{2 \times 5}{3 \times 5} = \frac{10}{15} \text{ and } \frac{4}{5} = \frac{4 \times 3}{5 \times 3} = \frac{12}{15}$$

Now $\frac{10}{15} + \frac{12}{15} = \frac{22}{15} = 1\frac{7}{15}$

Similarly $\frac{8}{9} - \frac{5}{6} = \frac{16}{18} - \frac{15}{18}$

$= \frac{1}{18}$

18 is the LCM of 9 and 6.

Shorter method

We added fractions above using this method:

$$\frac{3}{4} + \frac{4}{5} = \frac{15}{20} + \frac{16}{20} = \frac{31}{20} = 1\frac{11}{20}$$

Your work could also be laid out in the following way:

$$\frac{3}{4} + \frac{4}{5} = \frac{3(5) + 4(4)}{20}$$

$$= \frac{15 + 16}{20} = \frac{31}{20} = 1\frac{11}{20}$$

Adding and subtracting mixed numbers

To find $4\frac{3}{4} + 2\frac{1}{6}$, first add the whole numbers 4 and 2, then add the two fractions $\frac{3}{4}$ and $\frac{1}{6}$.

Thus $\quad 4\frac{3}{4} + 2\frac{1}{6} = 4 + 2 + \frac{3}{4} + \frac{1}{6}$

$$= 6 + \frac{9}{12} + \frac{2}{12}$$

$$= 6\frac{11}{12}$$

Another way

$4\frac{3}{4} + 2\frac{1}{6} = \frac{19}{4} + \frac{13}{6}$

$$= \frac{19(6) + 13(4)}{24}$$

$$= \frac{114 + 52}{24}$$

$$= \frac{166}{24} = \frac{83}{12}$$

$$= 6\frac{11}{12}$$

When subtracting mixed numbers such as $3\frac{1}{4} - 2\frac{3}{8}$, first change each number to an improper fraction and then subtract as follows:

$$3\frac{1}{4} - 2\frac{3}{8} = \frac{13}{4} - \frac{19}{8}$$

$$= \frac{26}{8} - \frac{19}{8} = \frac{7}{8}$$

Example 1

Simplify $1\frac{3}{4} + 4\frac{5}{6} - 3\frac{2}{3}$.

First add $1\frac{3}{4}$ and $4\frac{5}{6}$

$$1\frac{3}{4} + 4\frac{5}{6} = 1 + 4 + \frac{3}{4} + \frac{5}{6}$$

$$= 1 + 4 + \frac{9}{12} + \frac{10}{12}$$

$$= 5 + \frac{19}{12} = 5 + 1\frac{7}{12} = 6\frac{7}{12}$$

Now $6\frac{7}{12} - 3\frac{2}{3} = \frac{79}{12} - \frac{11}{3}$

$$= \frac{79}{12} - \frac{44}{12} = \frac{35}{12} = 2\frac{11}{12}$$

Now try it this way! $\quad 1\frac{3}{4} + 4\frac{5}{6} - 3\frac{2}{3}$

$$= \frac{7}{4} + \frac{29}{6} - \frac{11}{3}$$

Exercise 3.3

1. Copy and complete the fraction additions shown by these two diagrams:
   (no need to copy diagrams)

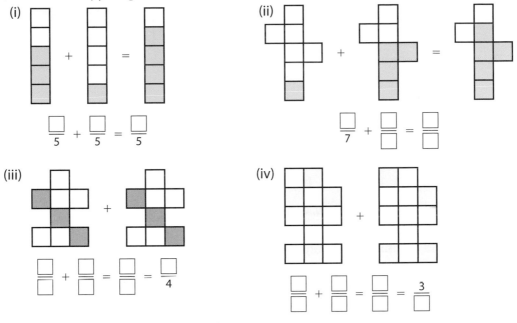

(i)

$$\frac{\square}{5} + \frac{\square}{5} = \frac{\square}{5}$$

(ii)

$$\frac{\square}{7} + \frac{\square}{\square} = \frac{\square}{\square}$$

(iii)

$$\frac{\square}{\square} + \frac{\square}{\square} = \frac{\square}{\square} = \frac{\square}{4}$$

(iv)

$$\frac{\square}{\square} + \frac{\square}{\square} = \frac{\square}{\square} = \frac{3}{\square}$$

2. Work out each of these and simplify your answer where possible.

   (i) $\frac{2}{5} + \frac{1}{5}$

   (ii) $\frac{3}{7} + \frac{2}{7}$

   (iii) $\frac{1}{9} + \frac{2}{9} + \frac{4}{9}$

   (iv) $\frac{4}{11} + \frac{2}{11} + \frac{1}{11}$

   (v) $\frac{8}{9} - \frac{2}{9}$

   (vi) $\frac{9}{10} - \frac{4}{10}$

   (vii) $\frac{5}{7} + \frac{4}{7} - \frac{6}{7}$

   (viii) $\frac{9}{13} - \frac{3}{13} + \frac{5}{13}$

   (ix) $\frac{7}{8} + \frac{5}{8} - \frac{3}{8}$

3. Simplify these calculations as far as possible:

   (i) $\frac{1}{4} + \frac{3}{8}$

   (ii) $\frac{3}{10} + \frac{2}{5}$

   (iii) $\frac{5}{6} + \frac{2}{3}$

   (iv) $\frac{3}{7} + \frac{1}{14}$

   (v) $\frac{5}{12} + \frac{3}{4}$

   (vi) $\frac{2}{5} - \frac{1}{15}$

   (vii) $\frac{2}{3} - \frac{1}{4}$

   (viii) $\frac{9}{14} - \frac{1}{7}$

   (ix) $\frac{11}{20} - \frac{1}{5}$

4. Work out each of the following and simplify your answers:

   (i) $\frac{1}{3} + \frac{2}{5} + \frac{1}{15}$

   (ii) $\frac{3}{8} + \frac{1}{6} + \frac{2}{3}$

   (iii) $\frac{5}{12} + \frac{3}{4} + \frac{1}{3}$

   (iv) $\frac{2}{9} + \frac{1}{3} + \frac{1}{6}$

   (v) $\frac{3}{4} + \frac{1}{2} - \frac{1}{3}$

   (vi) $\frac{7}{12} + \frac{1}{8} - \frac{1}{6}$

5. Work these out and simplify your answers:

   (i) $2\frac{1}{3} + 1\frac{1}{6}$

   (ii) $2\frac{1}{4} + 1\frac{1}{3}$

   (iii) $3\frac{1}{2} + 2\frac{3}{5}$

   (iv) $3\frac{3}{10} + 1\frac{4}{5}$

   (v) $1\frac{3}{4} + 2\frac{5}{12}$

   (vi) $4\frac{1}{5} + 1\frac{1}{3}$

   (vii) $2\frac{7}{10} + 1\frac{3}{5}$

   (viii) $3\frac{1}{5} + 2\frac{2}{3}$

   (ix) $3\frac{2}{3} - 2\frac{1}{2}$

6. Match each calculation with its result.

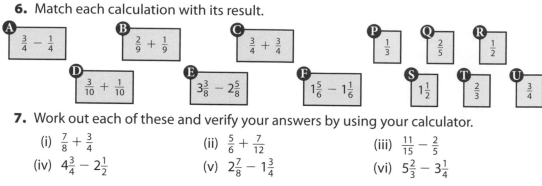

A $\frac{3}{4} - \frac{1}{4}$ **B** $\frac{2}{9} + \frac{1}{9}$ **C** $\frac{3}{4} + \frac{3}{4}$ **P** $\frac{1}{3}$ **Q** $\frac{2}{5}$ **R** $\frac{1}{2}$

D $\frac{3}{10} + \frac{1}{10}$ **E** $3\frac{3}{8} - 2\frac{5}{8}$ **F** $1\frac{5}{6} - 1\frac{1}{6}$ **S** $1\frac{1}{2}$ **T** $\frac{2}{3}$ **U** $\frac{3}{4}$

7. Work out each of these and verify your answers by using your calculator.

   (i) $\frac{7}{8} + \frac{3}{4}$ (ii) $\frac{5}{6} + \frac{7}{12}$ (iii) $\frac{11}{15} - \frac{2}{5}$

  (iv) $4\frac{3}{4} - 2\frac{1}{2}$ (v) $2\frac{7}{8} - 1\frac{3}{4}$ (vi) $5\frac{2}{3} - 3\frac{1}{4}$

8. Work out each of these and verify your answers by using a calculator.

   (i) $5\frac{3}{4} - 2\frac{1}{3}$ (ii) $4\frac{3}{10} - 2\frac{2}{5}$ (iii) $5\frac{2}{9} + 3\frac{1}{3}$

  (iv) $4\frac{3}{8} + 2\frac{1}{2} + 1\frac{3}{4}$ (v) $2\frac{7}{10} + 2\frac{3}{5} - 3\frac{1}{2}$ (vi) $3\frac{5}{8} + 2\frac{3}{4} - 4\frac{1}{6}$

9. In a magic square each row, each column and
each diagonal add up to the same number.
Copy and complete this magic square.

$5\frac{1}{3}$		
$\frac{2}{3}$	$3\frac{1}{3}$	6

Section 3.4 Multiplying fractions

If you study the diagram on the right, you will see that $\frac{1}{2}$ of $\frac{2}{3}$ is $\frac{1}{3}$.

Also $\frac{1}{2} \times \frac{2}{3} = \frac{2 \times 1}{2 \times 3} = \frac{2}{6} = \frac{1}{3}$.

This illustrates that 'of' is the same as 'multiply by'.

Now $\frac{1}{2}$ of $\frac{4}{5} = \frac{2}{5}$ and $\frac{1}{2} \times \frac{4}{5} = \frac{4}{10} = \frac{2}{5}$

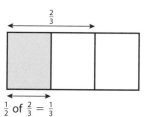

$\frac{1}{2}$ of $\frac{2}{3} = \frac{1}{3}$

> When multiplying two fractions, multiply the
> numerators together and the denominators together.

When multiplying mixed numbers such as $2\frac{1}{4} \times 1\frac{2}{3}$, change the mixed numbers to
improper fractions as follows:

$$2\frac{1}{4} \times 1\frac{2}{3} = \frac{9}{4} \times \frac{5}{3} = \frac{45}{12} = 3\frac{9}{12} = 3\frac{3}{4}$$

Example 1

Simplify   (i) $\frac{4}{5} \times \frac{2}{3}$ (ii) $2\frac{1}{3} \times 3\frac{1}{2}$

            $\frac{4}{5} \times \frac{2}{3} = \frac{8}{15}$ $2\frac{1}{3} \times 3\frac{1}{2}$

                                    $= \frac{7}{3} \times \frac{7}{2} = \frac{49}{6} = 8\frac{1}{6}$

Cancelling

Sometimes when multiplying two fractions, we can simplify our work by dividing the numerator and denominator by a common factor. This is know as *cancelling*.

Now $\quad \dfrac{3}{8} \times \dfrac{4}{9} = \dfrac{12}{72} = \dfrac{1}{6} \quad$ or $\quad \dfrac{1\cancel{3}}{\cancel{8}_2} \times \dfrac{1\cancel{4}}{\cancel{9}_3} = \dfrac{1 \times 1}{2 \times 3} = \dfrac{1}{6}$

Example 2

Work out $\quad$ (i) $\; 1\frac{3}{4} \times 2\frac{2}{3}$ $\qquad\qquad$ (ii) $\; 1\frac{3}{7} \times \frac{21}{35}$

$$1\frac{3}{4} \times 2\frac{2}{3} = \frac{7}{1\cancel{4}} \times \frac{\cancel{8}^2}{3}$$

$$= \frac{14}{3} = 4\frac{2}{3}$$

$$1\frac{3}{7} \times \frac{21}{35} = \frac{^2\cancel{10}}{_1\cancel{7}} \times \frac{^3\cancel{21}}{\cancel{35}_7}$$

$$= \frac{2 \times 3}{1 \times 7} = \frac{6}{7}$$

When using your calculator to work out $\frac{3}{4} \times \frac{2}{5}$, key in

$\boxed{\tiny\frac{\blacksquare}{\square}}\ \boxed{3}\ \boxed{\downarrow}\ \boxed{4}\ \boxed{\rightarrow}\ \boxed{\times}\ \boxed{\tiny\frac{\blacksquare}{\square}}\ \boxed{2}\ \boxed{\downarrow}\ \boxed{5}\ \boxed{\rightarrow}\ \boxed{=}$

The result is $\frac{3}{10}$.

To find the value of $2\frac{1}{3} \times 3\frac{1}{2}$, key in

$\boxed{\text{SHIFT}}\ \boxed{\tiny\frac{\blacksquare}{\square}}\ \boxed{2}\ \boxed{\rightarrow}\ \boxed{1}\ \boxed{\downarrow}\ \boxed{3}\ \boxed{\rightarrow}\ \boxed{\times}\ \boxed{\tiny\frac{\blacksquare}{\square}}\ \boxed{3}\ \boxed{\rightarrow}\ \boxed{1}\ \boxed{\downarrow}\ \boxed{2}\ \boxed{\rightarrow}\ \boxed{=}$

The answer is $8\frac{1}{6}$.

Note 1 If you convert $2\frac{1}{3} \times 3\frac{1}{2}$ to $\frac{7}{3} \times \frac{7}{2}$, it can be done much more quickly on a calculator.

To find $\frac{7}{3} \times \frac{7}{2}$, key in $\boxed{\tiny\frac{\blacksquare}{\square}}\ \boxed{7}\ \boxed{\downarrow}\ \boxed{3}\ \boxed{\rightarrow}\ \boxed{\times}\ \boxed{\tiny\frac{\blacksquare}{\square}}\ \boxed{7}\ \boxed{\downarrow}\ \boxed{2}\ \boxed{\rightarrow}\ \boxed{=}$

The result is $8\frac{1}{6}$.

Note 2 When multiplying a fraction by a whole number, e.g. $3\frac{1}{2} \times 8$, write 8 as $\frac{8}{1}$ and proceed as follows:

$$3\frac{1}{2} \times 8 = \frac{7}{2} \times \frac{8}{1} = \frac{56}{2} = 28$$

Exercise 3.4

Work out each of the following and give your answer in its simplest form.

1. $\frac{1}{2} \times \frac{3}{4}$ $\qquad\qquad$ **2.** $\frac{3}{4} \times \frac{1}{5}$ $\qquad\qquad$ **3.** $\frac{3}{4} \times \frac{3}{5}$

4. $\frac{4}{5} \times \frac{2}{3}$ $\qquad\qquad$ **5.** $\frac{4}{7} \times \frac{2}{3}$ $\qquad\qquad$ **6.** $\frac{3}{4} \times \frac{8}{9}$

7. $\frac{3}{4} \times \frac{4}{5}$ $\qquad\qquad$ **8.** $\frac{8}{9} \times \frac{3}{10}$ $\qquad\qquad$ **9.** $\frac{3}{4} \times \frac{2}{21}$

10. $\frac{5}{6} \times \frac{2}{15}$ $\qquad\qquad$ **11.** $\frac{7}{12} \times \frac{18}{35}$ $\qquad\qquad$ **12.** $\frac{3}{16} \times \frac{8}{9}$

13. $\frac{2}{3} \times \frac{6}{7} \times \frac{3}{4}$ **14.** $\frac{3}{7} \times \frac{5}{9} \times \frac{21}{5}$ **15.** $\frac{1}{2} \times \frac{7}{12} \times \frac{6}{7}$

16. $2\frac{2}{3} \times 1\frac{1}{4}$ **17.** $4\frac{1}{5} \times \frac{5}{7}$ **18.** $1\frac{4}{5} \times 2\frac{1}{3}$

19. $3\frac{3}{4} \times 1\frac{2}{5}$ **20.** $1\frac{2}{5} \times 2\frac{1}{7}$ **21.** $3\frac{3}{4} \times 1\frac{1}{5}$

22. $4\frac{3}{5} \times 5$ **23.** $1\frac{7}{8} \times 8$ **24.** $\frac{7}{10} \times 20$

25. $3\frac{5}{7} \times 14$ **26.** $28 \times 2\frac{3}{7}$ **27.** $\frac{5}{21} \times 14$

28. Work out each answer and use the code to change it to a letter. (You may need to simplify your answer.)

S	O	B	H	K	L	T	E	A	C	N	D
$\frac{2}{3}$	$\frac{3}{4}$	$1\frac{1}{2}$	$1\frac{2}{5}$	$1\frac{3}{5}$	$1\frac{4}{5}$	$2\frac{1}{3}$	$2\frac{1}{2}$	$2\frac{2}{3}$	$2\frac{3}{4}$	$3\frac{3}{4}$	$4\frac{3}{4}$

Then rearrange each set of letters to spell a piece of furniture.

  (i) $\frac{1}{4}$ of 19 $\frac{1}{5}$ of 8 $\frac{1}{3}$ of 2 $\frac{1}{4}$ of 10

  (ii) $\frac{1}{4}$ of 3 $\frac{1}{3}$ of 7 $\frac{1}{5}$ of 9 $\frac{1}{8}$ of 6 $\frac{1}{6}$ of 4

  (iii) $\frac{1}{2}$ of 3 $\frac{1}{4}$ of 11 $\frac{1}{5}$ of 7 $\frac{1}{4}$ of 15 $\frac{1}{2}$ of 5

29. Work these out. Cancel first and then simplify your answer where possible:

  (i) $\frac{3}{4} \times \frac{5}{7} \times \frac{2}{3}$ (ii) $\frac{9}{20} \times \frac{5}{6} \times \frac{4}{5}$ (iii) $3\frac{1}{3} \times 1\frac{4}{5} \times 2$

  (iv) $2\frac{3}{4} \times 1\frac{1}{11} \times \frac{1}{4}$ (v) $7\frac{1}{2} \times \frac{9}{10} \times 1\frac{1}{3}$ (vi) $3\frac{1}{5} \times 2\frac{1}{2} \times 1\frac{3}{4}$

Section 3.5 Dividing fractions

To find how many sixes in 24 we divide 24 by 6, i.e. $24 \div 6 = 4$.

In the same way, to find the number of *halves* in 3, we find $3 \div \frac{1}{2}$.

The diagram shows that there are 6 halves in 3, i.e. $3 \div \frac{1}{2} = 6$.

Thus $\frac{3}{1} \div \frac{1}{2}$ is the same as $\frac{3}{1} \times \frac{2}{1} = \frac{6}{1} = 6$.

Similarly $3 \div \frac{3}{5} = \frac{\cancel{3}}{1} \times \frac{5}{\cancel{3}_1}$

$$= 5$$

> To divide a number by a fraction, turn the fraction upside down and multiply.

Example 1

Work out   (i) $15 \div \frac{5}{8}$ (ii) $4\frac{1}{6} \div 1\frac{2}{3}$

  (i) $15 \div \frac{5}{8} = \frac{^3\cancel{15}}{1} \times \frac{8}{\cancel{5}_1} = \frac{24}{1} = 24$

  (ii) $4\frac{1}{6} \div 1\frac{2}{3} = \frac{25}{6} \div \frac{5}{3} = \frac{^5\cancel{25}}{_2\cancel{6}} \times \frac{\cancel{3}^1}{\cancel{5}_1} = \frac{5}{2} = 2\frac{1}{2}$

Exercise 3.5

1. Shane has $\frac{4}{5}$ of a bar of chocolate. He shares it equally between two people. What fraction of the bar do they each get?

2. Rewrite each of these as a multiplication and then work out the answer.
   - (i) $\frac{3}{4} \div \frac{1}{2}$
   - (ii) $\frac{5}{6} \div \frac{2}{3}$
   - (iii) $\frac{2}{5} \div \frac{9}{10}$
   - (iv) $\frac{7}{12} \div \frac{1}{6}$
   - (v) $6 \div \frac{3}{4}$
   - (vi) $12 \div \frac{4}{9}$
   - (vii) $16 \div \frac{8}{9}$
   - (viii) $27 \div \frac{3}{4}$

3. Work out each of the following:
   - (i) $3\frac{3}{4} \div \frac{3}{8}$
   - (ii) $2\frac{5}{8} \div \frac{3}{4}$
   - (iii) $2\frac{1}{10} \div \frac{3}{5}$
   - (iv) $2\frac{5}{8} \div \frac{7}{16}$
   - (v) $1\frac{1}{8} \div 2\frac{1}{4}$
   - (vi) $8\frac{1}{4} \div 1\frac{3}{8}$
   - (vii) $5\frac{5}{8} \div 6\frac{1}{4}$
   - (viii) $3\frac{1}{8} \div 3\frac{3}{4}$

4. Which diagram below matches $\frac{1}{4} \div 2$?

5. Work out each of these:
   - (i) $5\frac{3}{7} \div 1\frac{3}{7}$
   - (ii) $10\frac{5}{6} \div 3\frac{1}{4}$
   - (iii) $6\frac{2}{3} \div 2\frac{4}{9}$
   - (iv) $1\frac{4}{5} \div \frac{27}{10}$

6. Match each calculation to a diagram.

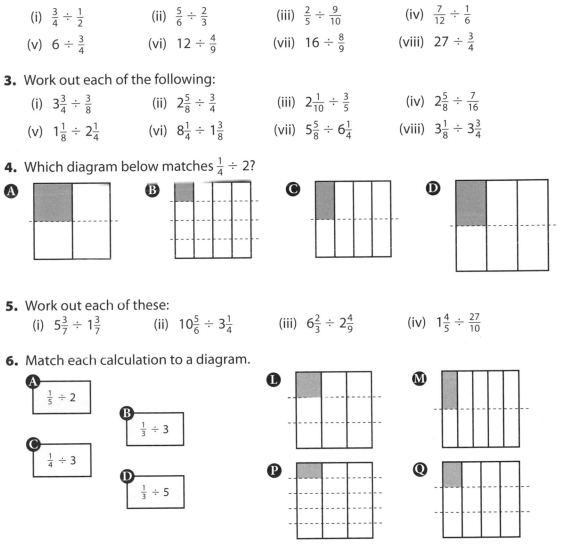

- **A** $\frac{1}{5} \div 2$
- **B** $\frac{1}{3} \div 3$
- **C** $\frac{1}{4} \div 3$
- **D** $\frac{1}{3} \div 5$

7. Simplify each of the following by first working out what is inside the brackets:
   - (i) $\left(\frac{3}{4} \times \frac{2}{9}\right) \div \frac{1}{12}$
   - (ii) $1\frac{1}{3} \times \left(\frac{3}{10} \div \frac{1}{2}\right)$
   - (iii) $\left(\frac{3}{4} \div \frac{7}{12}\right) \times 4\frac{2}{3}$

8. Denise has $\frac{1}{3}$ of a cake.
   She shares it equally between herself, her brother and her sister.
   What fraction of the cake do they each get?

9. Put these calculations into pairs which give the same answer.
Write down the answer to each pair.

A $\frac{1}{10}$ of $\frac{5}{6}$ **B** $\frac{1}{3} \times \frac{5}{6}$ **C** $\frac{1}{2} \times \frac{5}{6}$ **D** $\frac{5}{6} \div 2$

E $\frac{5}{6} \div 3$ **F** $\frac{1}{4}$ of $\frac{5}{6}$ **G** $\frac{5}{6} \div 4$ **H** $\frac{1}{10} \times \frac{5}{6}$

10. Simplify each of the following by first working out what is inside the brackets:

(i) $\left(\frac{3}{5} + \frac{1}{3}\right) \div \frac{2}{3}$ (ii) $\left(\frac{4}{9} + \frac{1}{3}\right) \times \frac{6}{7}$ (iii) $\frac{5}{8} \div \left(3\frac{1}{2} - 1\frac{1}{4}\right)$

11.

S	G	R	I	O	A	D	P	W	L	E	M
$\frac{1}{12}$	$\frac{1}{10}$	$\frac{1}{9}$	$\frac{1}{8}$	$\frac{1}{6}$	$\frac{3}{16}$	$\frac{1}{5}$	$\frac{1}{4}$	$\frac{3}{8}$	$\frac{1}{2}$	$\frac{2}{5}$	$\frac{3}{4}$

Work out each answer and use the code to change it to a letter.
Then rearrange each set of letters to spell a city.

(i) $\frac{4}{5} \div 2$ $\frac{1}{2}$ of $\frac{2}{9}$ $\frac{1}{2}$ of $1\frac{1}{2}$ $\frac{5}{6} \div 5$

(ii) $\frac{1}{10} \times \frac{5}{6}$ $\frac{1}{3}$ of $\frac{3}{4}$ $\frac{1}{16}$ of 3 $\frac{3}{8} \div 3$ $2 \times \frac{1}{18}$

(iii) $\frac{3}{5} \div 3$ $\frac{1}{2} \times \frac{2}{5}$ $\frac{1}{4}$ of 3 $\frac{1}{3} \times \frac{1}{3}$ $\frac{3}{8} \div 2$ $\frac{1}{4} \times \frac{1}{2}$

Section 3.6 Problems involving fractions

When solving problems involving fractions, you must decide whether to add, subtract, multiply or divide.

For example $\frac{3}{4}$ of 16 means $\frac{3}{4} \times \frac{16}{1} = \frac{48}{4} = 12$.

Example 1

Express 18 minutes as a fraction of an hour.
Give your answer in its simplest form.

To express one quantity as a fraction of another quantity, both quantities must be in the same units.

$\therefore \dfrac{18 \text{ minutes}}{1 \text{ hour}} = \dfrac{18}{60} \cdots \cdots$ both in minutes

$= \dfrac{3}{10} \cdots \cdots$ divide above and below by 6

Example 2

Ciara spent $\frac{3}{7}$ of her money and had €12 left.
How much had she at first?

If she spent $\frac{3}{7}$, she had $\frac{4}{7}$ left.

$\frac{4}{7} = €12$

$\therefore \frac{1}{7} = €3 \ldots\ldots$ divide by 4

$\therefore \frac{7}{7} = €21$

$\therefore$ she had €21 at first.

Exercise 3.6

1. Express the first quantity as a fraction of the second quantity, and give each fraction in its lowest terms:

   (i) 16, 24   (ii) 3 days, 1 week   (iii) 40 c, €2

   (iv) 24 mins, 2 hours   (v) €1.20, €3   (vi) 8 hours, 3 days

2. Hannah spends $\frac{1}{5}$ of her pocket money on sweets and $\frac{2}{3}$ on clothes.
   She saves the rest.
   What fraction of her pocket money does Hannah save?

3. The first $\frac{1}{2}$ of TANK is TA. The last $\frac{1}{3}$ of IRRITABLE is BLE.
   Put them together and you get TABLE.
   What words do these make?

   (i) The first $\frac{1}{3}$ of TRIANGLES and the second $\frac{1}{2}$ of STICKS

   (ii) The first $\frac{2}{5}$ of PRECIPICES and the last $\frac{2}{5}$ of VICTORIOUS

   (iii) The first $\frac{1}{3}$ of DISCUSSED, the first $\frac{1}{4}$ of APPLICATIONS and the last $\frac{3}{4}$ of FEAR

4. A journey to school consists of a $\frac{2}{5}$ km walk, then a $3\frac{1}{4}$ km bus journey, and finally a $\frac{1}{2}$ km walk from the bus stop to the school.
   Find the total length of the journey to school.

5. Find $\frac{3}{8}$ of €576.

6. In a bag of 56 coloured counters, $\frac{1}{4}$ are red, $\frac{2}{7}$ are blue and the rest are yellow.
   How many of the counters are yellow?

7. Emer bought a 3-hour blank video tape. She recorded programmes lasting $1\frac{1}{2}$ hours, $\frac{3}{4}$ hour and $\frac{2}{3}$ hour on this tape.
   How many minutes recording time were left on the tape?

8. Three quarters of a certain number is 27.
   Find (i) $\frac{1}{4}$ of the number.
         (ii) the whole number.

9. Alan spent $\frac{4}{9}$ of his money. If he had €65 left, how much had he at first?

10. How many $1\frac{1}{4}$ litre cartons of orange juice can be filled from a container holding 40 litres?

11. $\frac{3}{7}$ of the students in first-year are girls.
    If there are 64 boys in first-year, find the number of girls in the year.

12. $\frac{2}{5}$ of the spectators at a football match were in the terraces and the remaining 17 580 were in the stands. Find the total number of spectators at the match.

13. How many $\frac{1}{4}$ litre glasses can be filled from a container which contains $4\frac{1}{2}$ litres.

14. A ferry completes one crossing in $1\frac{1}{2}$ hours.
    What is the greatest number of crossings it can make in a 24 hour period?

15. Which of the letters on the line below corresponds to $\frac{5}{8}$?

16. A class of 30 students went to a fast-food bar.
    $\frac{3}{10}$ of them bought a hamburger, $\frac{2}{5}$ of them bought a pizza and the remainder bought chips.
    (i) What fraction of the students bought chips?
    (ii) How many students bought a pizza?

Test yourself 3

1. Express each of the following fractions in its simplest form:
   (i) $\frac{5}{15}$ (ii) $\frac{12}{16}$ (iii) $\frac{16}{24}$ (iv) $\frac{18}{30}$ (v) $\frac{21}{28}$

2. Express each of the following as an improper fraction (e.g. $1\frac{1}{4} = \frac{5}{4}$)
   (i) $1\frac{1}{2}$ (ii) $2\frac{1}{4}$ (iii) $3\frac{2}{3}$ (iv) $4\frac{3}{4}$ (v) $2\frac{4}{5}$

3. Copy and complete the following:
   (i) $\frac{1}{6} = \frac{?}{12}$ (ii) $\frac{2}{5} = \frac{6}{?}$ (iii) $\frac{4}{7} = \frac{12}{?}$

4. Perform the following operations and simplify your answers where possible:
   (i) $\frac{1}{2} + \frac{1}{3}$ (ii) $\frac{5}{8} + \frac{3}{4}$ (iii) $\frac{5}{6} + \frac{2}{3}$ (iv) $\frac{5}{7} + \frac{3}{14}$
   (v) $\frac{1}{2} - \frac{1}{3}$ (vi) $\frac{1}{3} - \frac{1}{4}$ (vii) $\frac{3}{4} - \frac{2}{3}$ (viii) $\frac{3}{4} - \frac{5}{12}$

5. To what fraction is each of the following arrows pointing?

6. Express each pair of fractions with the same denominator and then state the bigger fraction:
   (i) $\frac{3}{4}$ or $\frac{2}{3}$ (ii) $\frac{1}{3}$ or $\frac{2}{5}$ (iii) $\frac{2}{3}$ or $\frac{7}{12}$ (iv) $\frac{7}{10}$ or $\frac{3}{4}$

7. Express each of the following as a single fraction or whole number.
   (i) $\frac{3}{4} \times \frac{2}{5}$ (ii) $\frac{1}{4} \times 8$ (iii) $3\frac{1}{4} \times \frac{1}{2}$ (iv) $4\frac{1}{2} \times \frac{2}{3}$
   (v) $\frac{3}{4} \div \frac{1}{2}$ (vi) $\frac{5}{8} \div \frac{3}{4}$ (vii) $\frac{4}{9} \div \frac{2}{3}$ (viii) $2\frac{2}{3} \div \frac{2}{3}$

8. Work out each answer and use the code to change it to a letter. Then rearrange each set of letters to spell an item of food.

R	A	D	S	C	B	E	H	I	F	T	P
$\frac{6}{7}$	$1\frac{1}{5}$	$1\frac{1}{3}$	$1\frac{1}{2}$	$1\frac{2}{3}$	$2\frac{1}{4}$	$2\frac{2}{5}$	$2\frac{4}{5}$	$3\frac{1}{5}$	$3\frac{3}{5}$	$3\frac{3}{4}$	$6\frac{3}{4}$

   (i) $\frac{2}{5} \times 8$ $\frac{2}{3} \times 5$ $\frac{2}{5} \times 7$ $\frac{3}{4} \times 2$
   (ii) $\frac{2}{5}$ of 6 $\frac{3}{7}$ of 2 $\frac{2}{5}$ of 3 $\frac{2}{3}$ of 2 $\frac{3}{4}$ of 3
   (iii) $\frac{3}{10}$ of 4 $\frac{3}{5}$ of 2 $\frac{3}{8}$ of 4 $\frac{3}{4}$ of 9 $\frac{5}{8}$ of 6

9. Simplify each of these:
   (i) $\frac{8}{9} + \frac{2}{3}$ (ii) $2\frac{9}{10} - 1\frac{3}{5}$ (iii) $2\frac{2}{3} \times 2\frac{1}{4}$ (iv) $2\frac{4}{5} \div \frac{7}{10}$

10. A mother walks from home to the shop and then on to the school. If she then walks $1\frac{1}{2}$ km back to her home as show on the right, find how many km she walked.

11. Niamh spent $\frac{1}{4}$ of her pocket money and had €10.50 left. How much pocket money did she have at first?

12. 24 boys and 36 girls applied to go on a mountaineering course. $\frac{3}{4}$ of the boys and $\frac{2}{3}$ of the girls were selected. Find the total number that went on the course.

13. (i) What fraction of this figure is shaded?

    (ii) How many more squares would have to be shaded for $\frac{3}{4}$ of the figure to be shaded?

14. A farmer had 240 animals on his farm. $\frac{5}{8}$ of them were sheep, $\frac{1}{10}$ were pigs, six of them were horses and the rest were cows. How many cows did he have?

15. Simplify each of the following by first working out what is inside the brackets?
    (i) $\left(\frac{2}{3} \times \frac{1}{2}\right) \div \frac{3}{4}$
    (ii) $\left(3\frac{1}{7} - 1\frac{1}{2}\right) \times 14$
    (iii) $\left(1\frac{3}{5} + 2\frac{2}{3}\right) \times \frac{5}{8}$

16.

	Men	Women	Children
Fraction of people	$\frac{3}{10}$	$\frac{1}{10}$	A
Number of people	B	50	C

The table above shows information about the number of people watching a fireworks display.
    (i) Find the fraction marked A.
    (ii) Work out the numbers marked B and C.

For the problem solver...

1. A ball is dropped onto a hard surface. Each time it bounces, it rebounds to exactly one third of the height from which it fell. After the second bounce the ball rises to a height of 9 cm.
   From what height was it originally dropped?

2. Each morning Alan walks at a steady rate to school. When he has gone a quarter of the way he passes the clock tower; at one third of the way he passes the railway station. At the clock tower its clock shows 8.30 and at the railway station its clock shows 8.35.
   When does Alan leave his house and when does he reach school?

3. Johnny was 16 minutes late for school on Monday. Each day after that he hurries more and more so that he manages to halve the amount of time that he arrives late for school each day.
   On what day of the week does he arrive just 15 seconds late?
   A Monday   B Tuesday   C Wednesday   D Thursday   E Friday

4. A passenger fell asleep on a train when it was half way to his destination.
   He slept till he had half as far to go as he went while he slept.
   What fraction of the whole trip was he sleeping?

5. The numbers $\frac{1}{2}$, x, y, $\frac{3}{4}$ are in increasing order of size.
   The differences between successive numbers in this list are all the same.
   What is the value of y?

6. Each empty square contains either a number or a mathematical symbol ($+$, $-$, $\times$, $\div$).
   Copy the square and fill in the missing details.
   The colour squares are not included.

3	÷	2	→	
÷		÷		
8	÷		→	$\frac{1}{2}$
↓		↓		↓
		$\frac{1}{8}$	→	3

7. If to the numerator and denominator of the fraction $\frac{1}{3}$ you add its denominator 3, the fraction will double.
   Find a fraction which will triple when its denominator is added to its numerator and to its denominator.

chapter 4 Decimals

Key words

decimal point   decimals   units   tenths   hundredths   thousandths

digit   fractions   recurring decimals   rough estimates   rounding

Section 4.1 Decimals – Addition and subtraction

Hundreds	Tens	Units	•	Tenths	Hundredths	Thousandths
	5	4	•	6	5	3

A Formula One Grand Prix driver had his lap time recorded at 54.653 seconds.

This is a decimal number.

The decimal point separates the whole number from fractions.

In the number 54.653,

the digit 6 $= \frac{6}{10}$; the digit 5 $= \frac{5}{100}$; the digit 3 $= \frac{3}{1000}$

Thus $54.653 = 54 + \frac{6}{10} + \frac{5}{100} + \frac{3}{1000}$

$$= 54 + \frac{600}{1000} + \frac{50}{1000} + \frac{3}{1000}$$

$$= 54\frac{653}{1000}$$

If you examine the numbers below you will see how a decimal can be changed to a fraction and then simplified.

(i) $0.7 = \frac{7}{10}$

(ii) $0.25 = \frac{25}{100} = \frac{5}{20} = \frac{1}{4}$

(iii) $0.125 = \frac{125}{1000} = \frac{25}{200} = \frac{5}{40} = \frac{1}{8}$

> The first digit after the decimal point has 10 as denominator; the first two digits have 100 as denominator; the first three digits have 1000 as denominator.

Example 1

Find the value of the underlined digit in each of these:
  (i) 12.4<u>8</u>   (ii) 28.4<u>6</u>3   (iii) 6.75<u>4</u>   (iv) 3<u>5</u>.079

  (i)   In the decimal 12.48, the 4 represents $\frac{4}{10}$.
  (ii) In the decimal 28.463, the 6 represents $\frac{6}{100}$.
  (iii) In the decimal 6.754, the 4 represents $\frac{4}{1000}$.
  (iv) In the decimal 35.079, the 5 represents 5 units.

A **number line** may be used to represent decimals.

The number line below shows 10 divisions between 0 and 1.

Each division is worth 0.1.

A = 0.3
B = 0.8

Example 2

Write each of these fractions as a decimal:
  (i) $\frac{9}{10}$ (ii) $\frac{17}{100}$ (iii) $\frac{113}{1000}$ (iv) $\frac{6}{100}$ (v) $\frac{27}{1000}$

  (i) $\frac{9}{10} = 0.9$ (ii) $\frac{17}{100} = 0.17$ (iii) $\frac{113}{1000} = 0.113$
  (iv) $\frac{6}{100} = 0.06$ (v) $\frac{27}{1000} = 0.027$

Adding and Subtracting Decimals

Decimals are added and subtracted in the same way as whole numbers provided that the decimal points are lined up directly beneath one another.

Example 3

Find   (i) 146.076 + 12.34 + 1.6   (ii) 39.45 − 12.876

(i) 146.076
      12.34
       1.6
    ‾‾‾‾‾‾‾‾
     160.016

(ii) 39.450
      12.876
     ‾‾‾‾‾‾‾‾
      26.574

Exercise 4.1

1. Write the value of the underlined digit in each of the following:
   (i) 2.7̲4   (ii) 12.3̲6   (iii) 1.2̲74   (iv) 13.21̲7
   (v) 16.07̲3   (vi) 28.10̲9   (vii) 13̲6.8   (viii) 0.00̲7

2. Write the value of each underlined digit in words:
   (i) 2̲6.32   (ii) 14.5̲7   (iii) 1.26̲5   (iv) 0.70̲4

3. Write these numbers as decimals:
   (i) four and three tenths   (ii) sixteen and seven hundredths
   (iii) seventeen hundredths   (iv) six and three hundredths
   (v) twelve and twenty eight thousandths

4. Write the following decimals as fractions in their lowest terms:
   (i) 0.1   (ii) 0.3   (iii) 0.5   (iv) 0.8   (v) 0.6

5. Write each of these as a fraction and simplify your answer:
   (i) 0.25   (ii) 0.75   (iii) 0.28   (iv) 0.05   (v) 0.08

6. Write each of the following fractions as a decimal:
   (i) $\frac{9}{10}$ (ii) $\frac{1}{10}$ (iii) $\frac{5}{10}$ (iv) $\frac{8}{10}$ (v) $\frac{7}{10}$
   (vi) $\frac{16}{100}$ (vii) $\frac{28}{100}$ (viii) $\frac{25}{100}$ (ix) $\frac{75}{100}$ (x) $\frac{9}{100}$

7. Write as a decimal the number shown by each arrow:

8. Simplify each of these without using a calculator:
   (i) 12.24 + 6.72 + 14.4   (ii) 3.04 + 6.128 + 13.2
   (iii) 8.056 + 14.2 + 6.17   (iv) 0.462 + 1.8 + 3.07

9. Subtract each of the following:
   (i) 18.4 − 3.8   (ii) 14.05 − 1.62   (iii) 12.98 − 3.7
   (iv) 27.062 − 1.95   (v) 7.1 − 3.94   (vi) 3.016 − 0.99

10. Simplify each of these without using a calculator:
    (i) 26.84 + 5.06 − 12.97   (ii) 131.6 − 8.97 + 13.52
    (iii) 14.08 + 126.3 − 94.071   (iv) 39.01 − 16.94 + 27.494

11. Insert a decimal point in each of the following numbers:
   (i)   257 so that the 5 represents *five tenths*
   (ii) 147 so that the 4 represents *four units*
   (iii) 854 so that the 8 represents *eighty*
   (iv) 6253 so that the 3 represents *three hundredths*
   (v)   2146 so that the 6 represents *six thousandths*
   (vi) 14 so that the 4 represents *four thousandths*

12. What decimal of each of the following figures is shaded?
   (i)

   (ii)

13. Find the decimal that is half-way between the numbers in each of these pairs:
   (i)   0.5 and 0.6   (ii) 3.4 and 3.5   (iii) 4.6 and 4.7
   (iv) 7.6 and 8   (v)   2.46 and 2.47   (vi) 0 and 0.1

14. Rearrange each of these decimals in order of size, starting with the smallest.
   (i)   0.4, 0.3, 0.45, 0.36, 0.08, 0.5   (ii) 2.4, 2.52, 1.96, 2.73, 2.09, 2.17

15. In the number 138.274, which digit represents
   (i)   tens   (ii) units   (iii) hundreds   (iv) tenths   (v)   hundredths?

16. (i) Make the largest number you can with these
        cards. There must be at least one digit after the
        decimal point. The last digit must not be zero.

        5   6   0   8   .

   (ii) Make the smallest number you can with the cards above.
        There must be at least one digit before the decimal point.
        The first digit must not be zero.

17. **Puzzle**
   I am a four-digit number with the decimal _ _ . _ _ point in the centre.
   Just two of my digits are the same.
   My tens digit is smaller than my units digit.
   My units digit is the same as my tenths digit.
   My tens digit is one less than my hundredths digit.
   My digits add up to 11.
   What number am I?

Section 4.2 Multiplying and dividing decimals

1. Multiplying and dividing by 10, 100, 1000, ...

To multiply a decimal by 10, move the decimal point **one place** to the right, e.g.,

$$1.46 \times 10 = 14.6$$

When multiplying a number by **100** move the decimal point **2 places** to the right.

When multiplying a number by **1000** move the decimal point **3 places** to the right.

Examples: (i) $12.367 \times 100 = 1236.7$ (ii) $1.489 \times 1000 = 1489$

Similarly, when **dividing** by 10, 100 or 1000, move the decimal point 1, 2 or 3 places to the **left**.

Examples: (i) $28 \div 10 = 2.8$ (ii) $128.3 \div 100 = 1.283$
   (iii) $14.9 \div 1000 = 0.0149$

2. Multiplying decimals

If you multiply 8.4 by 1.2 on your calculator you will get the answer 10.08.

Notice that there is **one** digit after the decimal point in each of the numbers that we multiplied.

Notice also that there are **two** digits after the decimal point in the answer.

$$8.\underline{4} \times 1.\underline{2} = 10.\underline{08}$$
$$\text{one} + \text{one} = \text{two}$$

Similarly   (i) $1.46 \times 1.1 = 1.606$ (ii) $1.273 \times 9 = 11.457$
      (2 places) × (1 place) = (3 places)   (3 places) × (no place) = (3 places)

Rule

When multiplying two decimals, the number of digits after the decimal point in the answer will be equal to the sum of the numbers of digits after the decimal point in the two decimals to be multiplied.

Example 1

Find   (i) 14.72×1.8 (ii) 0.4×0.02

(i) 14.72×1.8 $= 26.496$
    (2 places) × (1 place) = (3 places)
    (To perform 14.72×1.8, first multiply the whole numbers 1472 and 18
    and then insert the decimal point in your answer.)
(ii) 0.4×0.02 $= 0.008$
    (1 place) × (2 places) = (3 places)

3. Dividing decimals

When dividing decimals by a whole number, keep the decimal points in line as shown below.

(i) 16.45 ÷ 5 is

$$5\overline{\smash{)}16.45} \atop 3.29$$

(ii) 77.16 ÷ 12 is

$$12\overline{\smash{)}77.16} \atop 6.43$$

When dividing a number by a decimal, e.g. $\dfrac{9}{0.3}$, change the denominator into a whole number as follows:

$$\frac{9}{0.3} = \frac{9 \times 10}{0.3 \times 10} = \frac{90}{3} = 30$$

Similarly

$$\frac{1.284}{0.12} = \frac{1.284 \times 100}{0.12 \times 100}$$

$$= \frac{128.4}{12} = 10.7$$

Exercise 4.2

(Do not use a calculator in these exercises.)

1. Write down the answer to each of these:

(i) 72 × 10   (ii) 12 × 100   (iii) 4 × 1000

(iv) 1.6 × 10   (v) 1.34 × 100   (vi) 14.8 × 100

(vii) 2.136 × 1000   (viii) 4.85 × 1000   (ix) 0.74 × 1000

2. Find the value of each of the following:

(i) 174 ÷ 10   (ii) 18.4 ÷ 10   (iii) 1.74 ÷ 10

(iv) 387 ÷ 100   (v) 12.8 ÷ 100   (vi) 1.8 ÷ 100

(vii) 387 ÷ 1000   (viii) 14.6 ÷ 1000   (ix) 8.9 ÷ 1000

3. Work these out:

(i) 2.3 × 100   (ii) 6.74 × 100   (iii) 86 ÷ 100   (iv) 100 × 0.34

(v) 3.28 ÷ 100   (vi) 4 ÷ 100   (vii) 0.047 × 100   (viii) 158 ÷ 100

4. Write down the answer to each of these:

(i) 1.2 × 4   (ii) 3.1 × 5   (iii) 8 × 0.12   (iv) 1.2 × 0.4

(v) 3.3 × 0.2   (vi) 2.3 × 0.3   (vii) 0.8 × 0.2   (viii) 0.7 × 0.12

5. Work out the value of each of these:

(i) 4.6 × 8   (ii) 12.34 × 4   (iii) 2.53 × 8   (iv) 1.2 × 0.6

(v) 14.8 × 0.8   (vi) 127 × 0.6   (vii) 42.5 × 0.06   (viii) 0.48 × 0.7

6. What goes in each box?

(i) ☐ × 3 = 0.9   (ii) ☐ × 0.2 = 1   (iii) ☐ × 3 = 1.2

(iv) 7 × ☐ = 2.8   (v) 0.2 × ☐ = 0.08   (vi) 1.1 × ☐ = 0.55

7. Work out each of these:
   (i) $12.8 \div 2$ (ii) $128.4 \div 4$ (iii) $4.08 \div 3$ (iv) $78.61 \div 7$

8. Work out each of these:
   (i) $\dfrac{0.8}{0.2}$ (ii) $\dfrac{4.2}{0.6}$ (iii) $\dfrac{13.85}{0.5}$ (iv) $\dfrac{6.14}{0.4}$

   (v) $\dfrac{4.8}{0.08}$ (vi) $\dfrac{20.4}{0.04}$ (vii) $\dfrac{0.92}{0.4}$ (viii) $\dfrac{1.08}{0.03}$

9. Choose one number from each box to multiply together to give these:

0.8	1.2	0.5	3

4	0.2	60	0.9

   (i) 4.8 (ii) 30 (iii) 2.7 (iv) 0.24
   (v) 0.6 (vi) 0.16 (vii) 0.1 (viii) 1.08

10. Use the fact that $48 \times 11 = 528$ to write down the answer to
    (i) 4.8×11 (ii) 48×1.1 (iii) 4.8×1.1
    (iv) 4.8×0.11 (vi) 0.48×0.11

11. Work out each of these:
    (i) $\dfrac{1.2 \times 0.4}{0.3}$ (ii) $\dfrac{12}{0.6 \times 0.5}$ (iii) $\dfrac{2.7 \times 0.3}{0.9}$ (iv) $\dfrac{0.12 \times 0.4}{0.8}$

12. A car on a motorway travels 26.4 m every second.
    How far does it travel in each of these times?
    (i) 10 seconds   (ii) 50 seconds   (iii) 2 minutes

13. You are told that $364 \div 14 = 26$.
    Using this information, write down the answers to these:
    (i) $\dfrac{36.4}{1.4}$ (ii) $\dfrac{3.64}{0.14}$ (iii) $\dfrac{36400}{14}$ (iv) $\dfrac{364}{1.4}$ (v) $\dfrac{3640}{0.14}$

14. Five friends go apple-picking. These are the amounts they pick.
         7.8 kg   9.43 kg   6.72 kg   11.27 kg   10.43 kg.
    They agree to put all the apples together and share out the weight equally.
    How much do they each get?

15. If 9 square metres of carpet costs €622.80, find the cost of one square metre.

16. How many pieces of timber, each 0.8 metres long, can be cut from a piece of length 25.6 metres?

17. Sheets of metal, 0.15 cm thick, are piled one on top of the other until they reach a height of 13.2 cm. How many sheets are there in the pile?

18. How many cups, each containing 0.3 litres, can be filled from a container holding 16.2 litres?

19. Four matching pairs of divisions give the same answer.
Which is the odd one out?

A 9.78 ÷ 0.6

B 10.5 ÷ 7

C 1.59 ÷ 3

D 2.08 ÷ 0.2

E 65.2 ÷ 4

F 6.09 ÷ 0.3

G 2.65 ÷ 5

H 72.8 ÷ 7

I 18.27 ÷ 0.9

20. Which **one** of the following is less than 0.8?

(i) 0.8×2 (ii) $\dfrac{0.8}{0.2}$ (iii) 0.8×1.2 (iv) $(0.8)^2$

Section 4.3 Rounding off decimals

The length of the line shown below is somewhere between 3.3 and 3.4 cm. We see an enlarged view of the ruler between 3 and 4 cm to illustrate the point A where the line ends.

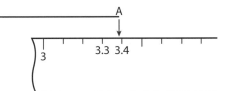

Notice that the arrow at the point A is nearer to 3.4 than to 3.3.

Thus we say that the length of the line is 3.4 cm, *correct to one decimal place.*

If the point A is 3.37 we can see that 3.37 is nearer to 3.4 than it is to 3.3.

When we omit some of the ending digits in a decimal, we are **rounding off** the given decimal to a certain number of decimal places.

Thus   (i) 3.86 = 3.9, correct to 1 decimal place as 86 is nearer to 90 than 80.

(ii) 7.43 = 7.4, correct to 1 decimal place as 43 is nearer to 40 than 50.

The following rules are important when rounding off decimals to a given number of decimal places.

> **1.** If the last digit is 5 or more, we increase the previous digit by 1.
>
> **2.** If the last digit is 4 or less, we leave the previous digit as it is.

Here are some examples:
  (i) 24.6 = 25, correct to the nearest whole number
 (ii) 1.278 = 1.3, correct to one decimal place
(iii) 16.425 = 16.43, correct to two decimal places

Expressing a fraction as a decimal

To change a fraction to a decimal, divide the top line by the bottom line.

$$\frac{3}{4} = 4\overline{)3.00} \qquad \frac{5}{8} = 8\overline{)5.000}$$
$$\phantom{\frac{3}{4} =} 0.75 \qquad \phantom{\frac{5}{8} =} 0.625$$

$$\frac{3}{4} = 0.75 \qquad \frac{5}{8} = 0.625$$

We will now express $\frac{2}{3}$ as a decimal:

$$3\overline{)2.0000}$$
$$0.6666 \ldots$$

Here we see that the sixes continue on and on …

This is an example of a **recurring decimal**.

When decimals continue on like that shown above, we generally give our answer correct to a given number of decimal places.

When using your calculator to express $\frac{3}{7}$, for example, as a decimal key in

If your calculator screen shows $\frac{3}{7}$, use the $\boxed{S \leftrightarrow D}$ key to change the fraction to a decimal.

Rough estimates

With the widespread use of electronic calculators, it is important to have a rough estimate of the answer so that you will know whether the answer you actually get is reasonable or not. The most common way to make a rough estimate is to round off whole numbers to the nearest 10, 100 or 1000 … and to round off decimals to one or two decimal places.

Example 1

By correcting each decimal to the nearest whole number, find the value of
$$\frac{3.16 \times 9.673}{5.38}$$

$$\frac{3.16 \times 9.673}{5.38} \approx \frac{3 \times 10}{5} = \frac{30}{5} = 6$$

(We use the symbol $\approx$ to denote *is approximately equal to*.)
The correct answer, using a calculator, is 5.68.

Exercise 4.3

1. Which whole number is the nearest to each of these?
   (i) 38.6   (ii) 12.4   (iii) 4.27   (iv) 15.96   (v) 23.5

2. Write these numbers correct to one decimal place:
   (i) 1.94   (ii) 13.73   (iii) 0.381   (iv) 3.152   (v) 6.049

3. Write these numbers correct to two decimal places:
   (i) 8.538   (ii) 0.348   (iii) 0.1792   (iv) 3.008   (v) 9.1592

4. Round these to the nearest kilometre:
   (i) 135.4 km   (ii) 87.47 km   (iii) 135.51 km   (iv) 327.89 km

5. Round these numbers to one decimal place:
   (i) 1.07   (ii) 0.762   (iii) 12.73   (iv) 0.05   (v) 1.75

6.

A	E	C	K	R	H	S	B	D
4.0	4.1	4.2	4.3	4.4	4.5	4.6	4.7	4.8

   Round each number below to one decimal place and find a letter for each one.
   Rearrange each set of letters to spell an item of food.
   (i) 4.0937, 4.03, 4.1875, 4.3453
   (ii) 4.477, 4.134, 4.059, 4.567, 4.235, 4.088
   (iii) 4.392, 4.778, 4.7341, 4.079, 4.032

7. The numbers in the rectangles are written to three decimal places in the loops.
   Find three matching pairs.

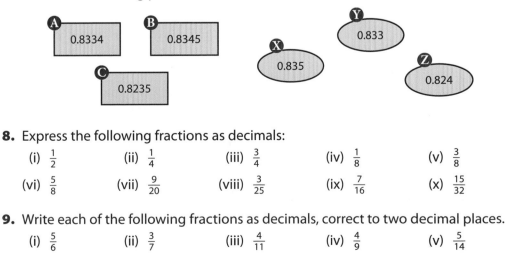

8. Express the following fractions as decimals:
   (i) $\frac{1}{2}$ (ii) $\frac{1}{4}$ (iii) $\frac{3}{4}$ (iv) $\frac{1}{8}$ (v) $\frac{3}{8}$
   (vi) $\frac{5}{8}$ (vii) $\frac{9}{20}$ (viii) $\frac{3}{25}$ (ix) $\frac{7}{16}$ (x) $\frac{15}{32}$

9. Write each of the following fractions as decimals, correct to two decimal places.
   (i) $\frac{5}{6}$ (ii) $\frac{3}{7}$ (iii) $\frac{4}{11}$ (iv) $\frac{4}{9}$ (v) $\frac{5}{14}$

10. By expressing each fraction as a decimal correct to two decimal places, find which is the greater in each of the following:

(i) $\frac{3}{5}$ or $\frac{4}{7}$ (ii) $\frac{5}{8}$ or $\frac{7}{11}$ (iii) $\frac{5}{9}$ or $\frac{7}{12}$ (iv) $\frac{5}{13}$ or $\frac{6}{15}$

11. Without using a calculator, write each number correct to the nearest whole number and then work out your answer:

(i) 11.8×7.4 (ii) 3.84×2.75 (iii) $43.8 \div 10.6$

(iv) $\dfrac{15.2 \times 6.8}{13.7}$ (v) $\dfrac{16.3 \times 8.54}{17.67}$ (vi) $\dfrac{12.37 \times 6.08}{3.49}$

12. Which *one* of the following is less than 0.6?

(i) 0.6×2 (ii) $\dfrac{0.6}{0.2}$ (iii) 0.6×1.2 (iv) $(0.6)^2$

13. Rewrite each number correct to one decimal place and then simplify without using a calculator:

(i) $\dfrac{1.48 \times 6.34}{0.27}$ (ii) $\dfrac{1.78 \times 0.33}{0.94}$ (iii) $\dfrac{1.84 \times 0.18}{3.62}$

Now use your calculator to find the exact value of each of the above, correct to one decimal place.

14. A group of 38 people are going to a concert. Tickets are €29.75 each.
  (i) Estimate roughly the total cost of the tickets.
 (ii) Is your rough estimate bigger or smaller than the exact amount?
     How can you tell without working out the exact amount?

15. Put these letters in order of size, starting with the smallest:

A: $\dfrac{0.1 + 0.2}{0.2 + 0.3}$ B: $\dfrac{0.2 + 0.4}{0.2 + 0.3}$ C: $\dfrac{0.1 + 0.2}{0.4 + 0.6}$ D: $\dfrac{0.1 + 0.4}{0.1 + 0.3}$ E: $\dfrac{0.3 + 0.4}{0.2 + 0.4}$

16. What is two and thirty four hundredths when written as a decimal?
    A: 0.234   B: 2.034   C: 2.34   D: 234.00   E: 23400

Test yourself 4

1. Write each of these as decimals:

   (i) $\frac{3}{10}$ (ii) $4\frac{7}{10}$ (iii) $\frac{15}{100}$ (iv) $\frac{67}{1000}$ (v) $1\frac{3}{100}$

2. Insert a decimal point in each of these numbers:
   (i) 328 such that the 2 represents *two tenths*
   (ii) 1495 such that the 9 represents *nine hundredths*
   (iii) 932 such that the 9 represents *ninety*
   (iv) 328 such that the 2 represents *two thousandths*.

3. (i) Write 123.6, correct to the nearest whole number.
   (ii) Write 1.476, correct to one decimal place.
   (iii) Write 12.062, correct to two decimal places.

4. Write down the answer to each of these:
   (i) 2.46×10 (ii) 1.34×100 (iii) $12.4 \div 10$ (iv) $412.8 \div 100$

5. Find the missing number in each calculation.
   (i) $\square \times 10 = 75.3$ (ii) $7321 \div \square = 73.21$
   (iii) $1000 \times \square = 45.63$ (iv) $17.3 \times \square = 17\,300$

6. To what decimal is each arrow pointing?

7. Given that $13.2 \times 5.5 = 72.6$, write down the value of each of these without further calculations:
   (i) 132×5.5 (ii) 1.32×0.55 (iii) 0.132×55

8.

A	B	E	H	I	G	L	N	P	R	T	W
2.0	2.1	2.2	2.3	2.4	2.5	2.6	2.7	2.8	2.9	3.0	3.1

Round each decimal below to one decimal place and find a letter for each one. Rearrange each set of letters to spell an animal.
   (i) 2.8604, 2.24, 2.138, 2.034
   (ii) 2.609, 2.2561, 2.1901, 1.964, 3.10131
   (iii) 2.51, 2.908, 2.412, 2.98, 2.1984
   (iv) 2.764123, 2.2461, 2.5543, 2.34452, 1.98361, 3.0499, 2.22109, 2.70671

9. Work out the answer to each of these:

    (i) 1.2×0.6 (ii) $1.2 \div 0.6$

Use these examples to write the missing word in each of these sentences:

    (a) Multiplying a positive number by a number between 0 and 1 gives an anwer that is _____ than the original number.

    (b) Dividing a positive number by a number between 0 and 1 gives an answer that is _____ than the original number.

10. The numbers in the rectangles are written to two decimal places in the loops. Find five matching pairs.

11. Express these decimals as fractions in their lowest terms:

    (i) 0.4   (ii) 0.25   (iii) 0.125   (iv) 0.08   (v) 0.16

12. Kate spent 0.4 of her money in one shop and 0.3 of it in a second shop. If she had €21.90 left, how much had she at first?

13. Simplify each of these without using a calculator:

    (i) $\dfrac{2.4 \times 1.2}{0.3}$ (ii) $\dfrac{0.48 \times 2}{0.06 \times 4}$ (iii) $\dfrac{3.1 - 1.9}{0.06 \times 20}$

14.

0.25		2.5
	0.9	
		0.8
12.6	1.2	

    (i) Which two of these numbers multiply together to give the **smallest** possible answer?

    (ii) Which two of these numbers, when multiplied together, give the answer which is closest to 1.

    (iii) Find the two numbers such that one divided by the other gives the **largest** possible answer.

15. In which of the following lists are the terms **not** increasing?

    A: $\frac{1}{5}$, 0.25, $\frac{3}{10}$, 0.5   B: $\frac{3}{5}$, 0.7, $\frac{4}{5}$, 1.5   C: $\frac{2}{5}$, 0.5, $\frac{7}{10}$, 0.9

    D: $\frac{3}{5}$, 0.5, $\frac{4}{5}$, 0.9   E: $\frac{2}{5}$, 1.5, $\frac{10}{5}$, 2.3

For the problem solver...

1. Put these cards in order from the smallest number to the largest .
What word do you get?

1.85	0.07	1.83	0.16	1.75	1.8
R	B	E	U	R	G

2. Jack has to cut a 10-metre pole into 1-metre lengths.
How long will it take him if he cuts one length every 3 minutes?

3. What is the value of $0.1 + 0.2 + 0.3 \times 0.4$?

4. What mathematical symbol can be placed between 2 and 3 to make a
number greater than 2 but less than 3?

5.

A	C	E	G	H	L	P	R	Y
1.5	1.25	0.2	0.5	1.7	0.3	0.4	2.5	0.82

Find the answers to these questions.
Then use the code above to change them to letters.
Rearrange each set of letters to spell a fruit.

(i) $4.1 \div 5$ (ii) $2.4 \div 6$ (iii) $10 \div 8$ (iv) $0.8 \div 2$
　 $10 \div 4$ $2.7 \div 9$ $8.5 \div 5$ $7.5 \div 5$
　 $5.1 \div 3$ $0.8 \div 4$ $3 \div 2$ $5 \div 2$
　 $2.5 \div 2$ $2 \div 5$ $1.6 \div 4$ $4 \div 8$
　 $1.6 \div 8$ $6 \div 4$ $1 \div 5$ $1.2 \div 6$
　 $7.5 \div 3$

6. Which of the following has the largest value?
(i) $0.5 + 0.25$ (ii) $0.5 - 0.25$ (iii) 0.5×0.25
(iv) $0.5 \div 0.25$ (v) $0.25 \div 0.5$

7. When Harry bought a train ticket he received €2.50 in change.
He noticed that for each coin in his change there was exactly one other
coin of the same value.
What was the coin of smallest value in Harry's change?
A 2c   B 5c   C 10c   D 20c   E 50c

5 Sets

Key words

element   null set   empty set (∅)   is an element of (∈)
is not an element of (∉)   equal sets   subsets   Venn diagram   union
intersection   cardinal number (#)   universal set   complement

Section 5.1 Describing a set

If you examine the three collections of items shown below, you will notice that the items in each collection are similar or **clearly defined**.
The first is a collection of cars.
The second is a collection of playing cards.
The third is a collection of road signs.

In mathematics we call each of these collections a **set**.
The items in a set are called the **elements** of the set.
The elements of a set must be clearly defined, that is, we should be sure whether or not a given object is an element of the set.

For example   (i)   the **days of the week** is a set
               (ii) the **pupils in my class** is also a set.

But **good television programmes** does not form a set as not everybody agrees on what a 'good programme' is.

Listing elements of a set

When it is possible to list the elements of a set, we write down the list inside a pair of chain brackets and separate each element from the next with a comma.
We generally use **capital letters** to name or denote sets.

If A = the set of whole numbers greater than 4 and less than 10, then
$$A = \{5, 6, 7, 8, 9\}$$

This is a **clearly defined set** as we are in no doubt that each of the elements 5, 6, 7, 8, 9 is greater than 4 and less than 10.

In any set an element is listed once only.

The letters of the word NAVAN could be listed in set form as {N, A, V}, that is, no letter is repeated.

A change in the order in which the elements are listed does not change the set.
The set {1, 3, 5, 7} could be listed as {3, 7, 5, 1} or {7, 5, 3, 1}.

Example 1

(i) List the elements of the set {letters of the word DIVISION}
(ii) Describe in words the elements of the set
{January, June, July}

(i) The set is {D, I, V, S, O, N}.

(ii) {January, June, July} is the set of months beginning with the letter J.

Exercise 5.1

1. Say whether each of the following could be accurately described as a mathematical set:
  (i) The counties of Leinster
  (ii) The players on my football team
  (iii) The tall pupils in my class
  (iv) The letters of the alphabet
  (v) The dangerous animals in the zoo
  (vi) The vowels in the word OPINION
  (vii) The big counties in Ireland.

2. Describe in words each of these sets:
  A = {Saturday, Sunday}
  B = {1, 2, 3, 4, 5, 6}
  C = {May, June, July}
  D = {v, w, x, y, z}
  E = {Kerry, Cork, Waterford, Tipperary, Limerick, Clare}
  F = {2, 4, 6, 8, 10}
  G = {a, e, i, o, u}

3. List the elements of the following sets using the { } notation:

A = {The first five letters of the English alphabet}

B = {The odd numbers between 2 and 14}

C = {The seasons of the year}

D = {The days of the week beginning with the letter T}

E = {The letters of the word SCIENCE}

F = {Counties in Ireland beginning with C}

G = {Vowels in the word MATHEMATICS}

H = {Colours of the rainbow}

4. Describe in words the sets shown below.

(i)

(ii)

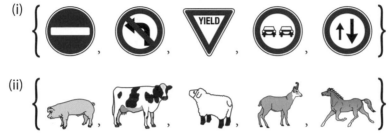

Section 5.2 Element of a set

We use the symbol ∈ to indicate that an element is a member of a given set.
We use the symbol ∉ to denote **is not an element of**.

For example if $A = \left\{ \vphantom{} \right.$ 〔cat〕, 〔dog〕, 〔rabbit〕 $\left. \vphantom{} \right\}$ 〔rabbit〕 ∈ A but 〔fox〕 ∉ A.

Similarly, if $B = \{1, 2, 3, 4\}$, $2 \in B$ but $8 \notin B$.

A set defined by a Rule

Take, for example, the set $A = \{$Spring, Summer, Autumn, Winter$\}$.

The set A could also be written using a **rule** to describe it as follows:

$A = \{x \mid x \text{ is a season of the year}\}$

This reads "*A is the set of all elements x, such that x is a season of the year.*"

Similarly, if $B = \{x \mid x \text{ is a whole number between 1 and 9 inclusive}\}$

then $B = \{1, 2, 3, 4, 5, 6, 7, 8, 9\}$

The null set $\varnothing$ or { }

A set that contains no elements is called the **null set** or **empty set**.

The null set is denoted by $\varnothing$ or { }.

The set of men who are more than
4 metres in height is an example of an empty set.

Do not confuse {0} with { }.

{0} is a set which has one member.

The null set is denoted by $\varnothing$ or { }.

> The null set is denoted by $\varnothing$ or { }.

Exercise 5.2

1. State whether each of the following is true or false:
- (i) $3 \in \{1, 3, 5, 7, 9\}$
- (ii) $v \in \{a, e, i, o, u\}$
- (iii) Tuesday $\in$ {The days of the week}
- (iv) Munster $\in$ {The counties of Ireland}
- (v) Metre $\in$ {Units of weight}

2. $A = \{x, y, z\}$, $B = \{3, 6, 9, 12\}$ and $C = \{5, 10, 15, 20\}$ are three sets.
Copy and insert the symbol $\in$ or $\notin$ in each of the following:

(i) $3 \ldots A$	(ii) $5 \ldots C$	(iii) $x \ldots A$
(iv) $y \ldots B$	(v) $12 \ldots B$	(vi) $z \ldots C$
(vii) $20 \ldots C$	(viii) $8 \ldots B$.	

3. Given $X = \{1, 2, 3, 4, 5\}$, $Y = \{a, b, c, d, e\}$, $Z = \{5, 10, 15\}$.
Say if each of the following is true or false:

(i) $b \in Y$	(ii) $6 \in Z$	(iii) $f \notin Y$
(iv) $5 \in X$	(v) $20 \notin Z$	(vi) $e \in Y$
(vii) $5 \notin X$	(viii) $10 \in Z$.	

4. List the elements of each of the following sets:
$A = \{x | x \text{ is a planet beginning with the letter } M\}$
$B = \{x | x \text{ is a vowel of the English language}\}$
$C = \{x | x \text{ is an even number between 1 and 13}\}$
$D = \{x | x \text{ is a number on a clockface}\}$
$E = \{x | x \text{ is a letter of the word PARALLEL}\}$
$F = \{x | x \text{ is an odd whole number between 2 and 14}\}$

5. Write the following sets in the form, $\{x \mid x \ldots\}$.

   (i) $A = \{1, 2, 3, 4, 5, 6, 7, 8\}$ (ii) $B = \{a, e, i, o, u\}$

  (iii) $C = \{2, 4, 6, 8, 10, 12, 14\}$ (iv) $D = \{May, June, July\}$

   (v) $E = \{1c, 2c, 5c, 10c, 20c, 50c, €1, €2\}$.

6. State whether each of the following is a null set:

    (i)   The set of months which begin with the letter T.

   (ii)   The set of men who have landed on the moon.

  (iii)   The set of pupils in your class who are under 8 years of age.

  (iv)   The set of whole numbers between $3\frac{1}{4}$ and $3\frac{3}{4}$.

   (v)   The set of women who are more than 100 years old.

  (vi)   The set of students in your class who study Nuclear Physics.

 (vii) $\{0\}$.

(viii)   The set of months of the year which begin with a vowel.

  (ix)   The set of foods that Old Mother Hubbard found in the cupboard.

   (x)   The set of odd numbers which are divisible by 2.

7. Can you think of any even numbers that are divisible by 5?
Is the set of even numbers that are divisible by 5 an empty set?

Section 5.3   Equal sets – Subsets

Two sets are **equal** if they contain exactly the same elements.

If $A = (2, 4, 6, 8, 10)$ and $B = \{8, 10, 6, 4, 2\}$, then $A = B$ as they both contain exactly the same elements even though they are listed in different ways.

Again, if $C = \{a, b, c\}$ and $D = \{x, y, z\}$
then $C \neq D$ as they do not contain the same elements.

Subsets

If $A = \{1, 2, 3, 4, 5\}$ and $B = \{3, 4\}$, we notice that all the elements in B are contained in A. We say 'B is a subset of A' and it is written $\boldsymbol{B \subset A}$.

The illustration below shows that the first set is a subset of the second set.

We use the symbol $\not\subset$ to denote 'is not a subset of'.

Set B is a subset of set A if every element of B is also an element of A.

> ## Example 1
>
> If $A = \{a, b, c, d\}$, write down a subset of A containing
>   (i)   2 elements   (ii)   3 elements.
>
>   (i) $\{b, c\}$ is a subset of A containing 2 elements.
>   (ii) $\{a, b, c\}$ is a subset of A containing 3 elements.

If $A = \{3, 4, 5\}$, then $\{3, 4, 5\}$ is a subset of A as all the elements in it are contained in A.

If $X = \{1, 2, 3\}$, then the subsets of X are
         $\{1\}, \{2\}, \{1, 2\}, \{2, 3\}, \{1, 3\}, \{1, 2, 3\}, \varnothing$

> For all sets A,
> $A \subset A$ and $\varnothing \subset A$.

The set X itself and $\varnothing$ are called **improper** subsets.
All the other subsets are called **proper** subsets.

Exercise 5.3

1. $A = \{1, 3, 4, 7, 9\}$ and $B = \{9, 3, 4, 1, 7\}$.
Explain why A and B are equal sets.

2. Which of the following sets are equal?
   $A = \{1, 3, 5, 7\}$ $B = \{7, 5, 9\}$ $C = \{5, 7, 9\}$ $D = \{1, 5, 7, 3\}$

3. Given $A = \{a, b, c\}$ and $B = \{x, y, z\}$.
Is $A = B$? Explain your answer.

4. If $X = \{\text{Letters of the word TITLE}\}$ and $Y = \{\text{Letters of the word LITTLE}\}$, write down the elements of set X and set Y. Is $X = Y$?

5. $A = \{5, 6, 7, 8, 9\}$ and $B = \{x|x \text{ is a whole number greater than 5 and less than 10}\}$.
Write down the elements of B and state if $A = B$.

6. $X = \{\text{Letters of the word PARALLEL}\}$ and $Y = \{\text{Letters of the word REPEAL}\}$.
Write down the elements of each set and say if they are equal.

7. If $A = \{1, 2, 3, 4, 5, 6, 7, 8, 9, 10, 11, 12\}$, write down the elements of the following subsets:
   (i)   The set of 2-digit numbers in A
   (ii) The set of even numbers in A
   (iii) The set of odd numbers less than 6 in A
   (iv) The set of numbers in A which are divisible by 3.

8. $A = \{1, 2, 3, 4, 5, 6\}, B = \{3, 4, 5, 6\}, C = \{3, 6, 9, 12\}, D = \emptyset$.
   State whether each of the following is true or false:
   (i) $B \subset A$ (ii) $B \subset C$ (iii) $D \subset B$ (iv) $C \subset A$ (v) $B \subset B$.

9. Say whether each of the following is true or false:
   (i) $\{6, 7\} \subset \{4, 5, 6, 7\}$ (ii) $\{a, b, c\} \subset \{a, c\}$.   (iii) $\emptyset \subset \{3, 4, 5\}$
   (iv) $\{1, 4, 9\} \subset \emptyset$ (v) $\{x, y, z\} \subset \{x, y, z\}$ (vi) $\{1\} \subset \{0, 1, 2\}$

10. If $A = \{a, b, c, d, e\}$, write down
    (i) two improper subsets of A (ii) three proper subsets of A.

11. Write down all the subsets of
    (i) $\{1, 2\}$ (ii) $\{x, y, z\}$

12. If $A = \{1, 3, 5, 7, 9, 11\}$ and $B = \{5, 7, 8, 9, 14\}$, write down a subset C of A which contains three elements such that C is also a subset of B.

13. Which of the following are true?
    (i) $2 \in \{1, 2, 3\}$ (ii) $\{2\} \subset \{4, 6, 8\}$ (iii) $\{p\} \subset \{o, p, q, r\}$
    (iv) $\{a, b, c\} \subset \{c, b, a\}$ (v) $\emptyset \subset \{l, m\}$ (vi) $\{1, 2\} = \{0, 1, 2\}$

14. If $A = \{a, b, c, d, e, f, g\}$, write down three sets B, C and D which are all subsets of A such that $C \subset B$ and $D \subset C$.

Section 5.4 Venn diagrams – Intersection and union of sets

A set can be illustrated by a circle with the elements represented by dots inside, each dot being labelled by a letter or number. This is called a **Venn diagram** in honour of the English mathematician, John Venn (1834–1923), who first used this type of diagram to represent sets.

The diagram on the right shows the set
$A = \{a, b, c, d, e\}$ illustrated by a Venn diagram.

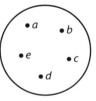

Subsets represented by Venn Diagrams

If $A = \{1, 2, 3, 4, 5\}$ and $B = \{3, 4\}$, then $B \subset A$.
This is shown in the Venn diagram on the right
where circle B is inside circle A.

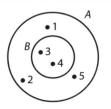

Intersection of two Sets

The crosshatched yellow lines in the given diagram represent the intersection of Main Street and High Street. It is the part of the street common to both.

Similarly, the intersection of two sets is the set of elements common to both.

> The intersection of two sets *A* and *B* is the set of elements that are in both *A* and *B*.
> *A* intersection *B* is written as **A ∩ B**.

The Venn diagram on the right shows two sets *A* and *B* with some elements common to both. The shaded area common to both sets is the intersection of the two sets.

From the diagram *A ∩ B* = {2, 6}.

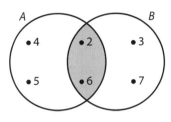

Example 1

If *A* = {*a, b, c, d, e, f*} and *B* = {*c, e, x, y*}, list the elements of *A ∩ B*. Draw a Venn diagram to illustrate the intersection.

A ∩ B = {*c, e*}.
The Venn diagram is shown on the right.

Union of sets

Union of sets

> The union of two sets *A* and *B* is found by putting together in a new set all the elements of *A* and of *B* without repeating any element.

A union *B* is written as **A ∪ B**.
If *A* = {1, 3, 5, 7, 9} and *B* = {7, 8, 9, 10}, then
A ∪ *B* = {1, 3, 5, 7, 8, 9, 10}.
In the Venn diagram on the right,
the shaded area represents A ∪ B.

Example 2

If *A* = {2, 4, 6, 8, 10} and *B* = {1, 2, 3, 4, 5}, list the elements of *A* ∪ *B* and
illustrate this by a Venn diagram.

A ∪ *B* = {1, 2, 3, 4, 5, 6, 8, 10}.

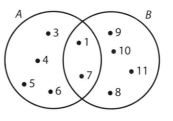

Venn diagram for A ∪ B

The cardinal number of a set (#)

The number of elements in a set is called the **cardinal number** of the set.
The symbol # is used to denote the cardinal number.

From the given Venn diagram,

$\#A = 6$ $\#B = 6$

$\#(A \cap B) = 2$ $\#(A \cup B) = 10$.

Exercise 5.4

1. What is the diagram on the right called?
   Now list the elements of *A*.
   What is #*A*?

   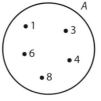

2. From the Venn diagram on the right, list the elements of
   (i) *A*   (ii) *B*
   (iii) *A* ∩ *B*   (iv) *A* ∪ *B*.

   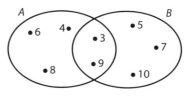

3. On the right are two sets A and B having some
elements in common.
(i) List the elements of A.
(ii) List the elements of B.
(iii) Name an element that is in B, but not in A.
(iv) Name an element that is neither in A nor B.
(v) List the elements that are common to A and B.

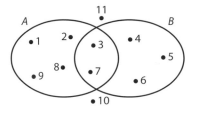

4. Two sets A and B are represented by the Venn diagram
on the right.
List the elements of
(i) A (ii) B
(iii) $A \cap B$ (iv) $A \cup B$.

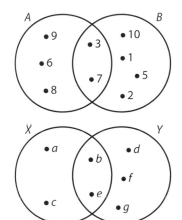

5. From the given Venn diagram list the elements of
(i) X (ii) Y
(iii) $X \cap Y$ (iv) $X \cup Y$.

6. Look at the Venn diagram on the right and say if each
of the following is true or false:
(i) $p \in A$ (ii) $r \in B$ (iii) $z \in B$
(iv) $r \in (A \cap B)$ (v) $z \in (A \cup B)$.

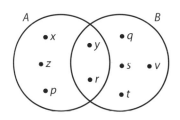

7. If $X = \{a, e, i, o, u\}$ and $Y = \{a, b, c, d, e\}$, draw a Venn diagram to illustrate this
information.

8. $A = \{1, 2, 3, 4, 5, 6\}$, $B = \{4, 5, 6, 7, 8\}$, $C = \{7, 8, 9, 10\}$
List the elements of each of these sets:
(i) $A \cap B$ (ii) $B \cup C$ (iii) $B \cap C$ (iv) $A \cap C$.

9. $A = \{$letters in the word SCIENCE$\}$, $B = \{$letters in the word NEARER$\}$
List the elements of   (i) A (ii) B (iii) $A \cap B$ (iv) $A \cup B$

10. From the Venn diagram on the right, list the elements of
(i) C (ii) D
(iii) $C \cap D$ (iv) $C \cup D$.

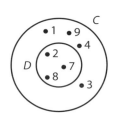

11. $A = \{0, 1, 2, 4, 8, 12\}$, $B = \{1, 3, 5, 8, 9\}$, $C = \{8, 9, 10, 11, 12\}$

List the elements of each of these:

(i) $A \cap C$ (ii) $A \cup B$ (iii) $B \cap C$

(iv) $A \cup C$ (v) $B \cup C$ (vi) $A \cap B$.

12. Using the Venn diagram on the right, write down

(i) #A (ii) #B

(iii) #(A ∩ B) (iv) #(A ∪ B).

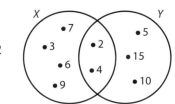

13. The Venn diagram on the right shows the elements of two sets X and Y.

Say if each of the following is true or false:

(i) $2 \in Y$ (ii) $15 \in X$ (iii) $4 \in (X \cap Y)$

(iv) $9 \in (X \cup Y)$ (v) $\#Y = 15$ (vi) $\#(X \cap Y) = 2$

(vii) $10 \in (X \cup Y)$ (viii) $\#X = 4$ (ix) $(X \cap Y) \subset X$.

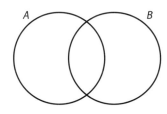

14. Copy the Venn diagram on the right and insert dots to represent this information:

$\#A = 4$, $\#B = 9$ and $\#(A \cap B) = 2$.

Section 5.5 The universal set – Complement of a set ———

Consider the following three sets:

$A = \{$pupils in the school over seventeen years of age$\}$

$B = \{$pupils in the school who study French$\}$

$C = \{$pupils in the school who play basketball$\}$

The three sets A, B and C are all based on 'the set of pupils in the school'. This set, from which all the other sets being considered are taken, is called the **universal set**. Thus the universal set may be described as the **background set** necessary when discussing various subsets.

In a Venn diagram a rectangle is used to represent the universal set.

It is denoted by the capital letter **U**.

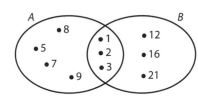

Complement of a set

The complement of a set A is the set of elements in the universal set U which are not in A. The complement of A is denoted by **A'** and is shown by the shaded area in the Venn diagram on the right.

Example 1

If $U = \{a, b, c, d, e, f, g, h, i\}$, $A = \{a, c, e, i\}$ and $B = \{e, f, g, h, i\}$, illustrate these on a Venn diagram and list the elements of

    (i) A' (ii) B' (iii) $(A \cup B)'$ (iv) $(A \cap B)'$

The Venn diagram is shown on the right.

    (i) A' is the set of elements of U which are not in A.

       ∴ $A' = \{b, d, f, g, h\}$

    (ii) $B' = \{a, b, c, d\}$

    (iii) $A \cup B = \{a, c, e, f, g, h, i\}$

       ∴ $(A \cup B)' = \{b, d\}$

    (iv) $(A \cap B) = \{e, i\}$

       ∴ $(A \cap B)' = \{a, b, c, d, f, g, h\}$

Exercise 5.5

1. What set does the shaded region of the given Venn diagram represent?

Use the Venn diagram to list the elements of

    (i) U (ii) A (iii) A'.

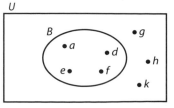

2. Use the given Venn diagram to list the elements of

    (i) B (ii) U (iii) B'.

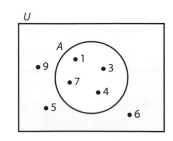

3. Use the given Venn diagram to list the elements
of each of these sets:

   (i) A (ii) B (iii) A'

   (iv) B' (v) $A \cup B$ (vi) $(A \cup B)'$.

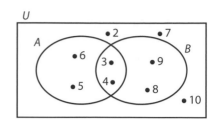

4. Using the Venn diagram on the right,
list the elements of

   (i) A' (ii) B' (iii) $A \cup B$

   (iv) $(A \cup B)'$ (v) $A \cap B$ (vi) $(A \cap B)'$.

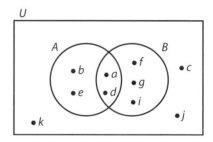

5. In the given Venn diagram each dot represents an element.
Write down

   (i) $\#A$ (ii) $\#A'$ (iii) $\#(A \cap B)$

   (iv) $\#B'$ (v) $\#(A \cup B)'$.

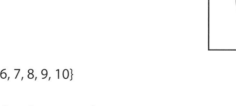

6. If $U = \{1, 2, 3, 4, 5, 6, 7, 8, 9, 10\}$
$A = \{1, 3, 5, 7\}$
$B = \{3, 4, 5, 6\}$, list the elements of

   (i) A' (ii) B' (iii) $A \cup B$ (iv) $(A \cup B)'$.

7. Given $U = \{1, 2, 3, 4, 5, 6, 7, 8, 9\}$
$A = \{1, 3, 5, 7\}$
$U = \{5, 6, 7, 8\}$
Copy the Venn diagram on the right and illustrate
the given information on it.

8. By examining the Venn diagram on the right, say whether each of the following statements is true or false:

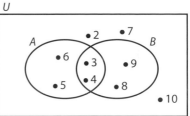

(i) $9 \in A'$ (ii) $3 \in (A \cup B)$

(iii) $4 \in B'$ (iv) $2 \in (A \cup B)'$

(v) $\#A' = 4$ (vi) $\#(A \cup B)' = 3$

(vii) $7 \in U$ (viii) $\#U = 10$

(ix) $\#(A \cap B) = 6.$

9. Examine the Venn diagram on the right and list the elements of the following sets:

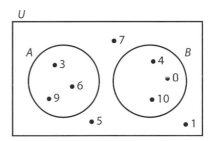

(i) A' (ii) B'

(iii) $A \cup B$ (iv) $(A \cup B)'$

(v) $A \cap B.$

10. What set is represented by the shaded region in each of the diagrams below?

(i)   (ii)

(iii)   (iv)

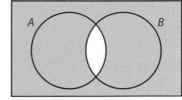

11. Given $U = \{1, 2, 3, 4, 5, 6, 7, 8, 9, 10, 11, 12\}$

$A = \{2, 3, 5, 7, 11\}$

$B = \{1, 3, 5, 7, 9, 11\}$

List the elements of the following sets:

(i) A' (ii) B' (iii) $A \cup B$ (iv) $(A \cup B)'$ (v) $(A \cap B)'.$

Investigate if $(A \cap B)' = A' \cup B'.$

Test yourself 5

1. List the elements of each of these sets:
   (i) A = {The even numbers between 3 and 11}
   (ii) B = {The counties in Ireland beginning with W}
   (iii) C = {The letters of the word COMMITTEE}
   (iv) D = {Vowels of the word REVISION}
   (v) E = {The first six multiples of 5}
   (vi) F = {x|x is a single digit natural number}

2. (i) If A = {m, a, t, h, s} and B = {e, x, a, m}, list the elements of
       (a) $A \cup B$ (b) $A \cap B$.

   (ii) If X = {3, 4, 5, 6, 7, 8} and Y = {1, 2, 7, 8},
       draw a Venn diagram to illustrate these sets.
       Now write down   (a) #($X \cap Y$)   (b) #($X \cup Y$)

3. In the Venn diagram on the right, list the
   elements of these sets:
   (i) X (ii) Y (iii) $X \cap Y$

4. A = {1, 3, 5, 7, 9}, B = {1, 2, 3, 4, 5}, C = {7, 8, 9, 10}
   List the elements of these sets:
   (i) $A \cap B$ (ii) $B \cap C$ (iii) $A \cup C$

5. From the given Venn diagram, list the elements of

   (i) P (ii) Q
   (iii) $P \cap Q$ (iv) $P \cup Q$

6. Use the given Venn diagram to write down the
   elements of each of these sets:

   (i) A (ii) U (iii) A'.

7. Use the given Venn diagram to list the elements
   of each of these sets:
   (i) A (ii) B (iii) $A \cap B$
   (iv) U (v) $A \cup B$ (vi) $(A \cup B)'$.

8. Describe the shaded area in each of the Venn diagrams below:

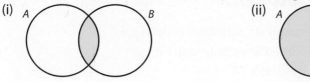

9. $A = \{1, 2, 3\}$, $B = \{a, b, c\}$, $C = \{b, c, d\}$ and $D = \{2, 1, 3\}$.
Which one of the following is true?
  (i) $A = B$ (ii) $B = C$ (iii) $A = D$ (iv) $A = B = C = D$.

10. Explain what is meant by the symbols, $A \subset B$.
Now copy each of the following and insert $\subset$ or $\not\subset$ in the space provided.
  (i) $\{a, b\} \ldots \{a, b, c, d\}$ (ii) $\{2, 3\} \ldots \{2, 3, 4, 5\}$
  (iii) $\{1\} \ldots \{2, 4, 6, 8\}$ (iv) $\{d, e, f\} \ldots \{a, b, c, d, e\}$

11. From the Venn diagram on the right, write down
  (i) $\#A$ (ii) $\#B$
  (iii) $\#(A \cap B)$ (iv) $\#(A \cup B)$.

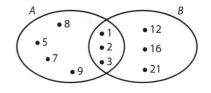

12. $A = \{2, 3, 4, 5\}$ and $B = \{4, 6, 8\}$.
Say if each of the following is true or false:
  (i) $5 \in A$ (ii) $6 \in (A \cap B)$ (iii) $2 \in (A \cup B)$ (iv) $\#A = 5$

13. Given $U = \{1, 2, 3, 4, 5, 6, 7, 8, 9\}$
       $X = \{1, 2, 3, 7\}$
       $Y = (2, 4, 7, 8)$
Copy the Venn diagram on the right and
on it illustrate the sets U, X and Y.
  (i) List the elements of Y'.
  (ii) List the elements of $X \cup Y$.
  (iii) Find $\#(X \cup Y)'$.
  (iv) Find $\#X'$.

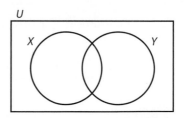

14. Copy the following statements, replacing the * sign in each case with the
appropriate symbol chosen from $\in, \notin, =, \cup, \cap, \subset, \not\subset$.
  (i) $3 * \{1, 2, 3\}$ (ii) $\{a, b\} * \{a, b, c\}$ (iii) $2 * \{1, 3, 5, 7\}$

  (iv) $\varnothing * \{5, 7, 9\}$ (v) $\{2, 3, 4\} * \{4, 2, 3\}$ (vi) $\{1, 2, 3\} * \{3, 4\} = \{3\}$.

For the problem solver...

1. Some letters are made using straight lines only (e.g. E):
Some are made using curved lines only (e.g. C):
Some are made using both (e.g. D).
Put the following letters into their proper places in the Venn diagram below:

A B C D E F G O

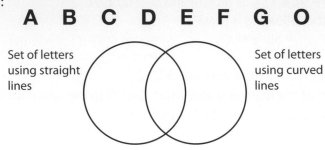

Set of letters using straight lines

Set of letters using curved lines

2. I am a 3 digit number. The product of my digits is 4.
I am an odd number less than 200. What am I?

3. Six stations lie at equal distances from each other along a railway line.
How much further is it from the first to the sixth, than from the first to the third?

4. A child's age increased by 3 years gives a number which has a whole number square root. Decreased by 3 years, the child's age gives the square root.
How old is the child?

5. The fraction $\frac{16}{64}$ is unusual since the digit 6, which occurs on both the top and the bottom, can be 'cancelled' to give $\frac{1}{4}$ and this is equal to $\frac{16}{64}$.
Which of these fractions has a similar property?
   A $\frac{12}{24}$ B $\frac{13}{39}$ C $\frac{15}{45}$ D $\frac{19}{95}$ E $\frac{24}{48}$

6. Karen writes down six different prime numbers, p, q, r, s, t, u, all less than 20, such that $p + q = r + s = t + u$.
What is the value of $p + q$?

7. The set A consists of positive whole numbers, n, such that the difference between $\sqrt{n}$ and 10 is less than 1.
How many elements are there in A?

Algebra

Key words

symbol	increase	decrease	expression	term
like terms	unlike terms	variable	constant	coefficient
substituting	brackets	index	indices	

Section 6.1

Symbols such as ▲, ● or ◆ are often used to stand for numbers.

Sometimes you can work out the value of the symbol.

Look at this example:

▼ + 8 = 12

We know that 4 + 8 = 12, so this means that ▼ = 4

You can also use the value of a symbol in a calculation.

If ● = 7, then 6 × ● = 42.

Writing in symbols

'3 more than 5' can be written as 5 + 3.

'6 less than 14' can be written as 14 − 6.

'10 increased by 4' can be written as 10 + 4.

In the same way

'5 more than ■' can be written as ■ + 5.

'7 more than n' can be written as n + 7.

'8 less than x' can be written as x − 8.

Exercise 6.1

1. Each symbol stands for a number. Write down its value.

    (i) ▲ + 3 = 5   (ii) ■ − 5 = 4   (iii) □ × 2 = 12   (iv) 3 + ◆ = 15

    (v) 9 − ● = 2   (vi) 5 × ■ = 55   (vii) ▼ ÷ 3 = 4   (viii) ◆ ÷ 10 = 3

2. Find the value of each of these symbols:

   (i) $11 - ◀ = 3$ (ii) $14 + ♣ = 21$

  (iii) $❱ + ❱ = 20$ (iv) $✻ + ✻ + ✻ = 30$

   (v) $□ - 6 = 14$ (vi) $◆ × ◆ = 16$

  (vii) $▲ × 4 = 20$ (viii) $✻ ÷ 6 = 5$

3. If $□ + ▲ = 12$, find three pairs of values for $□$ and $▲$.

4. If $● - ◆ = 9$, find three pairs of values for $●$ and $◆$.

5. If $● = 5$ and $■ = 3$, find the value of each of these expressions:

   (i) $● + 6$ (ii) $■ × 5$ (iii) $● - 2$ (iv) $7 + ■$

   (v) $3 × ●$ (vi) $6 ÷ ■$ (vii) $30 ÷ ●$ (viii) $2 × ■ + ●$

6. If $▲ = 18$, write down the value of each of these:

   (i) 6 more than $▲$ (ii) 3 less than $▲$ (iii) twice $▲$

  (iv) five times $▲$ (v) $▲$ less 8   (vi) twice $▲ + ▲$

7. $■$ stands for different numbers. Find its value in each of the following:

   (i) $■ + 6 = 10$ (ii) $■ - 3 = 5$ (iii) $7 + ■ = 14$

  (iv) $2 × ■ = 22$ (v) $■ ÷ 4 = 9$ (vi) $3 × ■ = 36$

8. $▲$ stands for a number. Write down each of these using symbols and numbers only:

   (i) 7 more than $▲$ (ii) 4 less than $▲$ (iii) twice $▲$

  (iv) $▲$ divided by 2   (v) $\frac{1}{3}$ of $▲$ (vi) $▲$ less 6

9. The first line in the table below has been completed.
Write down what should go in each shaded space in the remaining lines.

	Start number	Change	Result
	3	Increase by 7	$3 + 7 = 10$
(i)	9	Increase by 12	
(ii)	12		$12 + 6 = 18$
(iii)		Increase by 8	$21 + 8 = 29$
(iv)	$□$		$□ + 5$
(v)	$▼$	Increase by 8	
(vi)	$●$	Increase by 17	
(vii)		Decrease by 3	$16 - 3 = 13$
(viii)		Decrease by 12	$■ - 12$
(ix)	$▲$	Decrease by 36	
(x)	$❱$		$❱ - 9$

10. Each letter stands for a number. What is each number?

    (i) $a + 2 = 6$ (ii) $b + 3 = 12$ (iii) $c - 4 = 5$ (iv) $d - 2 = 9$

    (v) $9 - e = 3$ (vi) $2 \times f = 16$ (vii) $g + g = 12$ (viii) $h \div 3 = 6$

    (ix) $i + i + i = 12$

11. Write down what should be written in each of the shaded boxes below.
The first one is done for you.

	Start number	Change	Result
(i)	x	Increase by 6	$x + 6$
(ii)	a	Increase by 8	
(iii)	b	Decrease by 7	
(iv)	c	Double	
(v)	d		$d + 9$
(vi)	e		$e - 10$
(vii)	f	Multiply by 5	
(viii)	g		$3g$
(ix)	h		$h + k$

Section 6.2 Using Letters

James bought some DVDs but we don't know how many.
He also has seven of his own.
We could say that he bought x DVDs.
Now he has **$x + 8$** DVDs.

$x + 8$ is an **expression**.
x stands for an unknown number.

The expression $x + x + 2 + 5$ has four **terms**.
The expression can be simplified to $2x + 7$ which has 2 terms.
Notice that $x + x$ can be added to get $2x$.
$x + x$ can be added because they are **like terms**.

Consider the cars and vans below:

3 cars + **2** cars = **5** cars

What is   = ?

Three vans and two cars cannot be added as they are not like terms. In algebra, terms
with the same letter such as $2x$ and $3x$ can be added as they are **like terms**.

Thus $2x + 3x = 5x$ and $2y + 4y = 6y$.

However, $5x$ and $7y$ are **unlike terms** and cannot be added.

$2x + 3y + 4$ is an **expression** containing 3 terms. We don't know the values of x and y.

x and y can have different values in another expression.

That is why x and y are called **variables**. They are given this name because their values **vary**. The number **4** does not change. Since it is fixed, we call it a **constant**.

In **2x**, the number **2** tells us how many xs there are.

We call 2 the **coefficient** of x. Similarly 3 is the coefficient of y.

Notation

In algebra, the symbols $\times$ and $\div$ are not normally used.

Instead of writing $2 \times k$, we just write $2k$.

We write $\dfrac{a}{b}$ instead of $a \div b$.

Also   (i) $x + x + x = 3x$

          (ii) $2 \times a \times b = 2ab$

          (iii) $4 \times x \times y \times 3 = 4 \times 3 \times x \times y = 12xy$

          (iv) $2 \times a \times b \times c = 2abc$

> $1x$ is written as x.
> $1x + 1y$ is written as $x + y$.

Example 1

Simplify each of these by adding like terms:
   (i) $x + 2x + 3y + 5y$ (ii) $3a + 4b - a + 2b + 2a$

   (i) $x + 2x + 3y + 5y = 3x + 8y$

   (ii) $3a + 4b - a + 2b + 2a = \underline{3a - a} + 2a + 4b + 2b$
$$= 2a + 2a + 6b$$
$$= 4a + 6b$$

Exercise 6.2

1. Write each of the following without using the multiplication sign:
   (i) $5 \times a$ (ii) $4 \times b$ (iii) $4 \times 2 \times x$ (iv) $3 \times 4 \times y$
   (v) $4 \times 2c$ (vi) $5a \times 3$ (vii) $a \times b$ (viii) $4 \times a \times b$

2. Write these without the multiplication sign:
   (i) $2a \times 4b$ (ii) $3x \times 7y$ (iii) $3 \times ab$ (iv) $a \times b \times c$
   (v) $3xy \times 2$ (vi) $ab \times c$ (vii) $3xy \times 4z$ (viii) $2ab \times 5c$

3. Simplify each of the following by adding like terms:
  (i) $x + x + x$ (ii) $x + 2x + 3x$ (iii) $a + 2a + 3 + 4$
  (iv) $2b + 4 + 5b + 2$ (v) $3x + 4 + 2x + 6$ (vi) $x + y + 3x + 2y$

4. Simplify these by adding like terms:
  (i) $5x - 2x$ (ii) $3a - a$ (iii) $5x - 2x$
  (iv) $3a + 2 - a + 5$ (v) $6b - 2 + b - 4$ (vi) $3a - 2b + 2a + 4b$

5. Simplify each of these:
  (i) $12a + b + 3a + 5b$ (ii) $3x + 2y + 3 + 4x + 3y + 1$
  (iii) $5x - 4 + 2x + 8$ (iv) $7x - 4 - 3x + 7$
  (v) $6a + b + 3 + 2a + 2b - 1$ (vi) $3x + 4 + 2x - 6 + x + 3$

6. Simplify each of these expressions:
  (i) $ab + ab$ (ii) $3ab + 2ab$ (iii) $4xy - 2xy$
  (iv) $4cd + 5cd - 2cd$ (v) $2ab - 5ab + 4ab$ (vi) $5xy + 6xy - 7xy$

7. Simplify these expressions:
  (i) $2p + 3q - r + p - 4q + 2r$ (ii) $5k + 3 - 4k + 6 + k - 4$
  (iii) $2ab + c + 5ab - 4c$ (iv) $3xy + 2z + xy + 9z$
  (v) $6ab + 2cd - ab + 3cd$ (vi) $6x - xy + 5x - 7xy$

8. Find and simplify an expression for the perimeter (length all round) of each of the following figures:

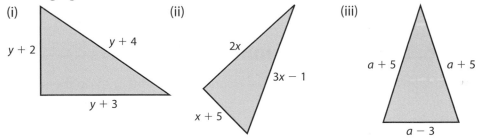

(i)   (ii)   (iii)

9. The number in each box is found by adding the numbers in the two boxes below it. Write an expression for the blue box as simply as possible.

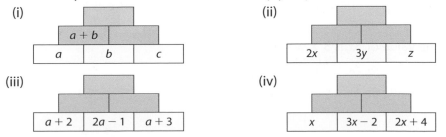

(i)   (ii)

(iii)   (iv)

10. Here are six cards containing expressions:

Ⓐ $x + 3$ Ⓑ $3x + 1$ Ⓒ $2x - 4$ Ⓓ $7 - x$ Ⓔ $2x - 6$ Ⓕ $3 - 2x$

(i)   Which two cards total $5x - 5$?

(ii)   Which two cards total $2x + 8$?

(iii)   Which two cards total $x + 3$?

(iv)   Which two cards total $10 - 3x$?

(v)   What is the total of all the expressions on the cards?

11. $3x + 5y - 8$ is an expression.

(i)   Name the two variables in this expression.

(ii)   Why are they called variables?

(iii)   Write down the coefficient of x.

(iv)   Write down the constant in the expression.

(v)   Are there any like terms in the expression?

12. An expression contains three terms.
The variable in one term is c; the variable in another term is d; there is also a term which is a constant.
What is the expression if

(i)   the coefficient of c is 4

(ii)   the coefficient of d is -3

(iii)   the constant term is a prime number between 6 and 10.

Section 6.3   Substituting numbers for letters

When a calculation contains more than one operation, remember to do them in the correct order.

Here are some examples:

(i) $3 + 4 \times 6 = 3 + 24 = 27$ ... multiply and divide before you add and subtract

(ii) $27 \div (7 - 4) = 27 \div 3 = 9$ ... do what is inside the brackets first

The rules for the order of operations in an **expression** are the same as the rules for arithmetic.

When $x = 3$, the value of $5x$ is $5 \times 3 = 15$.

When $x = 4$, the value of $3x + 7$ is $3 \times 4 + 7 = 12 + 7 = 19$.

When $x = 6$, the value of $3x \div (x - 3) = 3 \times 6 \div (6 - 3)$
$$= 18 \div 3$$
$$= 6$$

Example 1

If $x = 3$ and $y = 4$, find the value of
  (i) $3x$ (ii) $2x - y$ (iii) $2x + 3y - 6$ (iv) $2xy$

  (i) $3x = 3 \times 3 = 9$ (ii) $2x - y = 2 \times 3 - 4 = 6 - 4 = 2$
  (iii) $2x + 3y - 6 = 2 \times 3 + 3 \times 4 - 6$
  $\qquad\qquad\qquad = 6 + 12 - 6 = 12$
  (iv) $2xy = 2 \times x \times y$
  $\qquad\quad = 2 \times 3 \times 4 = 24$

Exercise 6.3

1. If $x = 2$ and $y = 3$, find the value of each of these:
  (i) $x + 2$ (ii) $3x$ (iii) $4y$ (iv) $6y - 8$
  (v) $2x + y$ (vi) $3x + 2y$ (vii) xy (viii) $5xy$

2. Find the value of each expression when $x = 5$.
  (i) $x + 3$ (ii) $5x$ (iii) $4x + 5$ (iv) $3x - 7$
  (v) $12 - x$ (vi) $15 - 2x$ (vii) $-3x + 20$ (viii) $9 - 3x$

3. If $a = 4$ and $b = 2$, find the value of
  (i) $a - b$ (ii) $6a + 3b$ (iii) $5a - 2b$ (iv) ab
  (v) $6ab - 2a$ (vi) $6a - 2ab$ (vii) $3ab + 6b$ (viii) $2a - b + 4ab$

4. Find the value of each expression when $y = 2$:
  (i) $6y$ (ii) $3(y + 4)$ (iii) $4(2y - 1)$
  (iv) $3(5y - 4)$ (v) $y(y + 3)$ (vi) $6y \times (2y + 1)$

5. If $a = 1$, $b = 2$ and $c = 3$, find the value of
  (i) $2a + b$ (ii) $3ab - c$ (iii) $4abc + 3c$
  (iv) $3bc - 4ab$ (v) $3abc - 2ac$ (vi) $5bc - 2ab$

6. Find the value of each expression when $x = 9$:
  (i) $\dfrac{x}{3}$ (ii) $\dfrac{x + 5}{2}$ (iii) $\dfrac{5x}{3}$
  (iv) $\dfrac{3x + 3}{10}$ (v) $\dfrac{2x - 6}{3}$ (vi) $\dfrac{18}{x}$

7. If $x = 1\frac{1}{2}$ and $y = \frac{1}{2}$, find the value of
  (i) $4x + 2y$ (ii) $3x + y$ (iii) $2x - 4y$
  (iv) $4x - 2y$ (v) $5x - 6y$ (vi) $8xy$

8. If $x = -2$, find the value of these expressions:
   (i) $x + 4$
   (ii) $2x$
   (iii) $2x + 8$
   (iv) $x - 6$
   (v) $3x - 2$
   (vi) $-2x$
   (vii) $-2x + 5$
   (viii) $6 - 2x$

9. Match these expressions to their answers when $p = -3$.

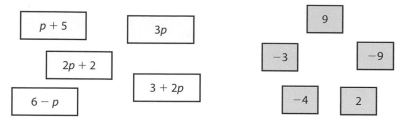

10.

A	B	C	D	E	F	G	L	N	R
-8	4	-9	3	-6	-10	-12	-2	-17	-7

   Find the value of each expression in the boxes below when $x = -5$.
   Use the code above to change your answers to letters.
   Rearrange the letters to spell the name of a country.

$4x + 3$	$x - 1$	$x - 3$	$2x$	$-4 + x$	$2x + 3$

11. Find the perimeter of the given figure when $h = 4$.

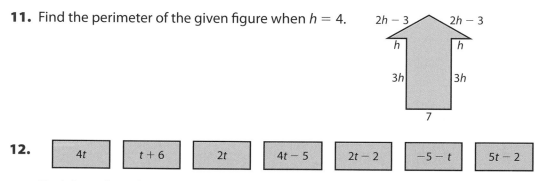

12.

$4t$	$t + 6$	$2t$	$4t - 5$	$2t - 2$	$-5 - t$	$5t - 2$

   Find the value of each of the expressions in the boxes above when $t = -3$.
   Use the code in question 10 above to find a letter for each answer.
   Rearrange the letters to spell the name of another country.

13. The expression $3d + 2$ gives the **total** number of dots needed to make a row with d blue dots.

   (i) Show that $3d + 2$ gives the correct total of dots for 5 blue dots.
   (ii) How many dots in total are needed to make a row with 15 blue dots?

14. In a magic square, each row, column and diagonal add up to the same number.

$a-b$	$a+b-c$	$a+c$
$a+b+c$	a	$a-b-c$
$a-c$	$a-b+c$	$a+b$

   (i) Show that this is a magic square if
      $a = 7, b = 2$ and $c = 3$.
   (ii) Now investigate if it is a magic square when
      $a = -2, b = 4$ and $c = -3$.

Section 6.4 Removing brackets

The expression $4(3 + 2) = 4(5) = 4 \times 5 = 20$.

$4(3 + 2)$ is a short method of writing $(3 + 2)$ multiplied by 4.

The multiplication sign is not visible.

We would get the same result to the question above if we multiplied each term inside the brackets by 4 and added the results, i.e.,

$$4(3 + 2) = 4 \times 3 + 4 \times 2$$
$$= 12 + 8 = 20$$

Similarly   (i) $3(x + 5) = 3 \times x + 3 \times 5 = 3x + 15$
   (ii) $5(2x + 4) = 5 \times 2x + 5 \times 4 = 10x + 20$
   (iii) $4(2a - 3b) = 4 \times 2a + 4 \times (-3b) = 8a - 12b$

If there is a minus sign outside the bracket, the sign of each term inside the bracket is changed when the bracket is removed.

Examples   (i) $-(2x + 3y) = -2x - 3y$
   (ii) $-(5x - 4) = -5x + 4$
   (iii) $2(x + 4) - (x - 3) = 2x + 8 - x + 3 = x + 11$
   (iv) $-3(2x + 5) = -6x - 15$
   (v) $-5(x - 3y) = -5x + 15y$

Example 1

Remove the brackets and simplify:
   $2(3x + 2y - 4) - 3(x - 3y + 2)$

$$2(3x + 2y - 4) - 3(x - 3y + 2) = 6x + 4y - 8 - 3x + 9y - 6$$
$$= 6x - 3x + 4y + 9y - 8 - 6$$
$$= 3x + 13y - 14$$

We have seen above that $3(x + 7) = 3x + 21$.

Look at the large rectangle here.

The length of the large rectangle is $(x + 7)$ and its width is 3.

Area $= 3(x + 7) = 3x + 21$.

The area of the yellow rectangle is $3x$.

The area of the green rectangle is 21.

The sum of the two areas is $3x + 21$, as found above.

Exercise 6.4

Remove the brackets in each of the following:

1. $4(x + 2)$
2. $3(a + 6)$
3. $4(2a + 7)$

4. $3(x + y)$
5. $5(2x + y)$
6. $4(2x + 3y)$

7. $6(2x - y)$
8. $3(x + 2y + 1)$
9. $6(2a + b + 3)$

Remove the brackets in each of these and simplify:

10. $6(a + 4) + 2(2a + 3)$
11. $7(x + y) + 3(2x - 3y)$

12. $5(2a + 3) - a + 4$
13. $5(a - b) + 2(2a + 3b)$

14. $5(x + 2y) - 3x + 2y$
15. $6(a + b) - 3a + b$

16. $2(3x - 2y) + 3x + 5y$
17. $3(a - 2) - 4(2a - 3)$

18. $8(a + b) - 4(2a + 3b)$
19. $3(x + 2y) - 2(2x - y)$

20. $4(2a - 3) - 2(a - 5)$
21. $3(2c + d) - 3(3c - 2d)$

22. $3(x + 2y + 1) + 2(2x + y - 3)$
23. $4(a + 3b + 1) + 2(a - 2b - 1)$

24. $3(2x - y + 4) + 2(x + y - 3)$
25. $3(a + b) + 4(2a - b) + 3a - b$

26. $4(x + y) + x - y + 2(x - y)$
27. $3(a - 2b) - 4(a - 2b) + 3a - b$

28. Find and simplify an expression for the perimeter of each of these figures:

(i)

(ii)

Section 6.5 Multiplication involving indices

You will have already learned that 5×5 can be written as 5^2.

Similarly (i) $a \times a$ can be written as a^2 (ii) $a \times a \times a$ can be written as a^3.

In the term a^2, **2** is called the **power** or **index**.

Now $a^2 \times a^2 = a \times a \times a \times a = a^4$
and $a^2 \times a^3 = (a \times a) \times (a \times a \times a)$
$\qquad\qquad = a \times a \times a \times a \times a = a^5$

> When multiplying the same number to two powers, add the indices.

To multiply $2x$ by $3x$, first multiply 2×3 and then multiply x by x.

$\therefore 2x \times 3x = 2 \times 3 \times x \times x$
$\qquad\qquad = 6x^2$

Similarly $3a \times 4b = 3 \times 4 \times a \times b = 12ab$

Example 1

Remove the brackets and simplify each of these:
  (i) $2x(x + 4) + 5x(2x - 1)$ (ii) $x(x + y) + 3x(4x - 3y) + 2xy$

  (i) $2x(x + 4) + 5x(2x - 1) = 2x^2 + 8x + 10x^2 - 5x$
$\qquad\qquad\qquad\qquad\qquad = 2x^2 + 10x^2 + 8x - 5x$
$\qquad\qquad\qquad\qquad\qquad = 12x^2 + 3x$
 (ii) $x(x + y) + 3x(4x - 3y) + 2xy = x^2 + xy + 12x^2 - 9xy + 2xy$
$\qquad\qquad\qquad\qquad\qquad\qquad\quad = x^2 + 12x^2 + xy - 9xy + 2xy$
$\qquad\qquad\qquad\qquad\qquad\qquad\quad = 13x^2 - 9xy + 3xy$
$\qquad\qquad\qquad\qquad\qquad\qquad\quad = 13x^2 - 6xy$

Evaluating expressions containing x^2

If $x = 3$, then $x^2 = 3 \times 3 = 9$.
If $x = 3$, then $4x^2 = 4 \times 3^2$
$\qquad\qquad\qquad = 4 \times 9 = 36$

> Work out the powers before multiplication

Example 2

Find the value of $2x^2 - 6x + 7$ when $x = 3$.

$\qquad 2x^2 - 6x + 7 = 2(3)^2 - 6(3) + 7$
$\qquad\qquad\qquad\quad = 2(9) - 18 + 7$
$\qquad\qquad\qquad\quad = 18 - 18 + 7 = 7$

Exercise 6.5

Write each of the following as a single term to a power, without using the multiplication sign:

1. 5×5 **2.** $4 \times 4 \times 4$ **3.** $a \times a$ **4.** $b \times b \times b$

5. $2 \times a \times a$ **6.** $3 \times x \times x$ **7.** $4 \times b \times b$ **8.** $a \times a^2$

9. $x^2 \times x^2$ **10.** $4 \times a \times a^2$ **11.** $2 \times 3 \times a \times a$ **12.** $4 \times x \times x^2 \times 5$

Remove the brackets and simplify each of the following:

13. $2(x^2 + 4) + 3(2x^2 + 5)$ **14.** $3(x^2 - 2) + 4(x^2 + 6)$

15. $x(x + 4) + 2x(x + 6)$ **16.** $2x(x + 2) + 3x(x - 1)$

17. $3x(2x + 1) + 4x(x - 3)$ **18.** $a(3a - 4) + 3a(2a - 3)$

19. $2x(2x - 6) - 3x(x + 5)$ **20.** $5a(a - 3) - 2a(a + 4)$

21. $3x(2x - 7) - 3x(2x - 4)$ **22.** $2a(3a - 4) - 3a(a - 7)$

23. $3(x^2 + 2x + 4) + 2(x^2 - 3x - 2)$ **24.** $4(a^2 + 2a - 1) - 2(2a^2 - 3a + 4)$

25. Evaluate each of the following when $x = 2$:
  (i) $2x$ (ii) x^2 (iii) $2x^2$ (iv) $5x^2$ (v) $4x^2 + 2x$

26. If $x = 2$ and $y = 3$, evaluate each of these:
  (i) $x^2 + y^2$ (ii) $3x^2 + y^2$ (iii) $2y^2 - x^2$ (iv) $x^2 + 3xy$
  (v) $2x^2 + 3y^2$ (vi) $4y^2 - 2x^2$ (vii) $3y^2 - 2xy$ (viii) $5xy - 2x^2$

27. (i) If $x = 2$, find the value of $x^2 - 3x + 5$.
  (ii) If $x = -3$, find the value of $x^2 - 4x - 6$.

28. If $a = 2$ and $b = -3$, find the value of each of these:
  (i) b^2 (ii) $4a^2$ (iii) $a^2 + 2b^2$ (iv) $3a^2 + 2b$
  (v) $2ab$ (vi) $2a^2b$ (vii) $2ab^2$ (viii) $b^2 - 4ab$

29. The area of a rectangle is the length multiplied by the breadth.
  Find the area of this rectangle when $x = 3$.

$3x - 1$

x ⬚ x

$3x - 1$

30. Match these expressions to the answers on the cards when $n = -3$.
  (i) n^2 (ii) $n^2 - 5$
  (iii) $3n^2 - 8$ (iv) $2(n^2 + 3)$
  (v) $n^2 - 2n + 6$

A 21 **B** 24 **C** 9

D 4 **E** 19

Section 6.6 **Multiplying two expressions**

What is $(2 + 3)(4 + 5)$?

Here we simplify what is inside each bracket and multiply the results.

Thus $(2 + 3)(4 + 5) = (5)(9) = 45$.

Here is another way to work out the answer.

$(2 + 3)(4 + 5)$ is twice $(4 + 5)$ + three times $(4 + 5)$

Thus $(2 + 3)(4 + 5) = 2(4 + 5) + 3(4 + 5)$

$\qquad\qquad\qquad\ = 2(9) + 3(9)$

$\qquad\qquad\qquad\ = 18 + 27 = 45$ ... as found above

Since algebra follows the same rules as arithmetic,
we multiply $(x + 2)(x + 3)$ as follows:

$(x + 2)(x + 3) = x(x + 3) + 2(x + 3)$

$\qquad\qquad\qquad\ = x^2 + 3x + 2x + 6$

$\qquad\qquad\qquad\ = x^2 + 5x + 6$

The area of the large rectangle below is $(x + 2)(x + 3)$.

By getting the area of each smaller rectangle, we can see that
$(x + 2)(x + 3) = x^2 + 5x + 6$.

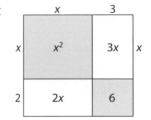

Example 1

Multiply (i) $(2x - 3)(3x + 4)$ (ii) $(2a + b)(a - 3b)$

(i) $(2x - 3)(3x + 4) = 2x(3x + 4) - 3(3x + 4)$

$\qquad\qquad\qquad\qquad\ = 6x^2 + 8x - 9x - 12$

$\qquad\qquad\qquad\qquad\ = 6x^2 - x - 12$

(ii) $(2a + b)(a - 3b) = 2a(a - 3b) + b(a - 3b)$

$\qquad\qquad\qquad\qquad\ = 2a^2 - 6ab + ab - 3b^2$

$\qquad\qquad\qquad\qquad\ = 2a^2 - 5ab - 3b^2$

Exercise 6.6

Multiply each of the following and simplify your answer:

1. $(x + 2)(x + 1)$

2. $(x + 1)(x + 3)$

3. $(x + 4)(x + 2)$

4. $(x + 5)(x + 2)$

5. $(x + 3)(x + 4)$

6. $(2x + 1)(x + 4)$

7. $(3x + 2)(x + 6)$

8. $(x + 5)(2x + 1)$

9. $(3x + 4)(2x + 1)$

10. $(x + 4)(x - 2)$

11. $(x - 3)(x + 5)$

12. $(x - 2)(2x + 1)$

13. $(3x + 2)(x - 3)$

14. $(3x - 1)(x + 4)$

15. $(5x + 2)(x - 4)$

16. $(x - 4)(x - 5)$

17. $(2x - 1)(3x - 2)$

18. $(4x - 3)(2x - 4)$

19. $(3x + 5)(2x - 1)$

20. $(5x - 2)(4x + 3)$

21. $(4x + 2)(2x - 3)$

22. $(2a + 3)(3a - 2)$

23. $(2a - 1)(5a + 2)$

24. $(4a + 1)(2a - 3)$

25. $(a + b)(c + d)$

26. $(x + y)(a + b)$

27. $(a + 2b)(c + 2d)$

28. $(2a - 3c)(3b - d)$

29. $(2a - 3b)(5a + 4b)$

30. $(x - 2y)(x + 3y)$

31. $(x + 2y)(x - 2y)$

32. $(3x + 2y)(3x - 2y)$

33. $(2x + y)^2$

34. $(x + 3y)^2$

35. $(2a - b)^2$

36. $(3x - 2y)^2$

37. Use the four smaller rectangles on the right to show that $(3x + 4)(2x + 3) = 6x^2 + 17x + 12$.

Test yourself 6

1. Simplify each of these expressions:
   (i) $5x + 3x - 4x$
   (ii) $4x + 5 + 6x - 3$
   (iii) $6x^2 - 2x + x^2 - 5x$
   (iv) $3a + 4b + a - 3b$
   (v) $2p - 3q + 3p + 5q$
   (vi) $a^2 - 4a + 6a + 5a^2$

2. If $x = 3$ and $y = 2$, find the value of each of these:
   (i) $6x$
   (ii) $2x + 3y$
   (iii) $6x - 2y$
   (iv) $x^2 + 2y^2$

3. (i) Express the perimeter of the given figure in its simplest form.
   (ii) Now find the length of the perimeter when $p = 5$ and $q = 1$.

   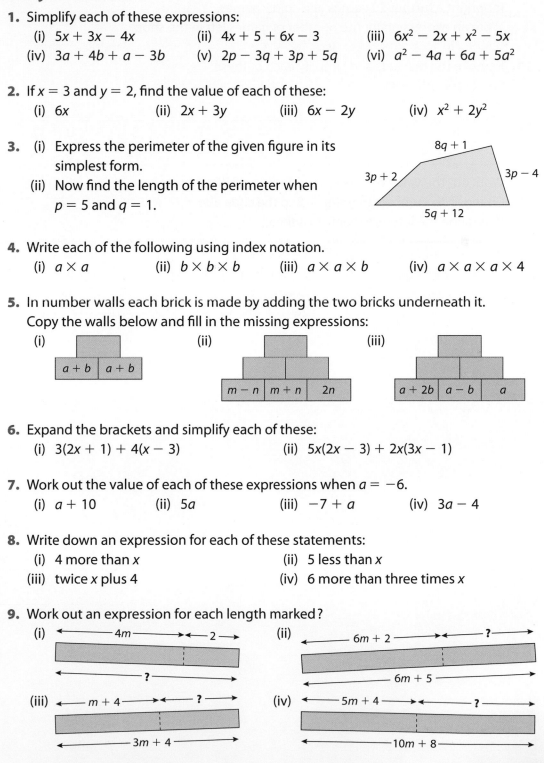

4. Write each of the following using index notation.
   (i) $a \times a$
   (ii) $b \times b \times b$
   (iii) $a \times a \times b$
   (iv) $a \times a \times a \times 4$

5. In number walls each brick is made by adding the two bricks underneath it.
   Copy the walls below and fill in the missing expressions:

   (i)
   (ii)
   (iii)

6. Expand the brackets and simplify each of these:
   (i) $3(2x + 1) + 4(x - 3)$
   (ii) $5x(2x - 3) + 2x(3x - 1)$

7. Work out the value of each of these expressions when $a = -6$.
   (i) $a + 10$
   (ii) $5a$
   (iii) $-7 + a$
   (iv) $3a - 4$

8. Write down an expression for each of these statements:
   (i) 4 more than x
   (ii) 5 less than x
   (iii) twice x plus 4
   (iv) 6 more than three times x

9. Work out an expression for each length marked?
   (i)
   (ii)
   (iii)
   (iv)

10. One Saturday a shop starts with x games.
It bought a further 20 games and sold y games.
Write an expression for the number of games left in the shop.

11. Remove the brackets and simplify each of these:
   (i) $(2x + 3)(x + 4)$ (ii) $(3x - 1)(2x + 5)$

12.

A	B	C	E	G	H	I	M	O	P	R	S	T	U	W
-2	-5	8	3	-3	0	-6	2	-1	5	1	-4	7	6	-9

Work out the value of the expressions in each list.
Change the numbers to letters using the code above.
Rearrange the letters to spell an animal.

(i)
$a - 1$ when $a = -2$
$b - 2$ when $b = -4$
$2 - c$ when $c = -3$

(ii)
$x + 9$ when $x = -2$
$y - 4$ when $y = 3$
$2z$ when $z = -1$
$2w + 1$ when $w = -2$

(iii)
$2a$ when $a = -2$
$b + 5$ when $b = -5$
$5 + 3c$ when $c = -2$
$2d + 5$ when $d = -1$
$-4 + e$ when $e = 5$

For the problem solver...

1. In a sequence of numbers, each term after the first three terms is the sum of the previous three terms. The first three terms are $-3, 0, 2$. Which is the first term to exceed 100?

2. The symbols $*, \nabla, \square, \bigcirc$ represent numbers. Use the clues in (a), (b) and (c) to answer part (d).
   (a) $* + \nabla = \square$ (b) $* = \nabla + \bigcirc$
   (c) $* + * + \nabla = \square + \bigcirc + \bigcirc$ (d) $\nabla = $ How many $\bigcirc$'s?

3. This square is on the door of a safe.
   The letters A, B, C, D and E stand for whole numbers.
   The red numbers show the sum of each row and column.
   $E = 3$
   To unlock the safe you must know what number the other letters stand for.
   What do they stand for?

E	E	D	C	14
C	B	C	A	21
B	B	D	A	15
C	A	E	D	16
19	16	13	18	

4. The letters J, M, C represent three different non-zero digits. What is the value of $J + M + C$?

   $$\begin{array}{cc} J & J \\ M & M \\ C & C \\ \hline J & M & C \end{array}$$

5. What is the value of ♥ if each row and each column has the total given?

			Total
♥	☀	♫	12
♫	♥	♥	11
☀	☀	♫	13
Total 12	11	13	

6. The symbols $*, \bigcirc, \triangle, \square$ represent weights. Use the information in (a), (b), (c) to answer part (d).
   (i) (a) $\triangle + \square = * + \bigcirc$ (ii) (a) $\bigcirc + \bigcirc + \square = * + \bigcirc$
       (b) $\square + \square = \triangle + \bigcirc$ (b) $* + * = \bigcirc + \bigcirc + \bigcirc$
       (c) $\triangle + * + * = \bigcirc$ (c) $\square + * = \bigcirc + \bigcirc$
       (d) $\bigcirc = $ How many $*$?   (d) $* = $ How many $\square$s?

7. The expression $n^2 - n + 11$ gives a prime number for all but one of these values of n. Which is the odd one out?
   $A\ n = 2$ $B\ n = 3$ $C\ n = 5$ $D\ n = 7$ $E\ n = 11$

Chapter 7

Percentages

Key words

per cent	fraction	decimal	equivalent fraction
increasing	decreasing	value-added tax	discount
cost price	selling price	profit	loss

Section 7.1 Percentages – Fractions – Decimals

The words **per cent** means *per hundred* or *out of every hundred*.

The symbol **%** is used to represent *per cent*.

Thus 10% means 10 out of every 100.

The diagram shows 100 squares.

25 of the squares are coloured red.

The amount of the diagram coloured red is

$$\frac{25}{100} = 25\%.$$

10% of the diagram is coloured green.

Fractions to percentages

$$\frac{1}{5} = \frac{1 \times 20}{5 \times 20} = \frac{20}{100} = 20\%$$

$$\frac{3}{4} = \frac{3 \times 25}{4 \times 25} = \frac{75}{100} = 75\%$$

Here we changed each fraction into an equivalent fraction with 100 as denominator.

This work may be shortened by multiplying each fraction by $\frac{100}{1}$.

Thus $\frac{1}{5} = \frac{1}{5} \times \frac{100}{1}\% = \frac{100}{5} = 20\%$

$\frac{3}{4} = \frac{3}{4} \times \frac{100}{1}\% = \frac{300}{4} = 75\%$

> To change a fraction to a percentage, multiply the fraction by $\frac{100}{1}$.

Example 1

Express   (i) $\frac{4}{5}$ (ii) $\frac{5}{8}$ as percentages.

(i) $\frac{4}{5} = \frac{4}{5} \times \frac{100}{1}\%$

$= \frac{400}{5} = 80\%$

(ii) $\frac{5}{8} = \frac{5}{8} \times \frac{100}{1}\%$

$= \frac{500}{8} = 62\frac{4}{8}\%$

$= 62\frac{1}{2}\%$

Percentages and decimals

If you examine the following you will see the close connection between decimals and percentages.

(i) $0.25 = \frac{25}{100} - 25\%$

(ii) $16\% - \frac{16}{100} - 0.16$

(iii) $0.8 = \frac{8}{10} = \frac{80}{100} = 80\%$

(iv) $12\frac{1}{2}\% = \frac{12\frac{1}{2}}{100} = \frac{12.5}{100}$

$- 0.125$

Rule   To change a decimal to a percentage, multiply by 100.

Percentage to decimals or fractions

$35\% = \frac{35}{100} = \frac{7}{20}$

Here we put the percentage over 100 and simplified the fraction.

Similarly, $35\% = \frac{35}{100} = 0.35$

Here again we divided the percentage by 100 to change it to a decimal.

Rule   To change a percentage to a decimal or fraction, divide the percentage by 100.

Here are some percentages you should memorise:

Fraction	$\frac{1}{10}$	$\frac{1}{5}$	$\frac{1}{3}$	$\frac{1}{2}$	$\frac{2}{3}$	$\frac{3}{4}$
Percentage	10%	20%	$33\frac{1}{3}\%$	50%	$66\frac{2}{3}\%$	75%

Exercise 7.1

1. Three figures, each with 100 squares, are shown below:

(a) (b) (c)

   (i)   What percentage of each square is coloured yellow?
   (ii) What percentage of each square is not coloured yellow?
   (iii) What fraction of each square is coloured yellow?
   (iv) What decimal of each square is coloured yellow?

2. Copy and complete each of these:

   (i) $\dfrac{28}{100} = \square\%$

   (ii) $\dfrac{54}{100} = \square\%$

   (iii) $\dfrac{\square}{100} = 15\%$

   (iv) $\dfrac{9}{10} = \dfrac{\square}{100} = \square\%$

   (v) $\dfrac{11}{20} = \dfrac{\square}{100} = \square\%$

   (vi) $\dfrac{14}{25} = \dfrac{\square}{100} = \square\%$

3. Express the following percentages as fractions in their simplest form:

   (i)   20%   (ii) 60%   (iii) 70%   (iv) 15%   (v)   25%
   (vi) 75%   (vii) 85%   (viii) 5%   (ix) 2%   (x)   24%.

4. Copy and complete the following:

$$7\tfrac{1}{2}\% = \dfrac{7\tfrac{1}{2}}{100} = \dfrac{7\tfrac{1}{2} \times 2}{100 \times 2} = \dfrac{\square}{200} = \dfrac{3}{\square}.$$

5. Change these percentages to fractions and simplify each fraction:

   (i) $33\tfrac{1}{3}\%$ (ii) $12\tfrac{1}{2}\%$ (iii) $2\tfrac{1}{2}\%$ (iv) $8\tfrac{1}{3}\%$ (v) $17\tfrac{1}{2}\%$

6.

| 0 | 0.1 | 0.2 | 0.3 | 0.4 | 0.5 | 0.6 | 0.7 | 0.8 | 0.9 | 1 |

| 0 | 10% | 20% | 30% | 40% | 50% | 60% | 70% | 80% | 90% | 100% |

Use the number line above to answer these questions:
   (i)   Write each of these decimals as a percentage:
   (a) 0·5   (b) 0·2   (c) 0·35   (d) 0·8   (e) 0·75
   (ii) Write each of these percentages as a decimal:
   (a) 20%   (b) 80%   (c) 70%   (d) 65%   (e) 95%

7. Change these fractions to percentages:

   (i) $\dfrac{18}{100}$ (ii) $\dfrac{47}{100}$ (iii) $\dfrac{3}{10}$ (iv) $\dfrac{7}{10}$ (v) $\dfrac{5}{20}$

   (vi) $\dfrac{2}{5}$ (vii) $\dfrac{3}{4}$ (viii) $\dfrac{17}{20}$ (ix) $\dfrac{4}{25}$ (x) $\dfrac{19}{50}$

8. Write these percentages as decimals:
    (i) 50%   (ii) 10%   (iii) 90%   (iv) 35%   (v) 45%
    (vi) 8%   (vii) $12\frac{1}{2}$%   (viii) 24%   (ix) 1%   (x) $24\frac{1}{2}$%

9. Express the following decimals as percentages:
    (i) 0·8   (ii) 0·4   (iii) 0·75   (iv) 0·45   (v) 0·15
    (vi) 0·07   (vii) 0·01   (viii) 0·125   (ix) 0·345   (x) 0·045

10. What percentage of each diagram is shaded?

(i)   (ii)   (iii)

11. Put these in three matching groups.

$\frac{4}{5}$ 80%   0.8   40% $\frac{4}{10}$

$\frac{3}{4}$ $\frac{2}{5}$ 75%   0.75

12. Write the following quantities in order, starting with the smallest:
    (i) 50% $\frac{1}{4}$ 20%   0·3 $\frac{2}{5}$
    (ii) $\frac{3}{10}$ 60% $\frac{1}{5}$ $\frac{1}{2}$ $\frac{1}{4}$ 0·45

13. Write these fractions and percentages as decimals:
    (i) $\frac{27}{100}$ (ii) $\frac{7}{100}$ (iii) 54%   (iv) $17\frac{1}{2}$%   (v) $2\frac{1}{2}$%

14. Find four matching pairs.
    What could match the odd one out?

40%   0.25   15%   0.15   0.4

0.8   70%   80%   0.7

15.

A	E	U	N	R	S	T	M	V
$\frac{1}{2}$	30%	40%	0·8	0·6	0·2	75%	$\frac{1}{4}$	$\frac{7}{10}$

Use this code to find a letter for each fraction, decimal or percentage below.
Rearrange each set of letters to spell a planet.

    (i) $\frac{3}{4}$ 0·5 $\frac{6}{10}$ 20%   80% $\frac{2}{5}$
    (ii) 0·4 $\frac{1}{5}$ 0·7 $\frac{8}{10}$ 0·3
    (iii) $\frac{3}{5}$ 50%   0·4 $\frac{1}{5}$ $\frac{4}{10}$ 80%

16. What percentage of each of the following figures is shaded?

(i)

(ii)

(iii)

Section 7.2 Working with percentages I ──────────

Finding a percentage of a quantity ─────────────

To find the percentage of a quantity, change the percentage to a fraction or decimal and multiply by the quantity.

> **Example 1**
>
> Find (i) 8% of 250   (ii) $37\frac{1}{2}$% of €320.
>
> (i) 8% of 250 $= \dfrac{8}{100} \times \dfrac{250}{1} = \dfrac{200}{10} = 20$
>
> (ii) $37\frac{1}{2}\% = \dfrac{37\frac{1}{2}}{100} = \dfrac{37\frac{1}{2} \times 2}{100 \times 2} = \dfrac{75}{200} = \dfrac{15}{40} = \dfrac{3}{8}$
>
> $\dfrac{3}{8}$ of €320 $= \dfrac{3}{8} \times \dfrac{320}{1} = €120$

When using a calculator to find the percentage of a quantity, write the percentage as a decimal.

Using the calculator:

    (i) To find 8% of €36, key in

       36 ⨯ 0·08 =

       The result is €2·88.

    (ii) To find 76% of 250 km, key in

       250 ⨯ 0·76 =

       The answer is 190 km.

Decimal equivalents		
1%	=	0·01
7%	=	0·07
$8\frac{1}{2}$%	=	0·085
16%	=	0·16
$16\frac{1}{2}$%	=	0·165
70%	=	0·7
85%	=	0·85
92·3%	=	0·923

Expressing one quantity as a percentage of another quantity

To express one quantity as a percentage of another quantity, first express as a fraction and then multiply by 100.

When comparing quantities make sure both quantities are in the same units.

Example 2

Express   (i) 72 as a percentage of 80
          (ii) 15 minutes as a percentage of $1\frac{1}{2}$ hours.

(i) 72 as a percentage of 80 is $\dfrac{72}{80} \times \dfrac{100}{1} = \dfrac{720}{8} = 90\%.$

(ii) 15 mins as a percentage of $1\frac{1}{2}$ hours is $\dfrac{15}{90} \times \dfrac{100}{1}$ ... $1\frac{1}{2}$ hours = 90 mins

$\dfrac{15}{90} \times \dfrac{100}{1}\% = \dfrac{150}{9} = \dfrac{50}{3} = 16\frac{2}{3}\%$

When using a calculator to express 13 as a percentage of 50, you need to find the value of $\frac{13}{50} \times \frac{100}{1}$.

Key in 13 $\div$ 50 $\times$ 100 $=$.

The answer is 26%.

Exercise 7.2

1. Write down the answers to these without written calculations:
   (i) 10% of 50   (ii) 20% of 40   (iii) 25% of 48   (iv) 5% of 300
   (v) 30% of 200   (vi) 40% of 120   (vii) 75% of 16   (viii) 11% of 600

2. Find each of the following:
   (i) 10% of 380   (ii) 40% of 680   (iii) 30% of 1680
   (iv) 15% of €420   (v) 45% of €140   (vi) 80% of €910.

3. To find $17\frac{1}{2}\%$ of 480, copy and complete the calculation on the right.

   10% of 480 = 48
   5% of 480 = ☐
   $2\frac{1}{2}\%$ of 480 = ☐
   ───────────────────
   $17\frac{1}{2}\%$ of 480 = ☐

4. Use the method used in question 3 to find each of these:
   (i) 15% of 120 km
   (ii) $22\frac{1}{2}$% of €450
   (iii) $37\frac{1}{2}$% of 800 kg

5. Which is the greater of these sums of money?
   $12\frac{1}{2}$% of €160 or $17\frac{1}{2}$% of €120

6. The table on the right gives the marks that a boy got for each subject in a test.
Find the percentage mark that he got in each subject.

Subject	Boy's marks	Total marks
Maths	58	100
Science	60	80
English	48	60
Irish	51	75
History	28	40
Geography	56	70
French	116	200

7. Express the first quantity as a percentage of the second in each of the following:
   (i) 12; 48
   (ii) 15; 75
   (iii) €6; €15
   (iv) 25c; €5
   (v) 60c; €5.00
   (vi) 12 mins; 1 hr 20 mins
   (vii) 90 cm; 3 m
   (viii) 8 days; 2 weeks and 6 days
   (ix) 36; 450

8. These labels show the percentage of fat in some foods.

Pizza 10% fat   Chips 15% fat   Croissants 20% fat   Hamburgers 35% fat   Margarine 80% fat   Dry roast peanuts 45% fat

How much fat is there in
   (i) a 300 g pizza
   (ii) 200 g of chips
   (iii) 120 g of margarine
   (iv) a 100 g hamburger
   (v) a 90 g croissant
   (vi) 300 g of peanuts?

9. Express each of these percentages as a decimal:
   (i) 14%
   (ii) 27%
   (iii) 35%
   (iv) 6%
   (v) 9%
   (vi) $9\frac{1}{2}$%
   (vii) 30%
   (viii) 36·5%
   (ix) 96·3%
   (x) 20·3%

10. Use your calculator to find each of the following:
   (i) 15% of 280
   (ii) 12% of 340
   (iii) 7% of 84
   (iv) 28% of 650
   (v) $34\frac{1}{2}$% of 600
   (vi) $1\frac{1}{2}$% of 650

11. Which is bigger, 23% of €85 or 48% of €55?

12. Find the sale price of this jumper.

€59   SALE 15% OFF

13. In a school of 1200 pupils 45% are boys.
  (i) How many are girls?
  (ii) 30% of the girls are under 13.
       How many girls are under 13?

14. A worker with a weekly wage of €750 got an increase of 5%.
  Find his new weekly wage.

15. Joan got 248 marks out of 400 in a Science examination.
  Express her marks as a percentage of the total.

16. In a French examination a boy got 336 marks out of 600.
  In an English examination he got 44 marks out of 80.
  In which examination did he achieve the higher percentage mark?

17. A worker with a weekly wage of €640 got an increase of €32 a week.
  What percentage increase did she get?

18. A theatre has 480 seats. During a certain show 24 seats were empty.
  What percentage of the seats was full?

19. Martin walks $\frac{1}{2}$ km to school and takes the bus for the remaining $4\frac{1}{2}$ km.
  What percentage of the total journey does he walk?

20. In a survey a group of people were asked how they learned to use a computer.
  The answers are listed as

Method	Number of people
Self-taught	33
Through work	18
From family or friend	5
At school	21
Other	3

  (i) How many people were asked in the survey in total?
  (ii) What percentage of this total were self-taught?
  (iii) What percentage learned at school?

21. A cake is described as '85% fat free'.
  (i) What percentage of the cake is fat?
  (ii) If the cake weighs 400 g, how much fat does it contain?

Section 7.3 Working with percentages II

Increasing or decreasing by a given percentage

The following examples will show how to increase or decrease a quantity by a given percentage without using a calculator.

Example 1

(i) Decrease €650 by 12%.
(ii) Increase 440 g by 35%.

(i) 1% of €650 = $\frac{650}{100}$ = €6.50
     12% of €650 = €6.50 × 12 = €78
     To decrease by 12%, we take €78 from €650 to get €572.

(ii) 1% of 440 g = 4·4 g
      35% of 440 g = 4·4 × 35 = 154 g
      440 g + 154 g = 594 g
      ∴ 440 g increased by 35% = 594 g.

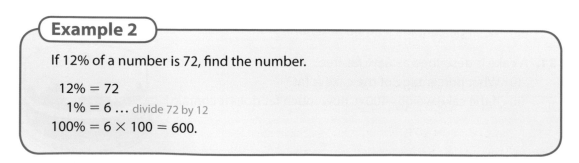

We will now use a calculator to work out the two calculations in Example 1 above.

(i) If an amount is decreased by 12%, we require 88% of the amount.
     88% = 0·88
     0·88 of €650 = 650 ⨉ 0·88 = . The answer is €572.

ii) If an amount is increased by 35%, we require 135% of the amount.
     135% = 1·35
     1·35 of 440 g = 440 ⨉ 1·35 = . The answer is 594 g.

Finding a quantity when given a percentage of it

If we are given a percentage of a quantity, we first find 1% and multiply this amount by 100 to find the total quantity which is 100%.

Example 2

If 12% of a number is 72, find the number.

12% = 72
 1% = 6 ... divide 72 by 12
100% = 6 × 100 = 600.

Exercise 7.3

1. Work out each of these without using a calculator:
   (i) Increase 90 by 10%
   (ii) Increase 60 by 20%
   (iii) Increase 150 by 30%
   (iv) Decrease 40 by 10%
   (v) Decrease 120 by 20%
   (vi) Decrease 200 by 5%

2. Work out these without using a calculator:
   Increase
   (i) 100 by 60%
   (ii) 300 by 65%
   (iii) 320 by 45%
   (iv) 280 by 15%
   (v) 480 by 5%
   (vi) €80 by 8%

3. Write these percentages as decimals:
   (i) 6%
   (ii) 15%
   (iii) 35%
   (iv) 70%
   (v) $7\frac{1}{2}$%.

4. To find 82% of 600, multiply 600 by 0·82 on a calculator.
   Now fill in the missing decimal in each of the following:
   (i) To find 38% of 700, multiply 700 by ☐.
   (ii) To find 60% of 580, multiply 580 by ☐.
   (iii) To find 13% of 270, multiply 270 by ☐.
   (iv) To find 6% of 300, multiply 300 by ☐.
   (v) To find 120% of 640, multiply 640 by ☐.
   (vi) To find $12\frac{1}{2}$% of 800, multiply 800 by ☐.

5. (i) Increase 240 by 10%.
   (ii) Increase 150 by 40%.
   (iii) Decrease €140 by 15%.
   (iv) Decrease 240 kg by $12\frac{1}{2}$%.
   (v) Increase €90 by 8%.
   (vi) Decrease 80 kg by 35%.

6. Find the weight of each of the following after the extra has been added:
   (i) A 450 g packet of cornflakes with 30% extra
   (ii) A 750 g container of yogurt with 10% extra
   (iii) A 250 g pizza with 15% extra.

7. If 11% of a number is 77, find the number.

8. If 20% of a sum of money is €70, find the sum of money.

9. If 15% of the price of a car is €2775, find the price of the car.

10. A bus company plans to increase its prices by 8%. At the moment the bus fare to town is €1.50. Calculate the new fare.

11. The shop price of a CD is €19.95.
   Calculate the online price if you save $22\frac{1}{2}$%.
   Give your answer to the nearest cent.

12. Deirdre spent 40% of her money in one shop and 35% of it in another.
   If she had €26.80 left, how much had she at first?

13. In a school there are 336 girls out of a total enrolment of 560 pupils.
    Find the percentage of boys in the school.

14. Dara got a wage increase of 5%.
    If his new wage is €892.50, find his wage before the increase.

15. A car is valued at €26 000. It depreciates in value by 20% in the first year and in the
    second year it depreciates by 15% of its value at the beginning of the year.
    Find the value of the car
    (i) after 1 year   (ii) after 2 years.

Section 7.4 Value-added tax (VAT) – Discount

Discount

A 15% discount means the price is reduced by 15%.
If you get a 15% discount on the price of an item, you now pay only 85% of the price.

Example 1

(i) A store offers a discount of 20% on all items during a sale.
   Find the sale price of a television set which had a marked price of €780.
(ii) A music shop offered a discount of €4.80 on DVDs with a marked price of
   €24.
   Express this discount as a percentage.

(i) If the discount is 20%, the sale price is 80% of the marked price.
   $80\% = 0{\cdot}8$
   $€780 \times 0{\cdot}8 = €624$
   ∴ the sale price is €624.

(ii) The percentage discount is

   Percentage discount $= \dfrac{€4.80}{€24} \times \dfrac{100}{1}\%$
   $\dfrac{\text{Discount}}{\text{Given price}} \times \dfrac{100}{1}\%$

   $= \dfrac{4{\cdot}80 \times 100}{24} = 20\%$

   ∴ the percentage discount is 20%.

Value-added tax (VAT)

Value-added tax or **VAT** is a government tax that is added to many of the things that we buy. In most shops the marked price of an item includes VAT and so we do not have to calculate it.

Sometimes the prices of more expensive items such as television sets and furniture are given without VAT. In these cases the shopkeeper calculates the VAT amount and adds it to the price of the item.

If an article is priced at €280 plus VAT at 23%, the full price can be worked out as follows:

1% of €280 = €2.80

23% = €2.80 × 23 = €64.40

∴ the full price = €280 + €64.40 = €344.40

 Using a calculator

100% + 23% = 123%

To find 123% we multiply by 1·23.

Full price = €280 × 1·23 = €344.40, as found above.

Example 2

The rate of VAT on electrical goods is 20%.
  (i) Find the selling price of a washing machine priced a €650 + VAT.
  (ii) If the selling price of a laptop, including VAT, is €576, find the price of the recorder before VAT is added on.

(i) 20% of €650 = 650 × 0·2 = €130

∴ selling price = €650 + €130 = €780.

(ii) €576 represents 100% + 20%, i.e. 120% of the price before VAT is added on.

$$∴ 120\% = 576$$

$$1\% = \frac{576}{120} = €4.80$$

$$100\% = 4.8 × 100 = €480$$

∴ the price before VAT is added is €480.

Exercise 7.4

1. Without using a calculator, find the sale price of each of these articles:

Article	Marked price	Percentage discount
DVD recorder	€800	15%
Electric iron	€40	20%
Bicycle	€780	25%
TV set	€950	$12\frac{1}{2}\%$

2. Find the sale price for each of these marked prices:

(i) Jumper: €45   (ii) Boots: €80

3. The price of a certain car is €27 500.
During the month of December the garage offers a discount of 15%.
What is the price of the car during December?

4. A man was given a discount of 20% when he bought a suit.
If he paid €256 for the suit, find the price of the suit before the discount by completing the following:

80% of the price = €256
1% of the price = ☐
100% of the price = ☐
Price before discount = ☐

5. A woman paid €200 for a coat after a discount of 20% was given.
Find the price of the coat before the discount was allowed.

6. Find the selling price of each of the following:
(i) a television set marked €800 + VAT at 20%
(ii) a bicycle marked €650 + VAT at 20%
(iii) a games console marked €420 + VAT at 15%
(iv) a lawn-mower marked €760 + VAT at 10%.

7. Find the cost of hiring a car for 8 days at €75 per day plus VAT at 15%.

8. Find the selling price of a suite of furniture marked €850 + VAT at 20%.

9. A dinner in a restaurant for 4 people cost €148.
Find the total bill when VAT at $12\frac{1}{2}\%$ was added on.

10. Without using a calculator find the total cost, including VAT, of each item.

€180

VAT is 21%

€700

11. A shopkeeper bought 200 pens at €2.40 each + VAT at 20%.
    Find the total cost of the pens.

12. A bill from a garage for a car service consisted of €240 for labour and €360 for parts. VAT at the rate of 10% for labour and 20% for parts was added to the bill.
    Find the total cost of the car service.

13. A man sold a house for €420 000.
    The auctioneer charged him fees of 1% of the sale price plus VAT at 21% on these fees.
    Find the amount of the bill from the auctioneer.

14. The price of an article is €33.60 when VAT at 20% is included.
    Find the price of the article before VAT is added on.

15. The price of a meal for 8 people in a restaurant is €264 after VAT at 10% is included.
    Find the price of the meal before VAT is added.

16. The price of a TV set, including VAT at 25%, is €750.
    Find the price of the TV set before VAT is added.

17. Angela bought a bicycle for €744. This price included VAT at 20%.
    Find the price of the bicycle before VAT was added on.

Investigation

Jack went to a builder's providers and bought building materials for €3750 plus VAT at 20%.

The providers told him that they would give him a discount of 10%.
Jack considered whether he should take the discount first and then pay VAT on the reduced bill

OR

Pay the VAT first and then get the discount on the total.
Which should be choose to get the cheapest price?

Section 7.5 Percentage profit and loss

When a trader buys an item for €8 and sells it for €10, he makes a **profit** of €2.
€8 is called the **cost price** and €10 is the **selling price**.
Traders generally express their profit as a percentage of the cost price.
For example, if an item is bought for €20 and sold for €25, a profit of €5 is made.
This profit expressed as a percentage of the price is

$$\frac{5}{20} \times \frac{100}{1} = \frac{500}{20} = \frac{50}{2} = 25\%$$

> Percentage profit (or loss) is
>
> $$\frac{\text{Profit (or loss)}}{\text{Cost price}} \times \frac{100}{1}\%$$

Example 1

A shopkeeper buys cameras at €180 and sells them at €216 each.
Find his percentage profit on the cost price.

Profit = €216 − €180 = €36

$$\text{Percentage profit} = \frac{\text{Profit}}{\text{Cost price}} \times \frac{100}{1}$$

$$= \frac{36}{180} \times \frac{100}{1} = \frac{36 \times 10}{18} = 20\%.$$

Example 2

By selling a jacket for €138, a store makes a profit of 15% on the cost price.
Find what the store paid for the jacket.

Since a profit of 15% was made, €138 represents 115% of the cost price.

The cost price is 100%.

$$\therefore 115\% = €138$$

$$1\% = \frac{138}{115}$$

$$100\% = \frac{138}{115} \times \frac{100}{1} = €120$$

∴ the store paid €120 for the jacket

Exercise 7.5

1. Find the selling price in each of the following:
- (i)   Cost price €20:   sold at a profit of 20%
- (ii) Cost price €32:   sold at a profit of 25%
- (iii) Cost price €80:   sold at a profit of 15%
- (iv) Cost price €60:   sold at a loss of 10%
- (v)   Cost price €8.20:   sold at a loss of 15%
- (vi) Cost price €120:   sold at a profit of $12\frac{1}{2}$%.

2. Find the percentage profit or loss in each of the following:
- (i)   Cost price €8:   selling price €10
- (ii) Cost price €20:   selling price €24
- (iii) Cost price €60:   selling price €63
- (iv) Cost price €120:   selling price €96
- (v)   Cost price €240:   selling price €312
- (vi) Cost price €16:   selling price €12.80.

3. A shopkeeper buys washing machines at €520 each and sells them at €598.
Find his percentage profit.

4. Find the three matching pairs out of the following:

A Cost price = €20 10% loss

B Cost price = €25 20% loss

C Cost price = €80 15% profit

D Cost price = €70 30% loss

P €92

Q €49

R €20

S €18

5. Find the cost price for each of these if
- (i)   the selling price is €10 and there is a 25% profit
- (ii) the selling price is €8.80 and there is a 10% profit
- (iii) the selling price is €57.60 and there is a 20% loss
- (iv) the selling price is €22.80 and there is a 5% loss
- (v)   the selling price is €1050 and there is a 40% profit.

6. A jeweller bought a gold ring for €550 and sold it at a profit of 40%.
Find the sale price.

7. A dealer bought a used car for €9000 and sold it for €9900.
Find his percentage profit.

8. An electrical shop buys MP3 docking stations at €360 each.
If they are sold at a profit of 15%, find the selling price.

9. A greengrocer buys kiwis in boxes of 50 at €24 per box.
If she sells the kiwis at 60 cent each, find her percentage profit.

10. A fashion shop makes a profit of 30% by selling a coat for €195.
Copy and complete the following to find the cost price of the coat

$$130\% = €195$$

11. When an item is sold for €121, a profit of 10% is made.
Find the cost price of the item.

12. By selling a bicycle for €720 a shopkeeper makes a loss of 10%.
(i) What did the shopkeeper pay for the bicycle?
(ii) At what price should he sell the bicycle to make a profit of 15%?

13. A dealer bought television sets at €800
each and sold them at a profit of 40%.
During a sale the selling price was reduced
by 10%.
(i) Find the selling price of a television
during the sale.
(ii) What was the dealer's percentage profit on television sets during the sale?

14. A shopkeeper bought 50 toys at €25 each.
He sold 40 of them at a marked price of €32.50.
He sold the remaining 10 toys after reducing the marked price by 20%.
(i) Find what the shopkeeper paid for the 50 toys.
(ii) Find the selling price of each of the remaining toys during the sale.
(iii) Find his total profit on the deal.
(iv) Work out his percentage profit.

15. During a sale the price of shirts is reduced by 20%.
If the sale price of a shirt is €48, what was the marked price before the sale?

16. A trader bought an article for €250 and then added on 20% to get his selling price.
(i) Find his selling price.
(ii) During a sale he reduced his selling price by 15%.
Find his percentage profit on the article during the sale.

17. A car dealer bought two cars; a Fiat for €8400 and a Ford for €9600.
He sold the Fiat at a profit of 20% and the Ford at a loss of 5%.
(i) Find the profit he made on the cars.
(ii) Find his percentage profit on the whole deal.

Test yourself 7

1. Express each of these as a percentage:
   (i) $\frac{1}{4}$ (ii) $\frac{2}{5}$ (iii) 0·34 (iv) 0·7 (v) $\frac{9}{10}$

2. Write each of these percentages as a fraction in its lowest terms:
   (i) 20% (ii) 25% (iii) 45% (iv) 5% (v) $87\frac{1}{2}$%

3. Work out these percentages.
   (i) 45 as a percentage of 60 (ii) 15 as a percentage of 75
   (iii) 32 as a percentage of 128 (iv) 42 as a percentage of 112

4.

40%	75%	30%	20%	50%	60%	25%	80%	70%

   Find a percentage from the box for each sentence.
   (i) Seven out of ten people watch the news on TV.
   (ii) One out of every two people who eat at McDonalds is under 12.
   (iii) In a survey it was found that maths was the favourite subject for three quarters of students.
   (iv) Two out of every five people go abroad for their summer holiday.
   (v) Six out of every twenty students play a musical instrument.

5. Work these out by first writing the percentages as fractions.
   (i) 20% of 60 (ii) 50% of 86 (iii) 25% of 36
   (iv) 10% of 3000 (v) 75% of 140 (vi) 90% of 1200
   (vii) 50% of 65 (viii) 25% of 24 (ix) 60% of 25

6. Copy and complete this table.

Fraction	Decimal	Percentage
$\frac{3}{4}$		
	0·6	
$\frac{7}{10}$		
		40%
	0·9	

7. What percentage of each of these figures is shaded?
   (i) (ii) (iii)

8. The pie chart shows how pupils in a class travel to school.
   30 pupils travel by car.
   (i) How many pupils are in the class?
   (ii) How many pupils walk to school?

9. Rachel's test scores are given in the table to the right.
   Copy and complete the table by working out Rachel's percentage score for each subject.

Subject	Score	Percentage
English	$\frac{35}{40}$	
Maths	$\frac{68}{80}$	
Geography	$\frac{28}{35}$	
History	$\frac{54}{60}$	
Science	$\frac{56}{64}$	

10. Write each of these lists in order of size, starting with the smallest:
    (i) $\frac{1}{4}$ 0·3   20% $\frac{2}{5}$ 10%
    (ii) $\frac{3}{5}$ $\frac{1}{2}$ $\frac{3}{4}$ 40%   0·78

11.

E	G	I	H	L	N	O	P	R	T	Y
$\frac{1}{2}$	20%	0.3	$\frac{1}{4}$	$\frac{2}{5}$	0.7	$\frac{3}{4}$	80%	0.6	90%	0·1

Use this code to find a letter for each fraction, decimal or percentage below.
Rearrange each set of letters to spell an animal.
   (i) 0·75, 30%, $\frac{7}{10}$, 0·4   (ii) $\frac{1}{5}$, 0·9, 60%, $\frac{3}{10}$, 50%

12. (i) If 40% of a number is 96, find the number.
    (ii) In the year 2000 the population of a town was 3840.
         In the year 2010 the population was 4128.
         What percentage increase is this?

13. (i) The price of a lawn-mower is €550 plus VAT at 15%.
        Work out the price when VAT is added on.
    (ii) A bill of €177.60 includes VAT at 20%.
         Find the amount of the bill before VAT was added on.

14. A greengrocer bought 40 punnets of strawberries at
    €3.60 a punnet. He sold 36 punnets at a profit of 40%
    but had to throw away the remaining 4 punnets.
    Find his percentage profit on the whole deal.

For the problem solver...

1. Copy and complete this cross-number puzzle.
Write the answer to each clue as a percentage.
Put one digit only in each box.

Clues across
- **1.** 54 out of 200
- **3.** 33 out of 50
- **5.** 13 out of 50
- **8.** 99 out of 100
- **10.** 102 out of 200
- **12.** 27 out of 50
- **14.** 38 out of 200

Clues down
- **2.** 300 out of 400
- **4.** 134 out of 200
- **6.** 87 out of 300.
- **7.** 100 out of 400
- **9.** 19 out of 20
- **11.** 110 out of 1000
- **13.** 23 out of 50

2. The kettle in Keith's kitchen is 80% full. After 20% of the water in it has been poured out, there are 1152 ml of water left. What volume of water does Keith's kitchen kettle hold when it is full?

3. In which of the following lists are the terms **not** increasing?
A: $\frac{1}{5}$, 0·25, 30%, 0·5   B: 60%, 0·7, $\frac{4}{5}$, 1·5
C: $\frac{2}{5}$, 0·5, 70%, 0·9   D: $\frac{3}{5}$, 50%, $\frac{4}{5}$, 0·9
E: $\frac{2}{5}$, 150%, $\frac{10}{5}$, 2·3

4. To make porridge, Goldilocks mixes together 3 bags of oats with 1 bag containing 20% wheat bran and 80% oats. All the bags have the same volume. What percentage of the volume of Goldilocks' porridge mixture is wheat bran?
A 5%   B $6\frac{2}{3}$%   C 20%   D $26\frac{2}{3}$%   E 60%

5. At halftime, St Jarlath's College had scored all of the points so far in their annual match against St Declan's.
In the second half, each side scored three points.
At the end of the match St Jarlath's had scored 90% of the points.
What percentage of the points in the match was scored in the second half?

6.

| S is 25% of 60 | 60 is 80% of U | 80 is M% of 25 |

What is S + U + M?
A 100   B 103   C 165   D 330   E 410

Key words

fundamental principle of counting   **chance**   **certain**   **impossible**
outcome   **equally likely**   **unlikely**   **even chance**   **fifty-fifty chance**
probability   **probability scale**   **random**   **spinner**   **fair**   **biased**

Section 8.1 Listing outcomes

When a dice is thrown you will get

1, 2, 3, 4, 5 or 6.

These are called results or **outcomes**.

If you toss a coin the outcomes are **head** and **tail**.

When this spinner is spun the number outcomes are

1, 2, 3, 4, 5, 6.

The colour outcomes are blue and green.

In the three examples above we have **listed** all the possible outcomes.

We will now list the outcomes when a dice is thrown and a coin is tossed.

Here is the list of possible outcomes:

H1, H2, H3, H4, H5, H6, T1, T2, T3, T4, T5, T6

Notice that there are 12 outcomes.

Notice also that there were **2** outcomes when a coin is tossed and **6** outcomes when a dice is thrown.

The **12** outcomes listed above could be found much more easily by multiplying **6** by 2 to get **12**.

The preceding example illustrates the **Fundamental Principle of Counting** which is given on the right.

> If one event has **m** possible outcomes and a second event has **n** possible outcomes, the two events have **m** × **n** outcomes.

> ### Example 1
>
> This is the choice for a two-course meal at *The Red Robin Cafe*.
>
> If a diner has a starter and main course, how many choices does she have?
>
> List the choices.
>
>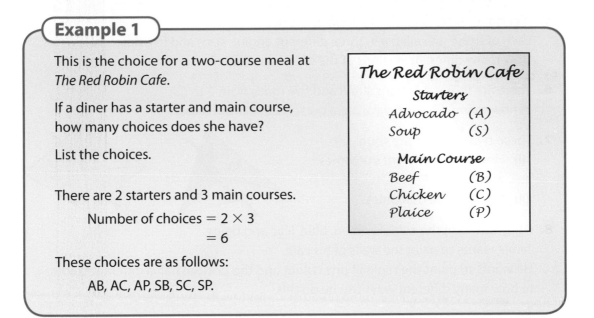
>
> There are 2 starters and 3 main courses.
>
> Number of choices = 2 × 3
> = 6
>
> These choices are as follows:
>
> AB, AC, AP, SB, SC, SP.

The **Fundamental Principle of Counting** can be extended to any number of events.

If a menu consists of 2 starters, 4 main courses, and 3 desserts, then a three-course meal can be selected in

2 × 4 × 3, i.e., 24 ways.

If an operation consists of choosing *x* **and** *y*, we **multiply** the numbers.

Exercise 8.1

1. A coin is tossed and this spinner is spun.
  (i) How many different outcomes are possible?
  (ii) List all these outcomes.

2. An 'early-bird' menu consists of 2 starters and 4 main courses. How many different 2-course meals can you have?

3. Two coins are tossed. List all the possible outcomes using H for head and T for tail.

4. A coin is tossed and this spinner is spun.
  (i) How many possible outcomes are there?
  (ii) List these outcomes.

5. A certain car is available in saloon or estate.
Each of these is available in three different engine sizes and five different colours.
How many different versions of the car are available?

6. There are four roads from A to B and five roads from B to C.
In how many different ways can a person travel from A to C?

7. These two spinners are spun.
  (i) How many different outcomes
     are possible?
  (ii) List all these outcomes.

8. Paint comes in the colours green, blue, lilac and beige.
Jamie wants to paint the walls of his cafe.
He wants to paint the top half one colour and the bottom half a different colour.
In how many different ways can he do this?

9. A code for a lock consists of one letter and one digit.
The letters can be A, B, C, D or E.
The digits can be 1, 3, 5, 7, 9.
How many different codes are possible?

10. A youth is dressing up for his first interview.
He has 5 shirts, 3 ties and 3 jackets to choose from.
If he is to wear a shirt, a tie and a jacket, how many different choices can he make?

11. A factory makes shirts as follows:

Material	silk	cotton	denim	
Size	small	medium	large	extra large
Sleeve	long	short		

Calculate how many different types of shirt the factory makes.

12. Three coins are tossed.
Make a list of all possible outcomes.
Start with HHH, HHT, …
How many different outcomes are there?

13. A lunch consists of a soup, a main course and a dessert.

The Restaurant offers   2 types of soup
                              3 main courses
                              4 desserts.

How many different lunch selections are possible?

14. A couple want to buy a house.
They can choose between a terraced, a
semi-detached or a detached house.
Each of these types comes with two
bedrooms, three bedrooms or four
bedrooms.
How many different choices of house do
they have?

Section 8.2 Chance and Probability

In the previous section we learned
how to list the **outcomes** when a
dice was thrown, a coin was
tossed or a spinner was spun.

We saw that tossing a coin has two possible outcomes.

These are **head** (H) or **tail** (T).

On any occasion no one knows what the outcome will be.

It is down to **chance**.

The coin is as **likely** to show a head as a tail.

There is an **even chance** that either will occur.

We could also say that there is a **fifty-fifty** chance of getting a head or a tail.

When a dice is thrown the possible outcomes are 1, 2, 3, 4, 5 or 6.

It is equally likely that any of these numbers will show in a single
throw of the dice.

We are equally likely to get green or blue when this spinner
is spun.

The probability scale

We know that some events are more likely to happen than others.

For example, it is more likely to rain in Ireland tomorrow than it is to get three months of
sunshine.

If we want to measure how likely something is to happen, we will begin the study of a
new branch of Mathematics called **probability**.

We first use a **probability scale** to show how likely any event is to happen.

A probability scale ranges from **certain** to **impossible**. This is shown in the diagram below.

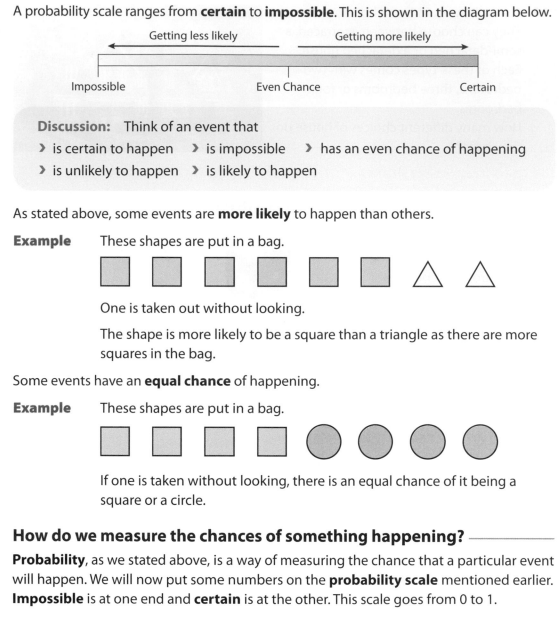

Getting less likely   Getting more likely

Impossible   Even Chance   Certain

Discussion: Think of an event that
> is certain to happen   › is impossible   › has an even chance of happening
> is unlikely to happen   › is likely to happen

As stated above, some events are **more likely** to happen than others.

Example   These shapes are put in a bag.

One is taken out without looking.

The shape is more likely to be a square than a triangle as there are more squares in the bag.

Some events have an **equal chance** of happening.

Example   These shapes are put in a bag.

If one is taken without looking, there is an equal chance of it being a square or a circle.

How do we measure the chances of something happening?

Probability, as we stated above, is a way of measuring the chance that a particular event will happen. We will now put some numbers on the **probability scale** mentioned earlier. **Impossible** is at one end and **certain** is at the other. This scale goes from 0 to 1.

0              $\frac{1}{2}$ 1

Impossible   Poor chance   Even Chance   Good chance   Certain

The probability of an event that is **impossible** to happen is **zero**.

The probability of an event that is **certain** to happen is **1**.

The probability of all other events is between 0 and 1.

The more likely an event is to happen, the closer the probability is to 1.

A probability scale may also be given in percentages or decimals.

The scale below goes from 0 to 100%.

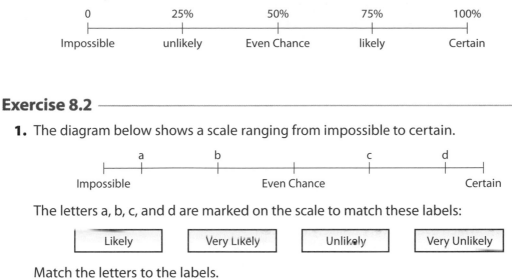

Exercise 8.2

1. The diagram below shows a scale ranging from impossible to certain.

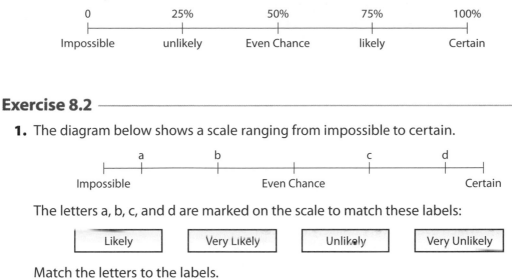

The letters a, b, c, and d are marked on the scale to match these labels:

| Likely | Very Likely | Unlikely | Very Unlikely |

Match the letters to the labels.

2. The probability scale below shows how likely the five events A, B, C, D and E are to happen.

  (i)   Which event is certain to occur?
 (ii)   Which event is very unlikely but possible to occur?
(iii)   Which event has an even chance of occurring?
(iv)   Which event is impossible?
 (v)   Which event is likely but not certain to occur?

3. Which of these labels best describes the likelihood of each of the events below occurring?

| Certain | Impossible | Even chance | Likely | Unlikely |

  (i)   Tomorrow a baby will be born in Ireland.
 (ii)   The next winner of the Lotto will be a woman.
(iii)   You score 8 when you roll an ordinary dice.
(iv)   It will rain in Galway sometime in the next week.
 (v)   Someone in your class will be absent one day next week.
(vi)   The next baby born will be a boy.
(vii)   Ireland will win the next soccer World Cup.

  (viii) The sun will set this evening.
   (ix) You will get an even number when you throw a dice.
    (x) You will do three hours homework tonight.
   (xi) You will live to be 200 years old.

4. The probability scale below shows the probability of the events A, B, C, D and E occurring.

   (i) Which event has 100% chance of happening?
  (ii) Which event has a 50% chance of occurring?
 (iii) Which event is impossible?
  (iv) Which event is very unlikely to occur?
   (v) Which event has a little more than an even chance of occurring?

5. Draw a scale like this one.

Write the letter which is beside each statement below on the line above to show how likely it is to happen.
A: A monkey will be driving the next car you see.
B: You will win the next raffle at your local club.
C: Clouds will appear in the sky tomorrow.
D: The traffic lights will be red when you reach a junction.
E: There will be twelve months in the next year.

6. All of these spinners are spun at the same time.

   (i) Which spinner has the greatest chance of stopping on green?
  (ii) Which spinner has the greatest chance of stopping on blue?
 (iii) Which spinner has an even chance of stopping on blue?
  (iv) Which spinner has the least chance of stopping on blue?

7. The probability scale below shows seven events, A, B, C, D, E, F and G.

A   B   C   D   E   F   G

Match each letter to the phrases or fractions or decimals given below:

| Impossible | 0.5 | $\frac{5}{6}$ | Likely | $\frac{1}{3}$ | Certain | Very Unlikely |

8. Make a copy of this probability scale.

0            $\frac{1}{2}$ 1

(i)
Impossible   Certain

Show where each of these events might be on the scale.
(The first one is done for you.)

  (i)   Your neighbour will live for 150 years.

 (ii) This spinner will stop on Red.

(iii) You will get a head when you toss a coin.

(iv) You will get 1 if you throw a fair dice.

 (v) A blue bead, without looking, will be drawn from the bag.

(vi) A red bead, without looking, will be drawn from the same bag.

9. Choose the probability 0, $\frac{1}{4}$, $\frac{1}{2}$, $\frac{3}{4}$ or 1 for the following events:

  (i)   Your next holiday will be to the moon.

 (ii) Picking a left shoe from a matching pair.

(iii) Scoring an even number with a throw of a dice.

(iv) Getting a diamond when a card is drawn from a deck
     of 52 playing cards.

 (v) Picking a red bead from this bag.

(vi) Next year Christmas will fall in the month of December.

10.

1 2 3 4 5 6 7 8 9 10

The numbers 1 to 10 are written on cards.
The cards are shuffled and then put face down in a line.

  (i) The first card is turned over. It is a 6. Is the next card to be turned over likely to
    be higher or lower than this? Why?

6

(ii) The next card turned over is a 4. Is the next card likely to be higher or lower than 4? Why?

(iii) The next two cards turned over are 7 and 5.

Is the next card to be turned over
(a) more likely   (b) less likely   (c) equally likely to be more than 5?
Explain your answer.

Section 8.3 Equally likely outcomes

We have already listed the outcomes when a dice is thrown.

Each of the numbers 1, 2, 3, 4, 5, 6 has the same chance of appearing.

These are called **equally likely outcomes**.

We are equally likely to get green, blue or yellow when this spinner is spun.

> **Example 1**
>
> A card is selected at random from these coloured digit-cards.
>
> 1 2 3 4 5 6
>
> When a card is selected at random, each card has the same chance of being selected.
>
> Write down the number of outcomes for these events:
> (i) the card is blue
> (ii) the number on the card is greater than 4
> (iii) the number on the card is at least 3
> (iv) the number on the card is even
> (v) the card is not red
> (vi) the card is blue and the number is even.
>
>   (i) 3   (ii) 2   (iii) 4   (iv) 3   (v) 4   (vi) 2

Exercise 8.3

1. When this spinner is spun, list all the possible outcomes.

List the possible outcomes if
  (i) a red number shows
 (ii) an even number shows
(iii) a green number shows
(iv) the number is 4 or more
 (v) the number is odd and red
(vi) the number is green and even.

2. A card is selected at random from these coloured digit-cards:

Write down the number of outcomes for these events:
  (i) The card is blue.
 (ii) The number on the card is 6 or more.
(iii) The number on the card is odd.
(iv) The card is green and the number is odd.
 (v) The card is not red and the number is even.

3. The cards below show numbers enclosed in a circle or a triangle.

Niamh selects a card at random.
Write down the number of outcomes for these events:
  (i) The card contains a circle.
 (ii) The card has an odd number on it.
(iii) The card has a circle and an even number on it.
(iv) The card has a triangle and an odd number.
 (v) The card has a multiple of 3 on it.
(vi) The card has a circle and a number that is 5 or more.

4. The cards in Question 3 are mixed and turned face down.
Niamh turns over one card.

It has ⬡6 on it. She turns over another card. Is it more likely that she gets a number

greater than 6 than a number less than 6?
Explain your answer.

5. State whether or not each of the following are equally likely events:
   (i)   Getting a head or getting a tail when a fair coin is tossed.

   (ii) Getting a yellow or getting a blue when this spinner is spun.

   (iii) Getting a black card or getting a red card when a card is drawn from a deck of 52 playing cards.

   (iv) Getting an even number or getting an odd number when a card is drawn from the five cards shown.

6. Here are three spinners

When all these spinners are spun
   (i)   which spinner has the greatest chance of landing on 4?
   (ii) which spinner has an even chance of landing on 2?
   (iii) which spinner has no chance of landing on 2?

All the spinners have the same chance of landing on a certain number.
   (iv) Which number is this?

7. Here are four spinners with different colours:

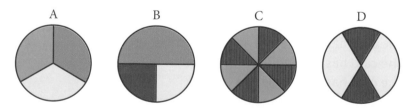

If the spinners are spun,
   (i)   Which spinner has an even chance of showing blue?
   (ii) Which spinner has an even chance of showing red?
   (iii) Which spinner has the least chance of showing yellow?
   (iv) Which spinner has one chance in three of showing yellow?
   (v)   Which spinner has one chance in four of showing red?
   (vi) Which spinner has the greatest chance of showing red?

8. The spinner shown has 12 equal sectors.

When the spinner is spun, write down the number of outcomes for these events:

(i) the spinner stops on pink

(ii) the spinner stops on a letter

(iii) the spinner stops on a number in a white sector

(iv) the spinner stops on a letter in a white sector

(v) the spinner stops on an even number.

Section 8.4 Calculating probability

When a coin is tossed, there are two **equally likely** outcomes.

They are head or tail.

The probability of getting a head is one chance in two.

We write this as P(head) = $\frac{1}{2}$.

> A favourable outcome is an outcome that you want.

For **equally likely outcomes**,

$$\text{Probability of an event} = \frac{\text{Number of favourable outcomes}}{\text{Number of possible outcomes}}$$

Example 1

Here are 12 cards of various colours with numbers on them.

Jane picks a card at random. Find the probability, as a fraction in its lowest terms, that she picks

(i) a blue card

(ii) a card showing 9

(iii) a red card

(iv) a 2-digit number

(v) a blue card with an odd number on it

(vi) a card that is not red.

(i) There are 4 blue cards.

$$\therefore \quad P(blue) = \frac{\text{Number of blue cards}}{\text{Total number of cards}} = \frac{4}{12} = \frac{1}{3}$$

(ii) There is one card showing 9.

$$\therefore \quad P(9) = \frac{1}{12}$$

(iii) There are 5 red cards.

$$\therefore \quad P(red) = \frac{5}{12}$$

(iv) There are three 2-digit numbers.

$$\therefore \quad P(\text{2-digits}) = \frac{3}{12} = \frac{1}{4}$$

(v) The blue cards with odd numbers are 7 and 11, i.e. 2 cards.

$$\therefore \quad P(\text{odd blue}) = \frac{2}{12} = \frac{1}{6}$$

(vi) The number of cards that are not red is 7.

$$\therefore \quad P(\text{not red}) = \frac{7}{12}$$

Exercise 8.4

1. These counters are put into a bag and one is selected at random.

(i) What is the probability that the selected counter is red?
(ii) What is the probability that the selected counter is green?
(iii) What is the probability that the selected counter is yellow or green?
(iv) What is the probability that the selected counter is not green?

2. Find the probability, as a fraction in its lowest terms, that this spinner lands on

(i) blue
(ii) red
(iii) green
(iv) red or yellow
(v) not blue
(vi) green or blue.

3. If I throw a fair dice, what is the probability that I get

(i) 4   (ii) an odd number   (iii) 5 or 6?

4. This spinner is equally likely to end on 1, 2, 3, 4 or 5.
   (i)   What is the probability of getting 4?
   (ii) What is the probability of getting 4 or more?
   (iii) What is the probability of getting an even number?

5. What is the probability of getting red on each of these spinners?
   (i)   (ii)   (iii)

6. Sean puts these beads into a bag.
   He picks one bead from the bag without looking.
   (i)   Which colour is Sean least likely to pick?
   (ii) What is the probability that he picks a yellow bead?
   (iii) What is the probability that the bead is not black?
   (iv) Sean wants all colours to have an equal chance of being picked.
         What beads does Sean need to add to the bag?
   (v)   If the probability of getting a yellow bead is to be twice the probability of
         getting a blue bead, what bead does Sean need to add to the bag?

7. When this spinner is spun, find the probability that it will stop on
   (i)   5   (ii)   8 or higher
   (iii) an even number   (iv)   the colour red
   (v)   the colour red or green (vi)   a red even number
   (vii) a colour that is not yellow
   (viii) green and an even number.

8. Sharon has 12 cards, as shown below.

   She picks a card at random. Find the probability, as a fraction in its lowest terms,
   that the card selected
   (i)   is yellow   (ii)   is blue
   (iii) is red or yellow   (iv)   shows an even number
   (v)   shows an even red number (vi) shows a 5
   (vii) shows a number that is 6 or more   (viii) is blue and shows an even number.

9. In a casino game a pointer is spun and you win the amount
shown in the sector where the pointer comes to rest.
Assuming that the pointer is equally likely to come to rest
in any sector, what is the probability that you win

   (i) €5   (ii) no money

(iii) €10 or €20   (iv) some money?

10. A card is drawn from a pack of 52 playing cards.
What is the probability that the card is

   (i) a red card   (ii) a spade   (iii) a king   (iv) a red king?

> There are four suits in a pack of cards: hearts and diamonds
> which are red; clubs and spades which are black.
> Each suit contains 2, 3, 4, 5, 6, 7, 8, 9, 10, jack, queen, king and ace.
> The picture cards are jack, queen and king.

11. A bag contains 5 red, 3 blue and 2 yellow beads, as shown.
One bead is taken out at random.
Find the probability that it is

  (i) red

 (ii) blue

(iii) not red

(iv) red or yellow.

12. A dice has its faces numbered 2, 4, 5, 5, 5, 7.
Find the probability of rolling

  (i) 7   (ii) 5   (iii) an even number   (iv) 5 or 7.

13. One card is selected at random from the nine
cards shown. Find the probability of selecting

  (i) an ace of diamonds

 (ii) an ace

(iii) a king

(iv) a red card.

14. One letter is chosen at random from the letters of the word *DEALING*.

  (i) Find the probability that the letter chosen is *G*.

 (ii) Find the probability that the letter chosen is a vowel.

(iii) Find the probability that the letter chosen is a vowel or *G*.

15. This box contains 9 counters.
The counters are either blue or green.
The probability of picking a blue counter is $\frac{4}{9}$.
  (i) How many blue counters are in the box?
 (ii) How many green counters are in the box?
(iii) If a black counter is added to the box, what now
      is the probability of picking a blue counter?

16. There are 15 cars in a car park. 7 are red, 6 are blue and 2 are silver.
Calculate the probability that the next car to leave the car park is
  (i) red   (ii) silver   (iii) not blue   (iv) red or silver.

17. At a fund-raiser for a school, class 5A makes a spinning wheel game, as shown.

What is the probability that the pointer lands on
  (i) 8   (ii) 6 or 8   (iii) an odd number
(iv) a multiple of 5   (v) a number that is even and greater than 5?

18. Seven of the eight discs shown have numbers on them.
The remaining disc is blank. Anne intends to write a
number on the disc before she puts them all into the bag.
  (i) What number should she write on the disc so that
     the probability of drawing a 3 is $\frac{3}{8}$?
 (ii) What number should she not write on the disc so
     that the probability of drawing a 1 is $\frac{1}{4}$?
(iii) What number should she write on the disc so that the probability of getting a
     5 is $\frac{1}{8}$?
(iv) If she wrote 4 on the disc what is the probability of getting a 4?

She wrote a number on the blank disc and put all the discs in the bag. If the
probability of then getting a 3 was $\frac{1}{4}$, say whether each of the following is *true*,
could be true or *false*.
(a) She wrote a 3 on the disc.
(b) She wrote a 4 on the disc.
(c) She could have written any number except 3 on the disc.

19. A fair six-sided spinner is numbered from 1 to 6, as shown.
The spinner is spun once. Copy the probability scale below
and on it mark A, B, C and D to correspond to the
following probabilities.
A: The spinner lands on an even number.
B: The spinner lands on 4 or 5.
C: The spinner lands on 8.
D: The spinner lands on a number which is less than 8.

20. The fair spinner shown is spun.
Work out the probability of the arrow pointing to: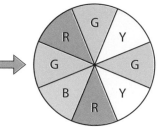
  (i) yellow (Y),
 (ii) green (G),
(iii) red (R),
 (iv) blue (B),
  (v) red or blue (R or B).

21. Elena has 3 different spinners.

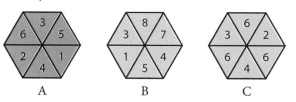

       A   B   C

She spins each spinner 100 times.

  (i) Draw a number line and draw arrows labelled A, B and C to show your estimate
of how many times each spinner will land on a six.

 (ii) Explain how you worked out your estimate for spinner C.

Test yourself 8

1. Write **impossible**, **unlikely**, **evens**, **likely** or **certain** for each of these:
   (i)   A rabbit will be driving the next bus you see.
   (ii) Someone in your class will be absent tomorrow.
   (iii) You will get a head when you toss a coin.
   (iv) You will have only one birthday next year.
   (v)   It will not rain in your area in the next week.

2.

   From the probability scale above, which letter best describes the following:
   (i)   impossible   (ii) even chance   (iii) very likely   (iv) certain
   (v)   very unlikely   (vi) likely   (vii) unlikely?

3. Barry spun this spinner.

   Copy and finish this list of possible outcomes.

   10, 15, ___, ___, ___, ___

   Do each of these outcomes have the same
   chance of happening? Explain.

4. Write down the probability that this spinner will land on these colours:
   (i)   yellow
   (ii) blue
   (iii) green
   (iv) either blue or green
   (v)   not blue.

5. A card game uses these ten digits.

   A card is chosen at random.
   (i)   How many possible outcomes are there?
   (ii)   What is the probability that the card chosen has an odd number?
   (iii) What is the probability that the card chosen has a 6 or greater on it?
   (iv)   What is the probability that the card chosen is yellow?
   (v)   What is the probability that the card chosen is yellow and has an even number
          on it?
   (vi)   What is the probability that the card is yellow or green?

6. This table shows the colours of 100 tickets sold in a raffle.

   All the tickets were put into a hat.

   One ticket was pulled out without looking.

   Find the probability that the colour of the ticket is

green	20
pink	60
blue	5
yellow	15
Total	100

      (i) yellow   (ii) pink

   (iii) yellow or blue   (iv) not green.

7. For each of the bags shown below,
      (i) find the probability of choosing a red bead
     (ii) find the probability of choosing a blue bead.

             A   B   C

8. In a game a person is given a choice of two bags to take a bead from.
   The person wins if they choose a red bead.

                     A   B

   Is it better to take a bead from bag A or bag B, or doesn't it matter?

   Give your reasons.

9. A letter is chosen at random from the word MATHEMATICS.
      (i) What is the probability that the letter is M?
     (ii) What is the probability that the letter is either A, E or I?
   (iii) What is the probability that the letter is not T?

For the problem solver...

1. The final score in a football match was 3 – 2.
   How many different half-time scores are possible?
   (Note: 1 – 0 is the same as 0 – 1.)

2. A ladybird has landed at point *P* on
   Sam's bow-tie.
   If it travels only along the edges
   of the bow-tie, but cannot travel
   along any edge more than once,
   how many different ways are there
   for it to get from *P* to *Q*?
   A 1   B 2   C 3   D 4   E 5

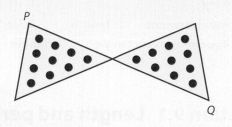

3. Mary has three brothers and four sisters.
   If they, and Mary, all buy each other an Easter egg, how many eggs will
   be bought?

4. A list of ten numbers contains two of each of the numbers 0, 1, 2, 3, 4.
   The two 0s are next to each other, the two 1s are separated by one
   number, the two 2s by two numbers, the two 3s by three numbers and
   the two 4s by four numbers.
   The list starts 3, 4, … .What is the last number?

5. Old Martha has 5 children, each of whom has 4 children, each of whom
   has 3 children, each of whom is childless. How many descendants does
   Old Martha have?

6. A box contains 6 blue socks and 8 white socks. If you reach into it in the
   dark, what is the least number of socks you must take out to be sure of
   getting
   (i)   a pair of the same colour
   (ii) 2 pairs?

7. Elaine said 'Two days ago I was 13; next year I will be 16.'
   What is the date today and when is her birthday?

8. You are told that 30 pupils have 25 different birthdays between them.
   What is the largest number of these pupils who could share the same
   birthday?
   A 2   B 3   C 4   D 5   E 6

Perimeter and area

Key words

measurement   length   breadth   perimeter   area
square   rectangle   triangle   base   perpendicular height

Section 9.1 Length and perimeter

The ruler shown gives measurements in centimetres (cm) and millimetres (mm).

The length of the red line is 4 cm 6 mm or 4.6 cm.

Since there are 10 mm in a centimetre it is easy to convert a length such as 8 cm 9 mm to the decimal 8.9 cm.

When measuring longer lengths such as the length of a football pitch, we use metres.

There are 100 cm in one metre (m).

> **Length**
> 10 mm = 1 cm
> 100 cm = 1 m

Perimeter

The **perimeter** of a shape is the distance around the edge of the shape.

The perimeter of this rectangle is

$$5 + 3 + 5 + 3 = 16 \text{ cm}$$

Since the opposite sides of a rectangle are equal in length, the perimeter can be written as

$$2 \times 5 + 2 \times 3 \quad \text{or} \quad 2(5 + 3) \text{ cm}.$$

For any rectangle

> Perimeter = $2(l + b)$
> where l = length and b = breadth.

Since the four sides of a **square** are equal in length

Perimeter of a square = $4 \times l$
where *l* is the length of a side.

Example 1

Find the perimeter of this figure in
(i) centimetres
(ii) millimetres.

(i) Perimeter = 6 cm + 8 cm + 2 cm + 9 cm
       = 25 cm
(ii) 25 cm = 25 × 10 mm
         = 250 mm

Exercise 9.1

1. Measure the length of each line below.
   Give your answer in centimetres and millimetres.
   (i) _____
   (ii) _____
   (iii) _____

2. Change these measurements so that they are all in centimetres:
   (i) 28 cm 5 mm   (ii) 360 mm   (iii) 76 mm   (iv) 1.5 m

3. Change these measurements to centimetres:
   (i) 3 m   (ii) 3.6 m   (iii) 0.7 m   (iv) 0.53 m

4. Copy and complete these:
   (i) 5 cm = ☐ mm   (ii) 45 mm = ☐ cm   (iii) 6.5 cm = ☐ mm
   (iv) 280 mm = ☐ cm   (v) 2.4 m = ☐ cm   (vi) 0.75 m = ☐ cm

5. Work out which of these measurements is bigger:
   (i) 25 cm or 80 mm   (ii) 8.5 cm or 90 mm   (iii) 24 cm or 0.25 m

6. What is meant by the perimeter of a shape?
Use your ruler to measure the perimeter of each of these figures.
Give each answer in centimetres and millimetres, e.g. 20 cm 8 mm.

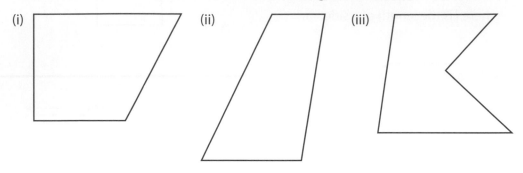

(i)   (ii)   (iii)

7. These rectangles have been drawn on 1 cm squared paper.
Find the perimeter of each figure in cm.

(i)   (ii)   (iii)

8. Work out the perimeter of each of these rectangles:

(i)   7 cm   9 cm

(ii)   18 cm   26 cm

(iii)   12 m   8.5 m

9. Find the perimeters of these shapes.

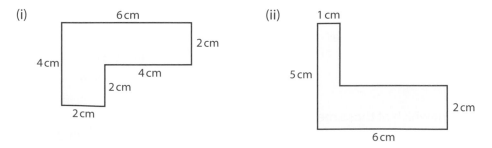

(i)   6 cm   2 cm   4 cm   4 cm   2 cm   2 cm   2 cm

(ii)   1 cm   5 cm   2 cm   6 cm

(iii)

(iv)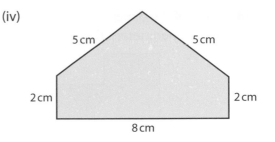

10. Work out the perimeter of these shapes:

(i)   8 cm   5 cm   4 cm   7 cm   12 cm

(ii) 2 cm   10 cm   2 cm   6 cm

(iii) 7 cm   2 cm   5 cm   4 cm

11. Work out the perimeter of each square.

(i)   11 cm

(ii)   15 cm

(iii)   8.5 cm

12. Work out the perimeter of each of these:

(i)   8 cm   5 cm   6 cm   14 cm

(ii)   14 cm   4 cm   10 cm   4 cm

(iii)   48 m   40 m   22 m   22 m

13. (i) Work out the perimeter of this shape.
   (ii) Show that the perimeter can be worked
       out by adding two of the lengths
       shown and doubling the answer.

27 cm   14 cm   28 cm   36 cm   22 cm   55 cm

14. Some of the dimensions are missing in these figures but it is still possible to work out the perimeters. Try them.

(i)   (ii)   (iii)

15. Find the perimeter of each shape. Explain your method.

(i)   (ii)

16. In each of these figures the perimeter is given.
Find the dimension marked **?** in each figure.

(i)   (ii)

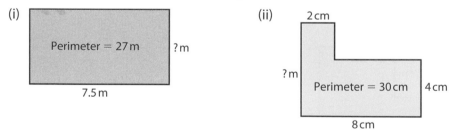

17. (i) The perimeter of the yellow rectangle is 24 cm and its base measures 4 cm.
Find the height of the rectangle.
(ii) Four of these rectangles are used to make the green logo.
Find the perimeter of this logo.

4 cm

Section 9.2 Area of rectangle and triangle

Area is the amount of space covered by a shape.

In the grid below each square has side of length 1 cm.

The area of each square is **1 cm²**.

It is pronounced *1 square centimetre*.

By counting the squares we can write down the area of each figure.

The **rectangle** on the right is 5 cm long and 3 cm wide.

Its area = 5 cm × 3 cm
$\qquad$ = 15 cm²

The area of a rectangle = length × breadth.

The area of a triangle

Since a diagonal bisects the area of a rectangle, it can be seen from the given diagram that the area of the shaded triangle is half the area of the rectangle.

Since the area of the rectangle is $b \times h$, the area of the triangle is half of $b \times h$.

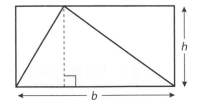

Area of triangle = $\frac{1}{2} \times$ base × height

In these triangles, *b* is the base and *h* is the **perpendicular height**.

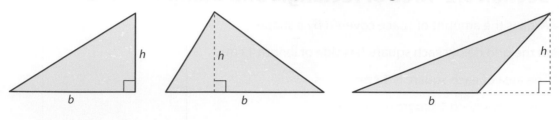

Finding the length or breadth

The area of the given rectangle is 28 cm² and its length is 7 cm.

Area = 28 cm²

7 cm

To find the breadth divide 28 by 7.

$$\therefore \text{ the breadth} = \frac{28}{7} = 4 \text{ cm}$$

Example 1

Find the area of the given figure.

The broken line divides the figure into two rectangles A and B.

Area of $A = 12 \text{ m} \times 7 \text{ m} = 84 \text{ m}^2$

Area of $B = 6 \text{ m} \times 4 \text{ m} = 24 \text{ m}^2$

Total area $= (84 + 24) \text{ m}^2$
$= 108 \text{ m}^2$

Example 2

Find the area of each of the triangles given below:

(i)　Area $= \frac{1}{2}$ base $\times$ perpendicular height

　　　$= \frac{1}{2} \times 10 \times 8$

　　　$= 40 \text{ cm}^2$

(ii)　Area $= \frac{1}{2} \times 12 \times 9$　　　　　　　　(iii)　Area $= \frac{1}{2} \times 7 \times 12$

　　　　$= 54 \text{ cm}^2$　　　　　　　　　　　　　　$= 42 \text{ cm}^2$

The area of a square

The area of this square is 9 cm² when you count the squares.

You get the same result if you multiply the length by the breadth, i.e.,

　　$3 \text{ cm} \times 3 \text{ cm} = 9 \text{ cm}^2$

Thus the area of a square is (length of side)²

Example 3

(i)　Find the area of the square with perimeter 40 cm.

(ii)　Find the perimeter of the square with area 81 cm².

(i)　If the perimeter is 40 cm, then each side is $\frac{40}{4} = 10$ cm.

　　Area $= 10 \text{ cm} \times 10 \text{ cm} = 100 \text{ cm}^2$

(ii)　Area $= 81 \text{ cm}^2$

　　$\therefore$　(side squared)² $= 81 \text{ cm}^2$

　　$\therefore$　length of side　$=$　9 cm

　　Perimeter is length of side $\times 4 = 9 \times 4$

　　　　　　　　　　　　　　$= 36 \text{ cm}$

Exercise 9.2

1. Find the area of each shape. Each square on the grid represents 1 cm².

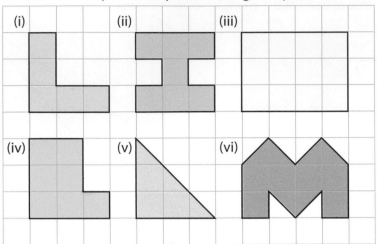

2. Estimate the area of this island.

   Each square represents 1 km².

3. Find the area of each rectangle shown below:

   (i) 7 cm, 9 cm

   (ii) 18 cm, 26 cm

   (iii) 12 m, 8.5 m

4. Work out the area of each of these rectangles:

   (i) 8 cm, 14 cm

   (ii) 15 cm, 7 cm

   (iii) 9 cm, 22 cm

5. Find the area of each square.

(i)

7 m

(ii)

15 cm

(iii)

22 mm

6. The area of the square shown is 25 m².

Find (i) the length of its side
(ii) the perimeter of the square.

Area = 25 m²

7. Find the length of the side of each square shown below:

(i) Area = 81 cm²

(ii) Area = 144 cm²

(iii) Area = 400 m²

8. Find the length (or breadth) of each of these rectangles:

(i) 12 cm

Area = 96 cm²

(ii) 12 m

Area = 240 m²

(iii) 18 mm

Area = 216 mm²

9. (i) Find the perimeter of the given figure.
(ii) Find the area of the figure by dividing
it into 2 rectangles.

8 cm

2 cm

4 cm

3 cm

10. Find the area of each of these figures.

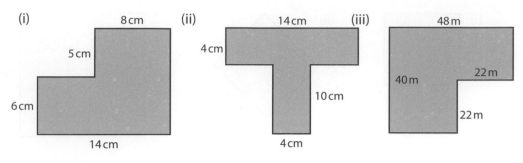

(i) 8 cm

5 cm

6 cm

14 cm

(ii) 14 cm

4 cm

10 cm

4 cm

(iii) 48 m

40 m

22 m

22 m

11. Work out the area of each of these floors.

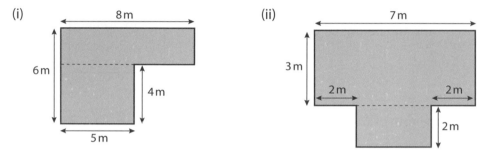

(i) 8 m

6 m

4 m

5 m

(ii) 7 m

3 m

2 m

2 m

2 m

12. Find the area of each of these triangles:

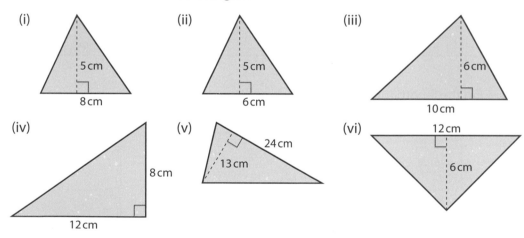

(i) 5 cm

8 cm

(ii) 5 cm

6 cm

(iii) 6 cm

10 cm

(iv) 8 cm

12 cm

(v) 24 cm

13 cm

(vi) 12 cm

6 cm

13. Work out the areas of these triangles:

(i) 7 cm

12 cm

(ii) 7 cm

9 cm

(iii) 12 cm

20 cm

14. Find the area of each of the four triangles A, B, C and D drawn on the centimetre grid:

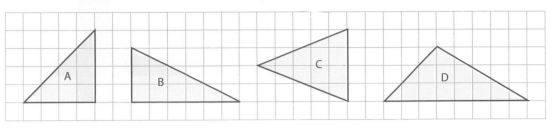

Verify your answer to triangle A by counting squares.

15. Find the value of *x* in each of these triangles:

(i)   (ii)   (iii)

Area = 16 sq. units   Area = 35 sq. units   Area = 27 sq. units

16. Find the areas of the following shapes which are comprised of rectangles and triangles:

(i)   (ii)   (iii)

17. Find the area that needs painting on each of these walls.

(i)   (ii)

157

18. Find the area of the blue region in this flag.

19. Work out the area of each of these shapes:

(i)

(ii)

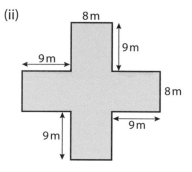

20. The diagram shows a square ABCD with a green square drawn inside.

ABCD has area 100 cm².

Calculate the area of the green square and explain how you found your answer.

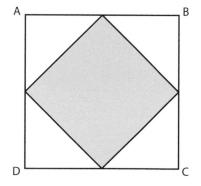

21. Find the area of the shaded border in each of these rectangles:

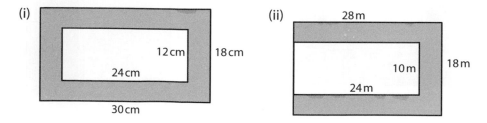

(i)

(ii)

This is the floor plan of an apartment.

Use it to answer questions **22–25.**

22. Find the floor area of
  (i) the living room   (ii) the hall.

23. Work out the floor area of the kitchen.

24. Find the cost of cleaning the bedroom carpet at €8 per square metre.

25. Find the cost of tiling the hall and WC if the cost of each square metre is €65.

Test yourself 9

1. Here are three rectangles and one square. Find the perimeter of each shape.

(i) 18 cm   12 cm

(ii) 10 cm   26 cm

(iii) 4.5 cm   15 cm

(iv) 23 cm

2. Work out the area of each figure in question **1.** above.

3. Measure these shapes and then find their perimeters.
Give each answer in centimetres and millimetres.

(i)

(ii)

4. Work out the area of each of these shapes.

(i) 3 cm   11 cm   4 cm   12 cm

(ii) 16 m   3 m   14 m   3 m

(iii) 5 mm   5 mm   10 mm   14 mm

5. Triangles X, Y and Z are drawn on a centimetre grid.
Work out the area of each triangle.

X   Y   Z

6. Find the areas of the following shapes which are composed of rectangles and triangles.

(i)   (ii)   (iii)

7. Work out the coloured areas of these diagrams.

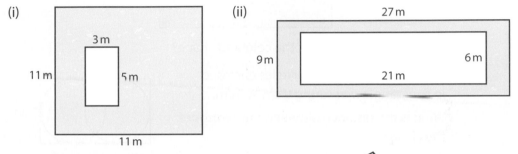

(i)   (ii)

8. The area of the given triangle is 40 cm².
Find the perpendicular height h cm.

9. Find   (i)   the perimeter
            (ii)   the area of this figure.

10. (i)   Copy and complete the table showing
how the area of a rectangle changes,
even though its perimeter is fixed at 28 cm.
(ii)   What can you say about the shape when it
has the largest area?
(iii)   A farmer has 100 m of fence and wants to
construct a rectangular enclosure with the
largest possible area. What is this area?

Length (cm)	Width (cm)	Area (cm²)
13	1	
12		
11		
10		
9		
8		
7		

For the problem solver...

1. The figure on the right shows an arrangement of ten square tiles.
   Which labelled tile could be removed, but still leave the length of the perimeter unchanged?

2. The shape below is made up of three rectangles, each measuring 3 cm by 1 cm.

   What is the perimeter of the coloured shape?

3. The diagram shows two circles enclosed in a rectangle measuring 9 cm × 5 cm.

   What is the distance between the centres of the circles?

   A   2 cm   B   2.5 cm   C   3 cm   D   3.5 cm   E   4 cm

   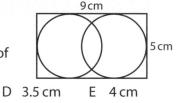

4. Each square in the given figure is 1 cm by 1 cm.

   What is the area of the triangle ABM?

   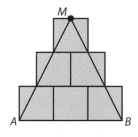

5. Four identical blocks of wood are placed touching a table in the positions shown in this side-on view.
   How high is the table?

6. Six touching circles of radius 10 cm are shown.
   Calculate the area of the triangle shaded.

   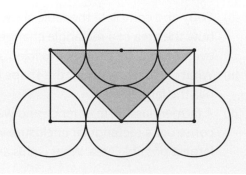

7. ABCD is a rectangle.
Explain why the two shaded
regions are equal in area.

8. Five identical rectangles fit
together as shown.
What, in cm², is the total
area which they cover?

Not to scale

15 cm

9. A goat in a large field is tethered to one end of a 10 metre rope. The
other end of the rope is attached to a ring which is free to slide along
a fixed horizontal rail, 10 metres long, in the middle of the field. Which
diagram shows the shape of the part of the field that the goat can reach?

A   B   C   D   E

20   20   ↕10   20   20

30   30   30   30   30

10. A 6 by 8 and a 7 by 9 rectangle overlap
with one corner coinciding as shown.
What is the area of the coloured region?
Give your answer in square units.

6

7

11. Four rectangular paper strips, each measuring 10 cm
by 1 cm, are laid flat on a table. Each strip is at right
angles to two of the other strips as shown.
What is the area of the table covered by the strips?

A 30 cm²   B 32 cm²   C 34 cm²   D 36 cm²   E 38 cm²

12. Which, if any, of the following shaded regions has an area different
from the other shaded regions?

A   B   C   D   E

Geometry 1
Points – Angles – Lines

Key words

line segment   right angle   acute angle   obtuse angle   reflex angle
straight angle   supplementary angles   interior angles   protractor
vertically opposite angles   alternate angles   corresponding angles
parallel   perpendicular   transversal   collinear

Introduction to Geometry

Think of ancient man-made structures such as the Pyramids of Egypt, the Tombs of Newgrange, Stonehenge in England and the Colosseum in Rome. All were built thousands of years ago and were designed by people who understood shapes, lines, triangles, circles and space. In a word, they were built by people who understood Geometry.

Around 600 BC–100 BC, the ancient Greeks took geometry to a whole new plane. They studied it, came up with proofs, and most importantly they wrote it down. The most famous book was called *Elements*, written by a very famous mathematician called Euclid.

Most of his Maths is still used today – just ask any architect. Our Geometry course is based on his work.

Section 10.1 Points – Lines – Line segments

On the right are 2 points, labelled A and B.

There is only one straight line that passes through the
points A and B.
We call that the line **AB**.
The line AB goes on forever, in both directions.

We can also name the line with a single lowercase letter
such as ℓ, m or n.

A line beginning at the point A and ending at the point B is
called the **line segment** AB.
It is written as [AB].

On the right we have a line segment [AB] which is
5 cm in length.
This is written as |**AB**| = **5 cm**.

The triangle on the right is made up of three line segments.
They are [AB], [AC] and [BC].

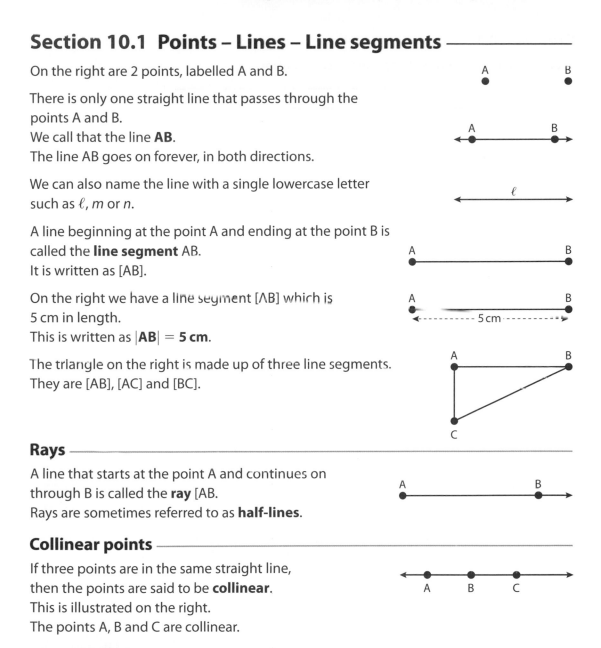

Rays

A line that starts at the point A and continues on
through B is called the **ray** [AB.
Rays are sometimes referred to as **half-lines**.

Collinear points

If three points are in the same straight line,
then the points are said to be **collinear**.
This is illustrated on the right.
The points A, B and C are collinear.

The plane

The flat surface on which points and lines are shown is called a **plane**. A plane contains
an infinite number of points. The Greek letter π is used to denote a plane.

The given diagram shows five points A, B, C, D and E.
The points C, E and B are collinear.
The points A, B and D are not collinear.
Why?

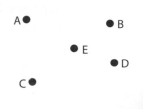

Exercise 10.1

1. Measure the length of each line in centimetres:
   (i) _____

   (ii) _____

   (iii) _____

2. Use your ruler to draw line segments having the following lengths:
   (i) 5 cm
   (ii) $6\frac{1}{2}$ cm
   (iii) 75 mm
   (iv) 46 mm

3. Describe in words each of the following diagrams:

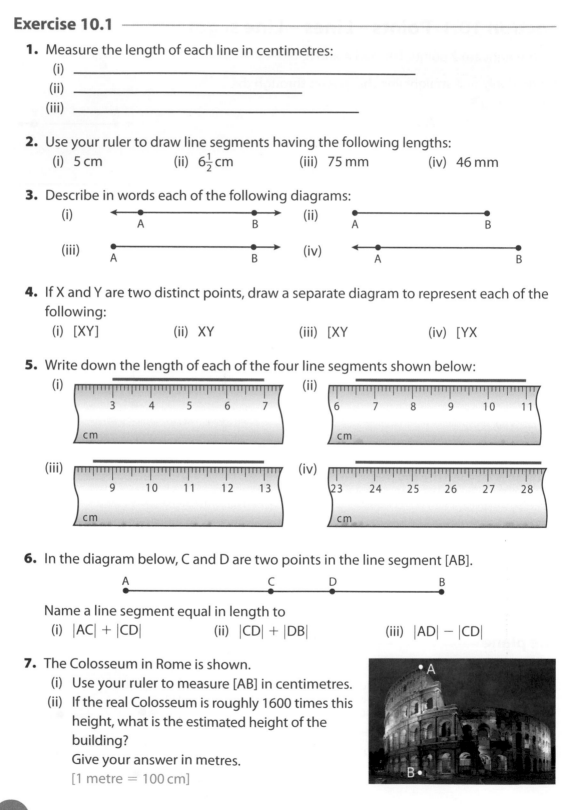

   (i) A B   (ii) A B
   (iii) A B   (iv) A B

4. If X and Y are two distinct points, draw a separate diagram to represent each of the following:
   (i) [XY]
   (ii) XY
   (iii) [XY
   (iv) [YX

5. Write down the length of each of the four line segments shown below:
   (i)
   (ii)
   (iii)
   (iv)

6. In the diagram below, C and D are two points in the line segment [AB].

   A   C   D   B

   Name a line segment equal in length to
   (i) |AC| + |CD|
   (ii) |CD| + |DB|
   (iii) |AD| − |CD|

7. The Colosseum in Rome is shown.
   (i) Use your ruler to measure [AB] in centimetres.
   (ii) If the real Colosseum is roughly 1600 times this height, what is the estimated height of the building?
   Give your answer in metres.
   [1 metre = 100 cm]

Section 10.2 Angles

The angle on the right is formed by rotating the line segment [OB] as indicated.
We use the symbol ∠ to denote an angle.
Thus ∠AOB is the angle on the right.

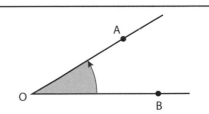

When the hand of a clock moves from one position to another we say that it has made or generated an **angle**.

When the hand of a clock starts at 12 and does a complete turn and stops again at 12, we say that it has done one complete **revolution**.

One complete revolution is divided into 360 parts.

Each part is called a **degree** (written **1°**).

360 degrees is written as 360°.

The Babylonians (2000 BC–1000 BC) loved the number 60 because it had so many factors. They also loved multiples of 60, i.e. 60, 120, 180 240, ...
That is why there are 60 seconds in a minute and 360° in a full revolution.

Naming angles

The shaded angle above can be named in three ways, namely
(i) ∠ABC   (ii) ∠CBA   (iii) ∠B

Right angle

A quarter of a revolution is called a **right angle.**
Therefore a right angle is 90°.

We use the symbol ⌐ to denote *right angle*.

90°

Straight angle

A half a revolution makes a **straight angle** or
two right angles.
A straight angle is 180°.

Other angles

| acute angle | obtuse angle | reflex angle |
| less than 90° | between 90° and 180° | more than 180° |

Ordinary angle

The given diagram shows two angles that can be called ∠AOB.

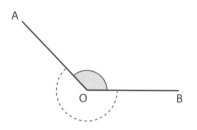

The shaded angle, which is less than 180°, is generally referred to as an **ordinary angle**.

Exercise 10.2

1. Use three letters to name each shaded angle below:

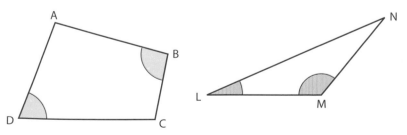

2. Use a single letter to name each shaded angle in the figures above.

3. Use a single letter to name these angles:
The letters you write down can be arranged to name an important river.
What is it?

4.

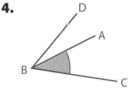

Jane named the shaded angle as ∠B.
Explain why this is not a good way to name it.
How should she name it?

5. Copy and complete the name of each angle in the box below.
The first letter is done for you. What sentence do they spell?

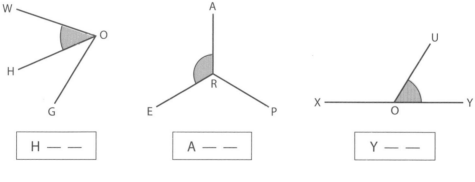

| H — — | | A — — | | Y — — |

6. Describe each of the angles show below:

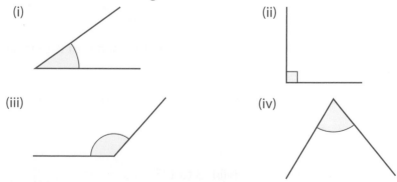

(i)

(ii)

(iii)

(iv)

7. Say if each of the following angles is acute, obtuse or reflex:

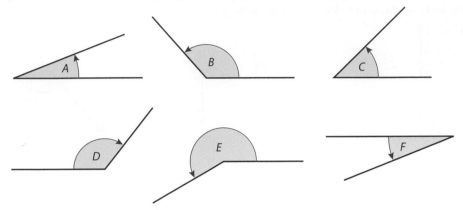

8. If one full turn is 360°, copy and complete the following table:

Fraction of turn	1	$\frac{1}{2}$	$\frac{1}{4}$	$\frac{1}{3}$	$\frac{1}{6}$	$\frac{1}{12}$
Angle (degrees)	360°					

9. What fraction of a complete revolution has the hand of the clock done in each of the following?

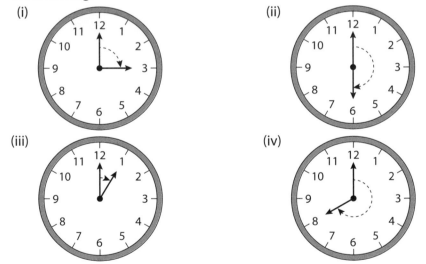

10. How many degrees are there in the angle between the two hands of the clocks in question 9 above?

11. How many degrees does the hand of a clock turn through when it goes from
   (i)   12 to 4   (ii)   12 to 2
 (iii)   3 to 9   (iv)   4 to 7
  (v)   5 to 9   (vi)   2 to 6
 (vii) 2 to 9   (viii)   3 to 11?

12. How many degrees are there in the angle between the two hands in each of these clocks?

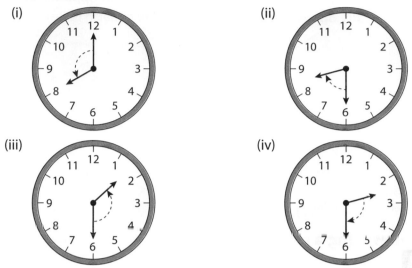

(i)

(ii)

(iii)

(iv)

Section 10.3 Calculating angles

Angles on a straight line

Angles on a straight line add up to 180°.

$$|\angle A| + |\angle B| = 180°$$

Any combination of angles on one side of a straight line add up to 180°.

$$|\angle A| + |\angle B| + |\angle C| = 180°$$

> Two angles which add up to 180° are called supplementary angles.

Angles at a point

Angles at a point add up to 360°.

$$|\angle A| + |\angle B| + |\angle C| + |\angle D| + |\angle E| = 360°$$

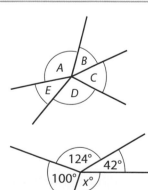

In this diagram, the three given angles add up to 266°.

$$x = 360° - 266°$$

$$\therefore \quad x = 94°$$

Vertically opposite angles

When two lines intersect, four angles are formed.
a and b are called **vertically opposite angles**.

Notice $|\angle a| + |\angle c| = 180°$

$\qquad |\angle b| + |\angle c| = 180°$

$\qquad \therefore \ |\angle a| = |\angle b|$

Similarly $\qquad |\angle c| = |\angle d|$

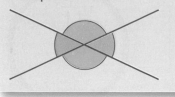

Vertically opposite angles
are equal in measure.

In the given figure

$|\angle b| = 54°$ ... vertically opposite angles

$|\angle a| = 180° - 54°$ ... angles in a straight line

$\qquad = 126°$

$|\angle c| = 126°$ ... vertically opposite angles

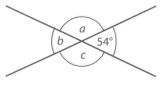

Measuring angles using a protractor

The instrument shown opposite is called
a **protractor**.

We use it to measure angles and draw
angles of given sizes.

The diagram shows that the size of the
angle is 50°.

50°

Drawing angles

Draw an angle of 74°.

74°

Draw a line.
Mark the vertex of
the angle.

Position the protractor as if you
were measuring an angle.
Mark a dot at 74°.

Draw a line from the
vertex through the
dot.

Protractor axiom	The number of degrees in an angle is always a number between 0 and 360.

An axiom is a
statement accepted
without proof.

Exercise 10.3

1. Find the size of the angle *A* in each of the following diagrams:

(i)   (ii)   (iii)   (iv)

2. Find the measure of the angle marked with a letter in each of the following diagrams:

3. Find the value of *x* in each of the following diagrams:

(i)   (ii)   (iii)

4. Find the size of the angle marked with a letter in each of the following:

5. Find the value of *x* in each of the following diagrams:

(i)   (ii)   (iii)

6. Write down the size of the angle marked with a capital letter in each of the following diagrams.

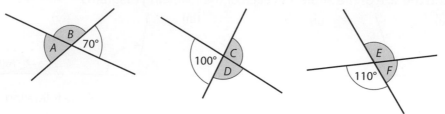

7. In each of the following diagrams, write down the sizes of the angles marked with a letter. Give a reason for your answer in each case.

(i)   (ii)   (iii)

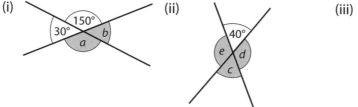

8. Find the value of y in each of the following figures:

(i)   (ii)   (iii)

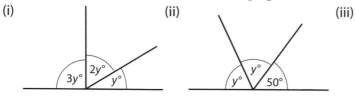

9. Find the value of x in each of these diagrams:

(i)   (ii)   (iii)

10. Use your protractor to measure these angles:

11. Use your protractor to draw angles of measure

    (i) 30°   (ii) 45°   (iii) 75°   (iv) 110°

12. Find the values of
the angles marked
A, B and C in the
given diagram.

13. Work out the size of the unknown angles.
Give a reason for each of your answers.

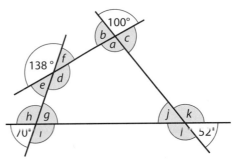

14. A designer is looking at folding stools.

    (i) If angle *p* is 100°, what is angle   (a) *q*   (b) *r* ?

    (ii) For safety reasons angle *p* must be greater than 120°.
        Which one of these statements must be true for
        angle *r* ?
        A: The angle *r* must be greater than 60°.
        B: The angle *r* must be less than 60°.
        C: The angle *r* must be equal to 60°.

        Give a reason for your answer.

Section 10.4 Angles and parallel lines

The two rails on a railway track are always the same distance apart.

The rail lines are **parallel**.
The lines ℓ and *m* are parallel.
It is written as $\ell \parallel m$.

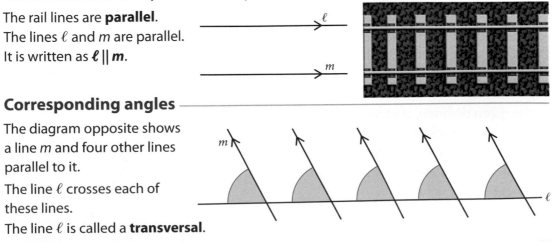

Corresponding angles

The diagram opposite shows
a line *m* and four other lines
parallel to it.

The line ℓ crosses each of
these lines.

The line ℓ is called a **transversal**.

All the shaded angles are in corresponding positions.

These angles are known as **corresponding angles**.

If you measure these angles you will find that they are all equal.

Here are some more corresponding angles.

Each pair is equal in measure.

> Corresponding angles are equal in measure.

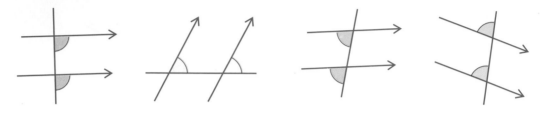

Alternate angles

The diagram on the right shows a line ℓ intersecting two parallel lines m and n.

The shaded angles are between the parallel lines and on alternate sides of the line ℓ.

These shaded angles are called **alternate angles** and are equal in size.

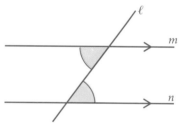

Other pairs of alternate angles are shaded in the diagrams below:

  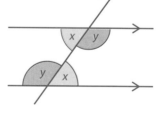

Theorem	If a transversal makes equal alternate angles on two lines, then the lines are parallel.

> Alternate angles are equal in measure.

In the given diagram, the transversal ℓ intersects the two lines m and n.
The equal alternate angles are marked.
The lines m and n are parallel because the alternate angles are equal.

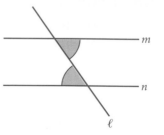

Interior angles

In the given figure, the lines ℓ and *m* are parallel.

The line *t* is a transversal.

The shaded angles shown are called **interior angles**.

These angles add to 180°.

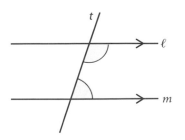

> ### Example 1
>
> Write down the size of the angles marked with letters.
>
>
>
> $|\angle a| = 115°$ ... vertically opposite angles
>
> $|\angle b| = 115°$ ... alternate angles
>
> $|\angle c| = 115°$ ... corresponding angles
>
> $|\angle d| + 115° = 180°$ ... angles in a straight line
>
> $|\angle d| = 180° - 115°$
>
> $|\angle d| = 65°$

Exercise 10.4

1. In each of the following diagrams write down the number of the angle that **corresponds** to the shaded angle:

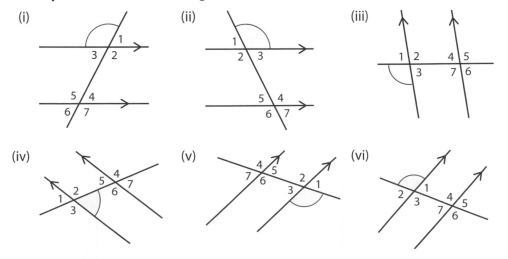

2. Write down the size of the angle marked with a letter in each of the following diagrams:

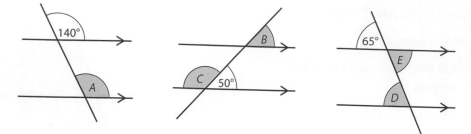

3. In each of the following figures write down the number of the angle which is **alternate** to the shaded angle:

(i)   (ii)   (iii)

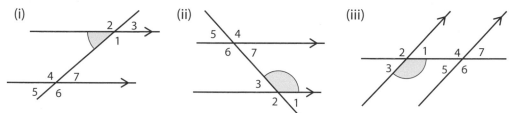

4. ℓ and *m* are parallel lines. Name

   (i) four pairs of vertically opposite angles
  (ii) two pairs of corresponding angles
 (iii) two pairs of alternate angles.

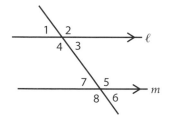

5. Write down the size of the angles marked with letters in the following diagrams:

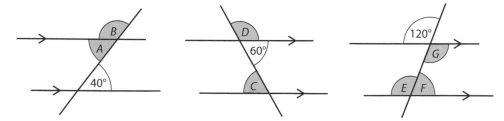

6. Find the size of the lettered angles. Give a reason for each answer.

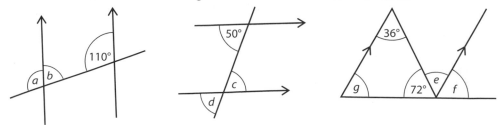

7. In this mechanism the two bars
   h and *k* stay parallel.
   Find angles x and y.

8. Find the size of the angles marked with letters in each of these diagrams:

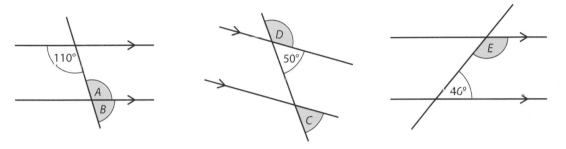

9. This diagram shows a lifting platform.
   The top always remains parallel to the base.
   (i) Angle *c* must not go above 35°.
      Which one of these statements about angle *b* is true?
      (a) Angle *b* must be equal to 35°.
      (b) Angle *b* must be greater than 35°.
      (c) Angle *b* must be less than or equal to 35°.
   (ii) If angle *c* must not go above 35°, what can you say about angle *a*?

10. In the given diagram ℓ and *m* are parallel lines.
   Copy and complete these statements to make them true.
   (i) *h* and ...... are corresponding angles.
   (ii) *e* and ...... are vertically opposite angles.
   (iii) *e* and ...... are alternate angles.
   (iv) *e* and ...... are interior angles.
   (v) *b* and ...... are corresponding angles.
   (vi) *b* and ...... are vertically opposite angles.
   (vii) *d* and ...... are interior angles.
   (viii) *a* and ...... are corresponding angles.
   (ix) *g* and ...... are vertically opposite angles.
   (x) *c* and ...... are alternate angles.

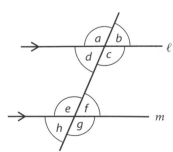

11. A snooker table is shown.

The ball follows a path from A to D.

AB is parallel to CD.

Find the size of the angles marked
V, W, X, Y, and Z.

12. The pictures show a gate and a shed door.
Find the angles marked with letters.

Section 10.5 Drawing parallel and perpendicular lines —

How to draw a line parallel to a given line ——————

We use a ruler and set square to draw a line parallel to a given line.
The diagrams below show the steps to be followed.

Given a line ℓ and a
point A.

Line up the set square
along the line ℓ. Hold the
ruler firmly along the side
of the set square.

Slide the set square along
the edge of the ruler until
you reach the point A.
Draw the line m parallel to ℓ.

Perpendicular lines

The lines ℓ and m intersect to form 4 right angles.

They are said to be **perpendicular** to each other.

It is written $\ell \perp m$.

Drawing a line perpendicular to a given line through a given point

Given the line segment
[AB] and a point P.

Place a ruler along AB. Place one side of the set square on the ruler, as shown. Move the set square until it reaches the point P. Draw a line ℓ through P.

The line ℓ is perpendicular to [AB] and it contains the point P.

Exercise 10.5

1. The diagram shows a right-angled triangle.

   (i) What is the size of the angle C?

  (ii) Name the side that is perpendicular to BC.

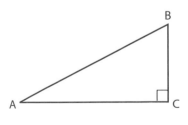

2. (i) Which line is perpendicular to SP?

   (ii) Which lines are perpendicular to PQ?

  (iii) Which line is parallel to QR?

Arrows indicate
parallel lines.

3. The diagram shows a rectangular box.
  (i)   Name two edges parallel to [AB].
  (ii) Name two edges perpendicular to [HG].
  (iii) How many edges are parallel to [DH]?
  (iv) Name three edges perpendicular to [BF].

4. Examine the diagram on the right and say if
each of the following is true or false:

  (i) $a \perp c$ (ii) $b \parallel c$
  (iii) $b \perp d$ (iv) $a \parallel d$
  (v) $d \parallel c$ (vi) $b \perp c$

5. Use a ruler and set square to draw three lines
perpendicular to the line ℓ shown on the right.

6. Copy the following diagrams and draw a line perpendicular to ℓ through the point
P in each case:

7. Copy the diagrams in Question 6 and use your ruler and set square to draw a line
through P parallel to ℓ in each case.

8. The diagram shows the shape ABCDE.
  (i)   Name two right angles.
  (ii) What line is perpendicular to [BC]?
  (iii) Name an acute angle.
  (iv) Name an obtuse angle.
  (v)   Name two parallel lines.

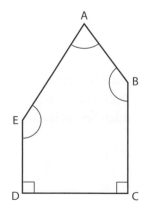

9. The diagram below shows some local roads near a village.

(i) Which road is parallel to Lacken Road?

(ii) Which road is perpendicular to River Road?

(iii) Name two roads perpendicular to Church Road.

10. Find the value of x in each of these figures:

(i)

(ii)

(iii)

11. In the given figure a, b and c are three straight lines. Find the value of x and the value of y.

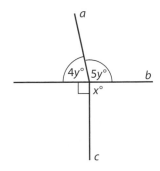

Test yourself 10

1. (i) Name the shaded angles.

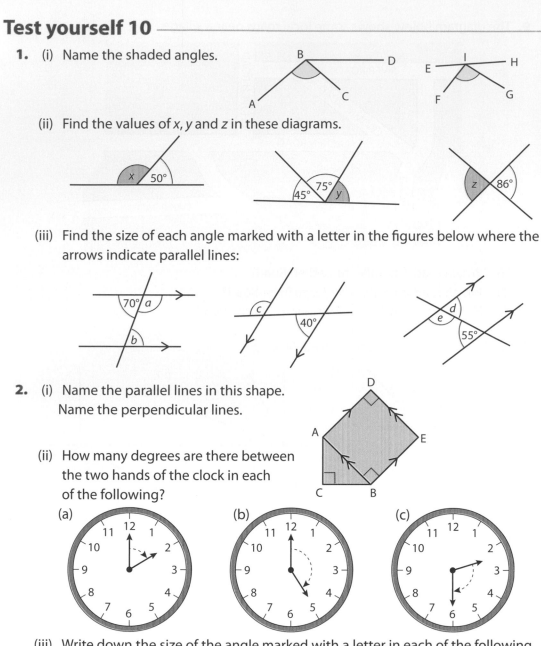

   (ii) Find the values of x, y and z in these diagrams.

   (iii) Find the size of each angle marked with a letter in the figures below where the arrows indicate parallel lines:

2. (i) Name the parallel lines in this shape.
      Name the perpendicular lines.

   (ii) How many degrees are there between the two hands of the clock in each of the following?

   (a) (b) (c)

   (iii) Write down the size of the angle marked with a letter in each of the following diagrams, where the arrows indicate parallel lines:

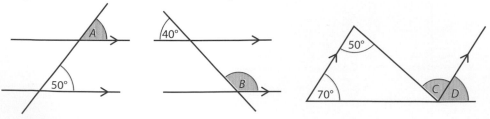

3. (i) Find the values of *a*, *b* and *c* in the following figures:

(ii) Calculate the angles marked with letters on this cot, fishing stool and workbench.

(iii) In the diagram on the right, the arrows
indicate that the lines are parallel.
Calculate the measures of the
angles *A* and *B*.

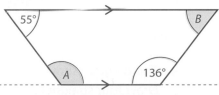

4. (i) Use a copy of this diagram.
Use your ruler and set square to draw
(a) a line through C that is perpendicular to AB
(b) a line through D that is parallel to AB.

(ii) Calculate the angles marked with letters in these diagrams:

(iii) In the diagram on the right, the lines containing
the arrows are parallel.
Calculate the sizes of the angles *A*, *B* and *C*.

For the problem solver...

1. Move two matches so that the circle is outside the glass shape.
   (You must retain the glass shape.)

2. Lines *AB* and *CD* are parallel and $|BC| = |BD|$.
   Given that *x* is an acute angle not equal to 60°, how many *other* angles in this diagram are equal to *x*?

3. How many squares in the given figure contain the dot?

4. The diagram shows 9 dots in the form of a square. Draw four straight lines so as to cross out every dot. You must not cross any dot more than once, nor retrace any line, nor lift the pencil from the paper until all nine dots have been crossed.

5. Remove three matches to leave just three identical squares.

6. This is a 1-metre square window. It gives more light than what was desired. Design a new window so that it will remain a square but give half the amount of light. Its height and width must still remain 1 metre. Any covering cannot be used to exclude the light.

Ratio and Proportion

chapter 11

Key words

ratio	simplest form	proportion	directly proportional
unitary method	inverse proportion	best buys	value-for-money

Section 11.1 Introducing ratio

Below we have one glass of concentrated orange squash and three glasses of water.

They are mixed together to make a diluted orange squash.

We say that the ratio of squash to water is 1 is to 3.

This is written as **1 : 3**.

The ratio of blue discs to red discs is 5 : 2.

The ratio of red discs to blue discs is 2 : 5.

From these two statements you can see that a **ratio** is used to compare one amount with another.

There are 12 boys and 18 girls in a class.

The ratio of boys to girls is 12 : 18.

We can simplify this ratio by dividing each part by 6.

> 12 and 18 have a common factor of 6.

Thus 12 : 18 simplifies to 2 : 3.

When you compare two or more quantities, they must be expressed in the same units.

$$4 \text{ days} : 2 \text{ weeks} = 4 \text{ days} : 14 \text{ days}$$
$$= 4 : 14$$
$$= 2 : 7 \qquad \text{... 2 is a common factor}$$

Example 1

Express the following ratios in their simplest form:

(i) $21:28$ (ii) $80\,cm:2\,m$ (iii) €1.25:€5   (iv) $\frac{1}{2}:\frac{3}{4}$

(i) $21:28 = 3:4$ ... divide both terms by 7

(ii) $80\,cm:2\,m = 80:200 = 8:20 = 2:5$

(iii) €1.25:€5 $= 125:500 = 25:100 = 1:4$

(iv) $\frac{1}{2}:\frac{3}{4}$ ... Here multiply each term by 4 to make whole numbers

$$\therefore \quad \frac{1}{2}:\frac{3}{4} = \frac{4}{2}:\frac{3\times 4}{4} = 2:3$$

Exercise 11.1

1. For the tile pattern on the right, find
  (i) the fraction of the pattern that is purple
  (ii) the ratio of purple tiles to white tiles
  (iii) the ratio of white tiles to the total number of tiles.

2. Express the shaded area as a ratio of the total area in each of the following diagrams:

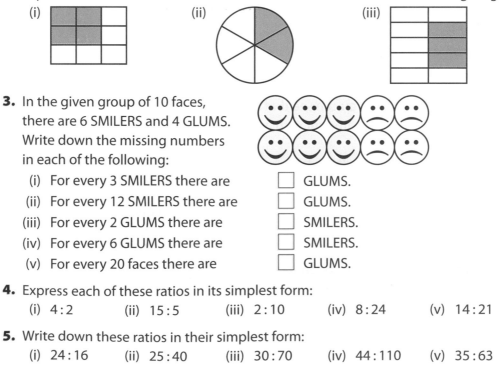

  (i)   (ii)   (iii)

3. In the given group of 10 faces, there are 6 SMILERS and 4 GLUMS. Write down the missing numbers in each of the following:

  (i) For every 3 SMILERS there are ☐ GLUMS.
  (ii) For every 12 SMILERS there are ☐ GLUMS.
  (iii) For every 2 GLUMS there are ☐ SMILERS.
  (iv) For every 6 GLUMS there are ☐ SMILERS.
  (v) For every 20 faces there are ☐ GLUMS.

4. Express each of these ratios in its simplest form:
  (i) $4:2$ (ii) $15:5$ (iii) $2:10$ (iv) $8:24$ (v) $14:21$

5. Write down these ratios in their simplest form:
  (i) $24:16$ (ii) $25:40$ (iii) $30:70$ (iv) $44:110$ (v) $35:63$

6. The recipe on the right gives the ingredients required for
   6 servings of *Lemon Ice Cream*.

   (i) How many egg yolks would be needed for 9 servings?

   (ii) How many ml of lemon juice would be needed for
   3 servings?

   (iii) How many grams of caster sugar would be needed
   for 18 servings?

   (iv) How many ml of double cream would be needed for 9 servings?

   (v) If 25 eggs yolks were used, how many servings could be made?

   > **Lemon Ice Cream**
   > (makes 6 servings)
   > 10 egg yolks
   > 200 g caster sugar
   > 50 ml lemon juice
   > 400 ml double cream

7.
   > **Fish Pie**
   > (serves 4)
   >
   > 500 g haddock
   > 400 ml milk
   > 60 g butter
   > 200 ml single cream
   > 2 eggs
   > 800 g potatoes

   The recipe on the left will make a fish pie to serve 4 people.

   (i) How many grams of haddock are needed to make a fish
   pie for 6 people?

   (ii) How many eggs are needed to make a fish pie for
   12 people?

   (iii) How many grams of potato are needed to make a fish
   pie for 10 people?

   (iv) If a fish pie contains 150 g of butter, how many people
   would it serve?

8. Fill in the missing number in each of these boxes:

   (i) $2 : 3 = 4 : \square$

   (ii) $3 : 5 = \square : 10$

   (iii) $3 : \square = 9 : 12$

   (iv) $2 : 7 = 6 : \square$

   (v) $5 : 15 = \square : 3$

   (vi) $7 : \square = 21 : 9$

9. Express each of the following ratios in its simplest form.
   Change both sides to the same units where necessary.

   (i) $10\,c : 50\,c$

   (ii) 5 days : 2 weeks

   (iii) 30 minutes : 2 hours

   (iv) $20\,c : €1$

   (v) $30 \text{ mins} : 1\frac{1}{2} \text{ hours}$

   (vi) 3 weeks : 7 days

10. In a mixed class there are 12 girls and 8 boys.
    What is each ratio in its simplest form?

    (i) the number of boys to the number of girls.

    (ii) the number of girls to the total number in the class.

11. A pets' home has 18 dogs, 12 cats, 9 rabbits and 3 mice.
    What is each ratio in its simplest form?

    (i) mice to cats

    (ii) mice to dogs

    (iii) rabbits to mice

    (iv) cats to the total number of pets.

12. Express each of the following ratios as whole numbers:

    (i) $\frac{1}{2} : 2$

    (ii) $\frac{1}{2} : \frac{1}{4}$

    (iii) $\frac{1}{4} : \frac{3}{4}$

    (iv) $\frac{1}{3} : \frac{2}{3}$

    (v) $\frac{3}{4} : 1\frac{1}{2}$

    (vi) $1\frac{1}{4} : 2$

    (vii) $\frac{3}{5} : \frac{7}{10}$

    (viii) $\frac{2}{5} : \frac{1}{2}$

13. A mortar mix is made by adding sand and cement in the ratio 4 : 1.

   (i) If 6 buckets of cement are used, how many buckets of sand are needed?

  (ii) If 10 buckets of sand are used, how many buckets of cement are needed?

 (iii) In a mortar mix 15 buckets in total were used. How many of these buckets contained cement?

Section 11.2 Dividing in a given ratio

Alan and Barbara share €60 between them in the ratio 2 : 3.
How much do they each receive?
The number of shares is $2 + 3 = 5$.
Each share is worth €60 ÷ 5 = €12.

Alan receives $2 \times €12 = €24$
Barbara receives $3 \times €12 = €36$

> Alan gets $\frac{2}{5}$
> Barbara gets $\frac{3}{5}$

Example 1

Divide €900 between A, B and C in the ratio 4 : 3 : 2.

$4 + 3 + 2 = 9$, so we make 9 divisions of the money.

> Each division is $\frac{1}{9}$ of the total.

A gets $\frac{4}{9}$ of €900 $= \frac{4}{9} \times \frac{900}{1} = €400$

B gets $\frac{3}{9}$ of €900 $= \frac{3}{9} \times \frac{900}{1} = €300$

C gets $\frac{2}{9}$ of €900 $= \frac{2}{9} \times \frac{900}{1} = €200$ ∴ A gets €400; B gets €300; C gets €200.

Example 2

In a school, the ratio of boys to girls is 6 : 5.
If there are 325 girls in the school, find the number of pupils in the school.

Boys : Girls $= 6 : 5$, so $\frac{6}{11}$ of the total are boys and $\frac{5}{11}$ are girls

∴ $\frac{5}{11} = 325$

    $\frac{1}{11} = 65$

    $\frac{11}{11} = 715$ ∴ there are 715 pupils in the school.

Exercise 11.2

1. Anna and Billy share €90 between them in the ratio 2 : 3.
    (i) What fraction of the €90 does Anna get?
    (ii) What fraction of the €90 does Billy get?
    (iii) How much money does each of them get?

2. Divide a prize of €400 between Claire and Dara in the ratio 5 : 3.

3. A box of 40 chocolates had milk and dark chocolates in the ratio 2 : 3.
   How many were milk chocolates?

4. Pat is 6 years old and Emer is 3 years old.
   Divide 36 sweets between them in the ratio of their ages.

5. (i) Divide €120 in the ratio 3 : 1   (ii) Divide €714 in the ratio 3 : 4.
   (iii) Divide €121 in the ratio 6 : 5   (iv) Divide €106.50 in the ratio 7 : 3.
   (v) Divide €864 in the ratio 5 : 4   (vi) Divide 1 hour 30 mins in the ratio 9 : 1.

6. Divide €1400 between three people in the ratio 4 : 2 : 1.

7. There are 90 pupils in first-year. The ratio of girls to boys is 5 : 4.
   How many boys are there in first-year?

8. A farmer had all his farm under two crops, beet and barley, in the ratio 3 : 4.
   If his farm consisted of 91 acres, how many acres were under each crop?

9. A prize is divided between *A* and *B* in the ratio 5 : 2.
   If *A* gets €165, find the total prize fund.

10. The ratio of nurses to doctors in a hospital is 7 : 1.
    If there are 91 nurses on the staff, find the number of doctors.

11. In a rectangle the ratio of length to width is 5 : 2.

28 cm

If the width is 28 cm, find the length.

12. The ratio of males to females in the crowd at
    a rock concert is 5 : 4.
    There are 360 males in the crowd.
    How many females are there?

13. The ratio of girls to boys on a school trip is 5 : 4.
Find the number of girls when there are these numbers of pupils:
  (i) 56 boys (ii) 72 boys (iii) 189 pupils altogether

14. Mortar that is used for interior walls is a mixture of sand, lime and cement in the ratio of 6 : 2 : 1.
  (i) How much sand is needed to make 60 kg of mortar?
  (ii) How much lime is needed to make 45 kg of mortar?
  (iii) To mix an amount of mortar, Tom uses 6 bucketfuls of lime. How many bucketfuls of sand will he need?

15. On a Saturday the football results gave a ratio of home wins to away wins to draws of 6 : 2 : 1. If there were 10 away wins, how many home wins were there and how many draws were there?

16. A prize fund is divided between A, B and C in the ratio 7 : 4 : 1.
If B receives €960, find the value of the total prize fund.

17. For a football team, the ratio of goals scored at home to goals scored at away games was 3 : 2.
  (i) If the team scored 45 goals, how many did they score at home?
  (ii) In a full season the team scored 24 goals in away games.
       How many goals did they score at home?

18. Sally makes breakfast cereal by mixing bran, currants and wheatgerm in the ratio 8 : 3 : 1 by mass.
  (i) How much bran does she use to make 600 g of the cereal?
  (ii) One day she only has 20 g of currants.
       How much cereal can she make? She has plenty of bran and wheatgerm.

19. Alan is 12 years old and Emer is 8 years old.
€5400 is divided between them in the ratio of their ages.
How much does each receive?
In eight years time another €5400 will be divided between them in the ratio of their ages at that time. How much will they each receive then?

20. Two squares and their perimeters are shown.
  (i) Write down the ratio of the lengths of their sides.
  (ii) Work out the ratio of their areas.

Perimeter = 20 cm

Perimeter = 28 cm

21. Three quarters of the junior members of a tennis club are boys and the rest are girls.
What is the ratio of boys to girls among the members?

22. First-year and second-year pupils are in an assembly.
The given table shows some facts about these pupils.
Work out the total number of girls in the assembly.

Year	boys : girls	Pupil data
1	4 : 5	84 boys
2	2 : 3	150 pupils

Section 11.3 Proportion

In the previous two sections we dealt with **ratio** which compares part to part.

In this section we will deal with **proportion** which compares part to whole.

In the given figure there are 4 red squares and 5 blue squares.

The proportion of red squares is $\frac{4}{9}$.

The proportion of blue squares is $\frac{5}{9}$.

> You can write a proportion as a fraction, decimal or percentage.

Example 1

In a football match Rovers had 25 shots at goal with 17 on target.
City had 20 shots at goal with 13 on target.
  (i)   Write the proportion of shots on target for each team as a fraction and as a decimal.
  (ii) Which team seems to be more accurate?
  (iii) Which did you find more useful, fraction or decimal, when answering part (ii)?

  (i)   Rovers: fraction $= \frac{17}{25}$;   decimal $= \frac{17 \times 4}{25 \times 4} = \frac{68}{100} = 0.68$

         City: fraction $= \frac{13}{20}$;   decimal $= \frac{13 \times 5}{20 \times 5} = \frac{65}{100} = 0.65$

  (ii) As 0.68 is greater than 0.65, Rovers seem to be more accurate.
  (iii) Decimals are more useful as it is usually much easier to compare decimals than compare fractions.

Direct proportion

If   1 apple costs 80 cent,
       2 apples cost €1.60
       3 apples cost €2.40

Apples 80c each

Here we can see that the number of apples and the prices increase in the same ratio, that is, they are **directly proportional**.

Similarly if   9 kg of potatoes cost €5.67

1 kg costs €5.67 ÷ 9 = €0.63

5 kg cost €0.63 × 5 = €3.15

In this example we found the cost of 1 kg first and then found the cost of 5 kg.

This method is generally called **the unitary method**.

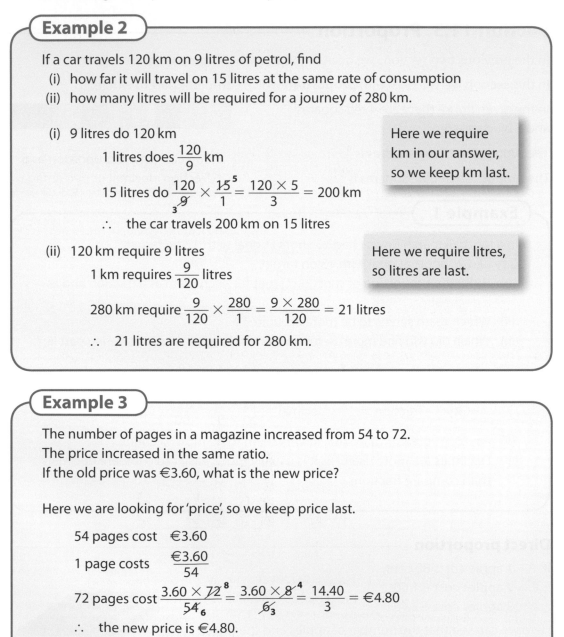

Example 2

If a car travels 120 km on 9 litres of petrol, find
 (i) how far it will travel on 15 litres at the same rate of consumption
 (ii) how many litres will be required for a journey of 280 km.

(i) 9 litres do 120 km

$$1 \text{ litres does } \frac{120}{9} \text{ km}$$

Here we require km in our answer, so we keep km last.

$$15 \text{ litres do } \frac{120}{\underset{3}{9}} \times \frac{\overset{5}{15}}{1} = \frac{120 \times 5}{3} = 200 \text{ km}$$

∴   the car travels 200 km on 15 litres

(ii) 120 km require 9 litres

$$1 \text{ km requires } \frac{9}{120} \text{ litres}$$

Here we require litres, so litres are last.

$$280 \text{ km require } \frac{9}{120} \times \frac{280}{1} = \frac{9 \times 280}{120} = 21 \text{ litres}$$

∴   21 litres are required for 280 km.

Example 3

The number of pages in a magazine increased from 54 to 72.
The price increased in the same ratio.
If the old price was €3.60, what is the new price?

Here we are looking for 'price', so we keep price last.

54 pages cost   €3.60

$$1 \text{ page costs } \quad \frac{€3.60}{54}$$

$$72 \text{ pages cost } \frac{3.60 \times \overset{8}{72}}{\underset{6}{54}} = \frac{3.60 \times \overset{4}{8}}{\underset{3}{6}} = \frac{14.40}{3} = €4.80$$

∴   the new price is €4.80.

Exercise 11.3

1. (i) What is the ratio of blue discs to red discs?
    (ii) What proportion of the discs are red?
         Give the answer as a fraction.
    (iii) What proportion of the discs are blue? Give the answer as a percentage.

2. There were 10 accidents on a busy road last month.
    7 were car accidents and 3 were cycle accidents.
    (i) Give the proportion of car accidents as a fraction.
    (ii) Give the proportion of cycle accidents as a percentage.
    (iii) What is the ratio of car to cycle accidents?

3. The table shows the choices made by a class of
    30 pupils going on a school trip.
    (i) Copy and complete the table.
    (ii) What proportion of boys want to go
         bowling?

	Boys	Girls	Total
Bowling	9	12	
Cinema	3	6	
Total			30

    (iii) What proportion of girls want to go bowling?
    (iv) What proportion of pupils want to go bowling?
    (v) What proportion of pupils going bowling are girls?
    (vi) Is bowling more popular among boys or girls?

4. The bar chart shows the number of A-grades achieved by a class of 24 pupils.

    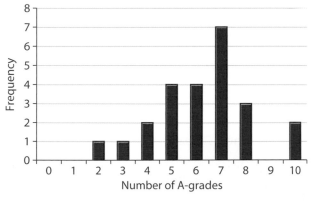

    (i) What proportion of the pupils achieved exactly 5 A-grades?
         Give your answer as a fraction in its simplest form.
    (ii) What proportion of the pupils achieved 5 or more A-grades?
         Give your answer as a fraction in its simplest form.
    (iii) What is the ratio of pupils achieving 5 A-grades to pupils achieving other results?

5. The tables below show pairs of values of x and y.
Which tables show x and y in direct proportion?

(i)
x	1	2	3
y	3	6	9

(ii)
x	1	3	5
y	7	9	12

(iii)
x	4	12	20
y	2	6	10

6. Copy and complete these tables so that x and y are in direct proportion.

(i)
x	5	7	9
y	10		

(ii)
x	8	9	
y	24		33

(iii)
x	10	18	
y		9	15

7. If 7 books cost €55.30, find the cost of nine books.

8. If 8 litres of milk cost €7.36, find the cost of 11 litres.

9. If 3 m of cloth cost €23.55, find the cost of 7 m.

10. If 12 m² of carpet costs €516, find the cost of 16 m².

11. A car travels 100 km on 8 litres of petrol. How far will it travel on 20 litres?

12. A recipe for making 12 scones requires 360 g of flour.
How many grams of flour are needed for 9 scones?

13. Lilian earns €45 for 5 hours work.
(i) What would she earn in 18 hours?
(ii) How many hours would she have to work to earn €207?

14. A car can travel 80 km on 6 litres of petrol.
How far can it travel on (i) 21 litres and (ii) 9 litres?

15. Franco uses this recipe to make pizzas for 4 people.
He wants to make a pizza for 10 people.
(i) What quantity of cheese does he need?
(ii) How many tomatoes does he need?
(iii) What quantity of bacon does he need?

Pizza
2 pizza bases
2 onions
250 g cheese
4 tomatoes
120 g bacon

16. A small plane flies 80 km in 15 minutes.
(i) How long will it take to fly 400 km? (ii) How far would it fly in 33 minutes?

17. A car can travel 100 km on €12 worth of petrol.
(i) How much would the petrol cost for a journey of 350 km?
(ii) How many km would the car travel on €30?

18. A model car is made to a scale of 1 : 50.
(i) The model has a length of 10 cm.
Calculate the length of the real car.
Give your answer in metres.
(ii) The real car has a height of 1.75 m. Calculate the height of the model car.

19. A secretary can type 320 words in 8 minutes.
   (i) At the same rate, how many words would she type in 10 minutes?
  (ii) How long would it take her to type 180 words?

20. The graph below shows that there is a direct proportion between pints and litres.
This graph can be used to change litres to pints and pints to litres.

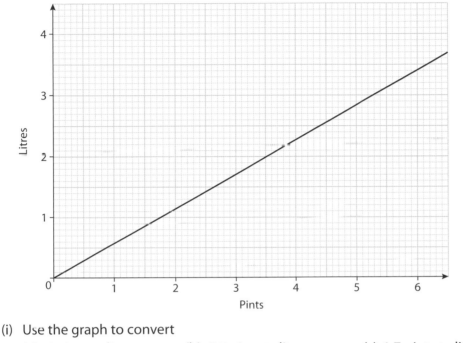

  (i) Use the graph to convert
     (a) 4 pints to litres   (b) 3.5 pints to litres   (c) 1.7 pints to litres
  (ii) Use the graph to convert
     (a) 3 litres to pints   (b) 1.5 litres to pints   (c) 0.9 litres to pints

     Use the graph to help you convert 15 pints to litres.

Section 11.4 Inverse proportion – Best buys

1. Inverse Proportion

If a car travels at a steady speed of 50 km/hr it will take it 4 hours to travel 200 km.
If it travels at 100 km/hr it will do the same journey in 2 hours.

Notice that the time taken to travel the journey decreases as the speed increases. This is an example of **inverse proportion** where an increase in one quantity causes a decrease in another quantity or vice versa.

Example 1

If 9 men can complete a job in 8 days, how long will it take 6 men to do the job if they work at the same rate?

(Here we are looking for time, so we keep time last.)

    9 men can do the job in 8 days

    1 man can do the job in 72 days   ... 9 times as long

    6 men can do the job in $\frac{72}{6} = 12$ days   ... $\frac{1}{6}$ as long as 1 man

2. Best buys

When shopping we often have to make choices between products which are packed in various sizes and priced differently. If we want to buy the item which gives the **better value for money**, we must compare prices using the same units.

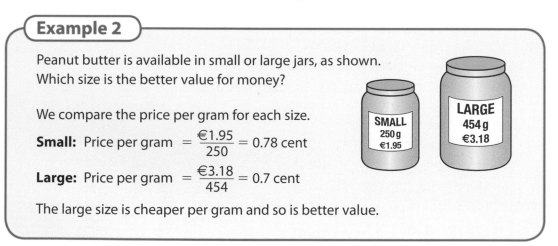

Example 2

Peanut butter is available in small or large jars, as shown. Which size is the better value for money?

We compare the price per gram for each size.

Small: Price per gram $= \dfrac{€1.95}{250} = 0.78$ cent

Large: Price per gram $= \dfrac{€3.18}{454} = 0.7$ cent

The large size is cheaper per gram and so is better value.

Exercise 11.4

1. Here are two bags of potatoes at a supermarket.
   (i) Work out the cost of 1 kg in the Family Pack.
   (ii) Work out the cost of 1 kg in the Value Pack.
   (iii) Which pack gives you more for your money?

POTATOES

3 kg
€2.94

POTATOES

5 kg
€5.20

Value pack   Family pack

2. Which box gives the best value?

3. A standard bottle of mineral water contains 1.5 litres and costs €1.92.
A large bottle contains 2.5 litres and costs €3.
  (i) What is the cost of one litre of water in the standard bottle?
 (ii) What is the cost of one litre in the large bottle?
(iii) In which bottle does the water work out cheaper?
(iv) Why might you prefer to buy the standard bottle?

4. A wholefoods store sells ground almonds in four sizes:
S: 200 g for €1.80   *M:* 300 g for €2.30   *L:* 500 g for €4.10   *EL:* 800 g for €7.00
Find the cost for 100 g in each size and decide which works out cheapest.

5. Asco bath lotion is sold in two sizes.
The large size contains 400 ml and costs €3.
The family size contains 1000 ml and costs €6.80.
Which size is the best value for money?
You must show your working.

6. Which of the two bottles of 'Active' drinks gives
the better value for money?

7. Toothpaste is sold in small, medium and large sizes.
The small size contains 75 ml and costs €2.40.
The medium size contains 125 ml and costs €3.50.
The large size contains 180 ml and costs €4.68.
Which size is the best value for money?

8. Fill in the missing numbers in the following lines:
    4 men take 6 days to build a wall.
    1 man takes ☐ days
    3 men take ☐ days.

9. If 6 men build a wall in 3 days, how long would it take

    (i) 1 man   (ii) 3 men to build the wall?

10. Three women can complete a house-to-house survey in 15 days.
How long would it take 5 women working at the same rate to complete the job?

11. When a dog eats 200 g of dogfood each day, a container lasts him 10 days.
How long would a container last him if he eats

    (i) 100 g per day   (ii) 400 g per day   (iii) 250 g per day?

12. A shopkeeper has enough money to buy 60 books at €9 each.
If the price of the books was increased to €12, how many of them could she buy for
the same amount of money?

13. A motorist driving 80 km per day has enough
petrol to last her 9 days. If she reduces her driving
to 45 km per day, how long will the petrol last?

14. Five women can complete a computer assignment in 12 days.
How long would it take

    (i) 10 women   (ii) 3 women to complete the assignment?

15. Three painters can paint an office block in 12 days.
    (i) How long would it take 4 painters to paint the block?
    (ii) If the office block had to be painted in 3 days, how many painters would be
needed?

16. It takes 5 lorries 18 days to remove the topsoil for an extension to a motorway.
    (i) How long would it take 15 lorries to remove the topsoil?
    (ii) How many lorries would be needed to remove the topsoil in 10 days?

17. A poultry farmer has enough corn to feed 30 hens for 9 days.
    (i) How long would the corn last 15 hens?
    (ii) How many hens could be fed with the corn for 6 days?

18. Tap A can fill a bath in 12 minutes.
Tap B can fill it in 6 minutes.
    (i) What fraction of the bath does tap A fill in 1 minute?
    (ii) What fraction of the bath does tap B fill in 1 minute?
    (iii) If both taps are working together, what fraction of
the bath will they fill in 1 minute?
    (iv) How long will it take both taps working together to
fill the bath?

Test yourself 11

1. Express each of these ratios in its simplest form:
   (i) 5 : 30   (ii) 6 : 9   (iii) 20 : 30   (iv) 21 : 28   (v) 24 : 16

2. Ava and Barry share €90 between them in the ratio 7 : 2.
   (i) What fraction of the €90 does Ava get?
   (ii) What fraction of the €90 does Barry get?
   (iii) How much money does each of them get?

3. (i) What proportion of the given figure is shaded?
   Give your answer as a fraction.
   (ii) What is the ratio of the shaded area to the total
   area of the square?
   (iii) If the area of the shaded portion is 36 cm², find the area of the whole square.

4. Darina uses this recipe to make apple crumble.
   She wants to make it for 10 people.
   (i) How much flour does she need?
   (ii) How much butter does she need?
   (iii) How many apples does she need?

Apple crumble
for 4 people

4 large apples
50 g butter
100 g sugar
200 g flour

5. Mr Brown makes some compost.
   He mixes soil, manure and leaf mould in the ratio 3 : 1 : 1.
   Mr Brown makes 75 litres of compost.
   How many litres of soil does he use?

6. The ratio of elephants to tigers in a safari park is 5 : 4.
   If there are 300 elephants in the park, how many tigers are there?

7. A prize fund is divided between *A* and *B* in the ratio 5 : 2.
   If *A* gets €330, find the total prize fund.

8. If 7 kg of meat cost €64.75, find the cost of 9 kg of the meat.

9. Ecowash washing liquid can be bought in four sizes.

Large 3 litre	Standard 1 litre	Economy 1.5 litre	Travel 0.5 litre
€6.48	€2.28	€3.39	€1.55

   (i) Find the cost of 1 litre for each size.
   (ii) Write the sizes in order of price per litre, the cheapest first.

10. €900 is divided between Sarah, Jack and Ciara in the ratio 1 : 2 : 3.
    How much does each receive?

11. A tin of biscuits contains enough for 12 people if each person eats 6 biscuits. If the
    same number of biscuits was divided among 8 people, how many would each receive?

12. (i) What proportion of this figure is red?
         Give your answer as a percentage.
     (ii) Express the ratio red : green in its lowest terms.

13. Write down the missing numbers for each of these ratios:

     (i) $3 : 5 = 9 : \square$ (ii) $3 : \square = 9 : 21$ (iii) $\square : 4 = 3 : 12$

14.

     Mortar is made by mixing 5 parts by weight of sand with 1 part by weight of
     cement.
     (i) How many kg of sand is in 90 kg of mortar?
     (ii) If there are 100 kg of sand in the mortar, how many kg of cement does it
          contain?

15. A car travels 110 km on 8 litres of petrol.
     How far will it travel on 20 litres?

16. The three angles of this triangle are in the ratio 4 : 3 : 2.
     Find the sizes of the three angles.

17. On a full tank of petrol of 40 litres, a car completed 420 kilometres.
     (i) What distance would you expect the car to complete with 22 litres of petrol in
          the tank?
     (ii) How many litres of petrol would you need to travel 630 kilometres?

18. A 500 g packet of *Healthy Flakes* costs €3.20.
     A 750 g packet of *Healthy Flakes* costs €4.50.
     Which size packet is the better buy?
     Show all your calculations and explain your answer clearly.

19. This packet of sugar cubes   How much would you expect to
     costs €1.92.   pay for this packet?

For the problem solver...

1. My watch gains four minutes every hour. I put it right when I get up at 7 am. What time does my watch show when school ends at 3.45 pm?

2. I want to cut a long strip of metal into four shorter pieces. If each cut takes twice as long as the previous one, and the first takes one minute, how long will the job take?

3. A car with five tyres (four road tyres and a spare) travelled 30 000 km. All five tyres were used equally.
   How many kilometres' wear did each tyre receive?

4. Michael and Meg are brother and sister. Meg has three times as many brothers as sisters, but Michael has the same number of bothers as sisters. How many children are there in the family?

5. If six towels on a clothes line take two hours to dry, how long do three similar towels (on the same line) take to dry?

6. Obtain a sheet of paper in each of these sizes: A3, A4 and A5.
   (i) How are the sheets related to each other?
   (ii) Investigate the ratio of the length to the width for each size. What do you find?

7. This problem was first posed by the Abbot of Canterbury in the 8th century.
   'One hundred bushels of corn were distributed among one hundred people in such a way that each man received three bushels, each woman two bushels, and each child half a bushel. Given that there are five times as many women as men, how many children are there?'

8. Twenty four 20c coins are lined up side by side. Every second 20c coin is then replaced by a 10c coin. Then every third coin in the resulting row is replaced by a 5c coin. Finally every fourth coin in the row is replaced by a 2c coin. What is the final value of the line?
   A €1.32   *B* €2.32   *C* €2.42   *D* €2.64   *E* €3.02

9. If it takes 5 men 5 days to plough 5 fields, how long does it take 1 man to plough 1 field, working at the same rate?

10. In the figure, $\frac{3}{4}$ of the smaller square is shaded and $\frac{6}{7}$ of the larger square is shaded. What is the ratio of the shaded area of the smaller square to the shaded area of the larger square?
    A $\frac{1}{2}$ *B* $\frac{4}{7}$ *C* $\frac{3}{4}$ *D* $\frac{6}{7}$ *E* $\frac{7}{8}$

12 Collecting Data

Key words

survey	tally chart	primary data	secondary data	numerical data
discrete data	continuous data		categorical data	ordinal data
simple random sample	population	questionnaire	bias	representative

Section 12.1 Collecting data – Surveys and Experiments

Television has become a large part of many people's lives.
Lots of questions could be asked about people's attitudes to TV.

- What programmes do thirteen year olds like best?
- How much TV do children under six watch each day?
- What percentage of households watch TV during meal-time?

To answer these questions you would need to do a **survey**.

A **survey** is a way of finding information from people for a particular purpose. It involves

- asking questions
- recording what people say
- presenting the information in a way that makes it easy to understand.

Companies will sometimes ask their customers to complete a questionnaire. They can then use the information to find ways in which they can improve the service that they offer.

Planning a survey

Before you begin a survey you need to plan it carefully using these steps.

1. **What do you want to find out?**

   You must have a clear idea of the purpose of the survey and what you want to find out.

   Example How much pocket money do first-year pupils get each week?

2. **Decide what data you need to collect.**

   Example In relation to the pocket money from the question above, you need to give amounts of money that the pupils receive in the response boxes.

   > Data is information that you or somebody else collects.

   These could be the choices that are given:

   €1–€5 ☐   €5–€10 ☐   €10–€15 ☐   More than €15 ☐

   Always ask questions that will give answers that are suitable to work with.
   Keep the questions simple and clear.
   Avoid anything too personal.
   Do not ask too many questions.

3. **Decide where to collect the data from and how much to collect.**

   Example When dealing with the amount of pocket money first-year pupils get each week you must decide on
   - the number of pupils you want to survey
   - where you will find these pupils so that you get a result that will adequately represent all first-year pupils.

Collecting data

When data is being collected for simple surveys a **data collection sheet** or **tally chart** is generally used.

Here is a tally chart from a traffic survey.

Type of vehicle	Tally	How many
Bus	ЖН ЖН ІІ	12
Car	ЖН ЖН ЖН ЖН ІІ	22
Lorry	ЖН ІІ	7
Van	ЖН ЖН І	11
Motorcycle	ЖН ЖН ЖН	15

> ЖН represents 5.

Activity

We want to find what is the most commonly-used vowel in the English language.

Each student in the class makes a tally chart similar to the one shown.

Select about 80 words from any of your textbooks and fill in the tally chart.

Count the number of times each vowel appears.

Letter	Tally	How many
a		
e		
i		
o		
u		

If the person beside you uses a different 80 words compare the results.

List the three most popular vowels by adding the results from all the students in the class.

Exercise 12.1

1. The tally chart shows the number of glass bottles put into a bottle bank one day.
   (i) How many green bottles were put into the bottle bank?
   (ii) How many brown bottles were put into the bottle bank?

Colour of glass	Tally
Clear	JHT JHT JHT II
Brown	JHT JHT JHT JHT I
Green	JHT JHT JHT

2. The tally chart below shows the colours of cars in a car park.

Colour of car	Tally	Frequency
Black	II	
Blue	JHT JHT III	
Green	IIII	
Red	JHT JHT I	
Silver	JHT II	
White	JHT JHT IIII	
	Total	

   (i) How many blue cars are recorded?
   (ii) How many cars are recorded altogether?
   (iii) What is the most popular colour?

3. Denise carried out a survey to find how students travelled to school.
Her frequency table looked like this:

Method of travel	Tally	Frequency
Walk	ЖТ ЖТ ЖТ ЖТ ЖТ III	A
Car	ЖТ ЖТ II	B
Bus	ЖТ ЖТ ЖТ ЖТ III	C
Bicycle	ЖТ	D
Taxi	II	E

  (i)   Write down the values for A, B, C, D and E.

 (ii)   What is the most common way of travelling to school?

(iii)   What fraction of the students cycled to school?

(iv)   Which two methods of travel were used by exactly one half of the students?

4. Here are the colours of 40 cars in a car park.

red	red	blue	green	white	red
blue	red	red	blue	white	green
red	white	white	blue	red	white
blue	blue	green	black	white	blue
red	silver	silver	blue	red	red
silver	white	white	red	blue	green
red	blue	silver	white		

  (i)   Copy and complete the tally chart below:

Colour of car	Tally	Frequency
Red		
Blue		
Green		
White		
Silver		
Black		

 (ii)   How many white cars are in the car park?

(iii)   What is the most popular colour?

(iv)   Which colour represents 25% of the total?

5. The ages, in years, of 40 people are shown below.

43	24	33	26	35	15	27	34	19	20
42	49	34	56	37	19	21	50	39	29
54	57	30	28	26	18	20	34	3	33
9	10	1	27	12	47	11	7	25	37

Copy and complete the **grouped** tally chart for the data given.

Age (years)	Tally	Frequency
0–9		
10–19		
20–29		
30–39		
40–49		
50–59		

> When data has a wide range of values, it can be sorted into groups or classes.

(i)   What is the width of each class interval?
(ii) How many people are in the class interval 30–39?
(iii) How many people are less than 20 years old?
(iv) How many people are 40 years of age or older?

6. The numbers of birds in a garden are recorded at the same time each day over a 50-day period. These numbers are given below.

4	24	11	24	3	7	8	12	23	14
22	15	5	6	7	8	11	3	8	25
3	7	5	7	17	9	1	13	7	12
1	2	8	18	13	12	3	6	6	9
17	15	11	9	8	17	7	14	16	4

Construct a tally chart similar to Q5 above using groups of
1–5,   6–10,   11–15,   16–20,   21–25.

(i)   On how many days were there 16 or more birds in the garden?
(ii) Which group had the highest number of birds?
(iii) On how many days were there between 11 and 20 (inclusive) birds in the garden?

7. Let all the students in the class write down the different countries they have visited. Use a tally chart to record the numbers who visited the following countries: Spain, France, UK, Italy, Portugal, Germany, Holland, USA.

(i)   Which of these eight countries was visited most often?
(ii) Which of these countries was the least visited?
      Give a reason why this country was the least visited.

Section 12.2 Types of data

1. **Primary and Secondary data**

   Data you collect yourself is called **primary data**.

   Data you look up in books, newspapers or on the internet is called **secondary data**.

   Example (i) Counting the number of cars passing the school gate is
   primary data.

   (ii) Looking at records to see how many babies were born each day in
   May is **secondary data**.

2. **Numerical data**

   Data which can be counted or measured is called **numerical** data because the
   answer is a **number**.

   Numerical data can be **discrete** or **continuous**.

   (i) **Discrete data**

   Data which can be counted is called discrete data.

   Here are some examples of discrete data.

   (a) The number of cars in the school car park.

   (b) The number of rooms in a house.

   (c) The number of goals scored by a football team in each of their matches
   over a season.

   (ii) **Continuous data**

   Data which is measured on some scale is called **continuous data**.

   When you measure a person's height, you cannot get an exact measurement.
   It could be 1.8 m or 1.81 or 1.79 m, or …

   It depends on the accuracy of the measuring device.

   Here are some examples of continuous data:

   (a) The temperatures in a seaside resort over a number of hours.

   (b) The weights of students in your class.

   (c) The length and width of your classroom.

3. **Categorical data**

   Lucy was collecting data about the colours and makes of cars in a large car park.

   She recorded the colour data like this:

   Notice that the colour of a car is not a number.

   The colours fall into groups or **categories**
   such as blue, red, silver, black, …

   Data such as this is called **categorical data**.

Colour of car	Tally
Blue	ЖЖ II
Red	ЖЖ ЖЖ I
Silver	ЖЖ III

Here are examples of categorical data:
- gender (male, female)
- favourite colour (red, blue, green, …)
- type of bird (duck, goose, robin, eagle, …)

Categorical data that involves **order** such as first division, second division, third division, … is generally referred to as **ordinal data**.

Other examples of ordinal data are
 (i)   very often, often, sometimes, rarely, very rarely
 (ii) lower income group, middle income group, higher income group
 (iii) January, February, March, …

Example 1

State whether the following data is discrete, continuous or categorical.
 (i)   The numbers of desks in the classrooms of your school.
 (ii) The temperatures of babies in a crèche.
 (iii) The types of animals on a farm.
 (iv) The numbers of goals scored by football teams on a Saturday.
 (v)   The speeds of cars passing a certain point on a racing track.
 (vi) The heights of the trees in a public park.

(i) Discrete	(ii) Continuous	(iii) Categorical
(iv) Discrete	(v) Continuous	(vi) Continuous

Exercise 12.2

1. State whether each of the following is primary data or secondary data:
 (i)   Counting the number of lorries passing the school gate
 (ii) Asking each student in your class the day of the week on which they were born
 (iii) Finding information for a holiday by looking at brochures
 (iv) Using the internet to find out how many gold, silver and bronze medals US athletes won at the Beijing Olympics
 (v)   Standing outside a supermarket and asking the customers about a new product
 (vi) Checking motoring magazines to find the number of Ford, Toyota and Volkswagen cars sold in January.

2. State whether each of the following is numerical data or categorical data:
   (i) The number of horses that ran in each of the six races at a meeting.
  (ii) The cost of posting each of seven parcels.
 (iii) The hair colours of the students in your class.
 (iv) The types of crop grown on a tillage farm.
  (v) The numbers of jigsaw pieces in a selection of jigsaw boxes.

3. Rory bought a new golf bag.
   He wrote down   (i) the colour of the bag
                        (ii) the number of pockets in the bag.
   State whether each of these data types is numerical or categorical.

4. Each of the following data types is numerical.
   State whether each is discrete or continuous.
   (i) The number of eggs used for making each of seven different-sized cakes.
  (ii) The numbers of motorbikes sold by a garage each month in the past year.
 (iii) The time taken to solve a Rubik's cube.
 (iv) The speed of an aeroplane two minutes after take-off.
  (v) The number of bedrooms in each house on my street.
 (vi) The number of occupants in each car passing a school gate.

5. Consider this statement:
   The weight of a parcel and the cost of its postage.

   Which part of the data is (i) discrete (ii) continuous?

6. There are three pieces of data in this sentence:
   'Niall bought a 5-door car for €18,000 and drove home at a steady speed of 40 km/hr.'
   (i) What are the three pieces of data?
  (ii) State whether each is discrete or continuous.

7. Five eggs and 200 grams of flour are included in a recipe for a cake.
   State whether each piece of data is discrete or continuous.

8. For each of these types of data write down whether it is discrete or continuous.
   (i) The marks gained by the pupils in your class in a maths test.
  (ii) The shoe sizes of the pupils in your school.
 (iii) The times taken to finish a 100-metre race at an athletics meeting.
 (iv) The area of your sports hall.
  (v) The numbers of buttons on a selection of jackets.

9. Mr and Mrs Jones were carrying out a survey.
   They asked members of their sports club these three questions.
   (i) How many times did you visit the sports club last week?
   (ii) How many children are there in your family?
   (iii) How long did it take you to travel to the sports club?
       (a) Is this data primary data or secondary data?
       (b) Give an example of discrete data which they collected.
       (c) Name the continuous data which they collected.

10. A garage lists the cars that it sells in the following way:
    small cars, economy cars, family cars, executive cars, luxury cars
    Describe this data by selecting **two** words from the following list:
    discrete, categorical, continuous, ordinal

Section 12.3 Sampling

If you are carrying out a survey in a mixed school and question the first two students on each class register, you may end up asking all boys or all girls.
Ideally you should ask everyone in the school, but this may not be practical as the numbers may be too big and it would take too long to complete the survey. Instead you could ask a limited number of students the relevant questions and hope that the results will be representative of the whole school.

In statistics we call this limited group **a sample**.
You need to make sure that each student in the school has an equal chance of being picked to be part of the survey. For example, five students from each class could be selected by drawing their names from a hat. This is called a **simple random sample**.

When you question a random sample you should get a result that is very similar to the one you would get if you questioned all the members of the group. The size of a sample is important. If it is too small, the results may not be reliable. If the sample is too large, the data may take too long to collect and it may also be too costly.

A population

If you carry out a survey in a single school, then all the pupils in that school are referred to as the **population**. In statistics a population is everybody or everything that could be included in a survey. For example, if you want to find out how people in a large company travel to work, then the population is all the people who work for that company.
If you are going to ask questions of some of the people in this picture, the **population** being considered is **all** the people in the football stadium.

Bias

The sample you select for your study is very important. If the sample is not random and does not fairly represent the whole population, the results may be **biased**. If bias exists, the results will not give you a clear picture of the whole population.

> In a **random** sample, every member of the group has the same chance of being selected.

Example 1

Cian wants to do a survey to find out if people are in favour of a new pedestrian crossing near a school.
Which of these three groups should he ask?
Give a reason for your answer.
  (i)   Car drivers using the road.
  (ii) Local residents.
  (iii) Mothers of children attending the school.

The most suitable group would be local residents as they are the most likely to give a response that would represent the whole population.
Car drivers are more likely to say that they do not want a new pedestrian crossing.
The mothers are very likely to want the new crossing as they would be very concerned about the safety of their children.

Activity

Select a random sample of five pupils from your class.

Ask them to write down the number of children (including themselves) in their families.

Write down the number of families with 1 child, 2 children, 3 children, …

Now find the percentage of the five families who had 1 child, 2 children, etc.

Repeat this exercise with all the students in your class.

Compare the percentage results of the sample with those of the whole class.

Do you think the sample was big enough?

Exercise 12.3

1. Niamh is doing a survey to find out how far the pupils in her school travel to get to school. One day she asked every pupil at the school bus stop.
   Explain why the sample is likely to be biased.

2. James wanted to do a survey to find out if people thought *Coldplay* was a good pop group.
   Which of the following groups is the most suitable for the survey?
   Explain your answer.
   (i) The students in his school.
   (ii) People attending a Coldplay concert.
   (iii) People in a nursing home.

3. David is doing a survey to find out which sports people most like to watch.
   He stands outside a football stadium and questions people as they leave.
   Explain why this survey may be biased.

4. Ciara wants to do a survey to find out how often people take exercise each week.
   Which of the following groups is the most suitable for her survey?
   Give the reasons for your selection.
   (i) People walking in the park.   (ii) People in a town centre.
   (iii) Members of the local sports centre.

5. Hannah wanted to do a survey to find out if people were in favour of banning cars and lorries from the city centre.
   She surveyed all car and lorry drivers near the city centre for one hour on a particular day.
   Explain why this sample may be biased.

6. Rachel is doing a survey to find out what students thought of the meals in the school canteen.
   She asks every fifth person going into the canteen for lunch.
   Explain why this may not be a good sample.

7. A supermarket thinks that as many men as women shop at their store.
   To investigate this they set up a survey one Saturday morning between 9 a.m. and 10 a.m. where they count the number of men and women going into the store.
   Do you think that a survey done on a Saturday morning would give a true picture of what happens over the course of a full week?
   Give two reasons for your answer.

Section 12.4 Questionnaires

A **questionnaire** is a set of questions designed to obtain information or data from individuals.

There are two main ways in which a questionnaire can be used.
- A person (or interviewer) asks the questions and fills in the responses.
- People are given a questionnaire to complete in their own time and the completed questionnaire is either returned or collected.

When you are writing questions for a questionnaire, the following points should be kept in mind.

1. **Questions should be clear, short and easily understood.**

   Example

   Questionnaire

   1. How do you generally travel to school? Tick one box

   Walk ☐   Bus ☐   Car ☐   Train ☐   Cycle ☐   Other ☐

   2. How long does it take you (in minutes)?

   1–10 ☐   11–20 ☐   21–30 ☐   31–40 ☐   >40 ☐

2. **Start with simple questions to encourage the person who is completing the questionnaire.**

   Example

   Questionnaire

   1. Are you male or female?   Male ☐   Female ☐

   2. Have you visited the new leisure centre?   Yes ☐   No ☐

3. **Avoid leading questions.**
   These are questions that suggest a particular response.

   Example

   Questionnaire

   1. Do you think that politicians are overpaid?

   Yes ☐   No ☐

   2. Don't you agree that people drink too much alcohol?

   Yes ☐   No ☐

4. **Avoid questions that may upset or embarrass people.**

   Example

   > Avoid personal questions like 'How old are you?'.

   Questionnaire

   1. Have you ever stolen goods from your local store?
      Yes ☐   No ☐

   2. Have you ever driven a car while over the drink-drive limit?
      Yes ☐   No ☐

Whenever you undertake a survey it is advisable to first do a **pilot survey**. A pilot survey is one that is carried out on a very small scale to make sure the design and questions in the survey are likely to produce the information required. It should, in particular, identify problems with the wording of the questions and the likely responses.

Exercise 12.4

1. Give a reason why each of the following questions is unsuitable to put in a questionnaire.
   A: What age are you?
   B: Do you agree that RTE 1 provides the best news coverage?
   C: The new supermarket seems to be a great success.
      Do you agree?
   D: How many times did you have a shower or bath in the past week?
   E: How much money do you earn each week?
   F: Are you young, middle-aged or old?
   G: Wouldn't you agree that the government is doing a good job?

2. This question appeared on a questionnaire:
   Q: All sensible people like dogs. Do you like dogs?
   This is an example of a **biased** question.
    (i) Explain why it is biased.
    (ii) Write two other questions that would be considered biased.

3. Here are two questions from a survey about the amount of homework given to pupils in St. Jude's High School.
   A: Do you agree that pupils in this school are given too much homework?
      Yes ☐ No ☐
   B: The amount of homework set to pupils in this school is: [Tick one box.]
      Not enough ☐   About right ☐   Too much ☐   Don't know ☐
   Which of these two questions is the more suitable for a questionnaire?
   Explain your answer.

4. Here is a question and the response boxes given in a questionnaire.

Q: How many hours of TV do you watch?   1 ☐   2 ☐   3 ☐
Suggest how you would improve the question and responses for this survey.

5. A market research company intended to ask the following question in a questionnaire:

How old are you?
 (i) Why is this question unacceptable?
 (ii) Rewrite the question to make it more acceptable.

6. Jane is doing a survey about how often people have a meal out in a restaurant.
Here are two questions she has written.

Q1. How often do you eat out?   ☐ A lot   ☐ Sometimes   ☐ Never
Q2. What food did you have the last time you ate out?
    (i) Give a reason why each of these questions is unsuitable.
    (ii) Write a better version of Q1 by being more specific in the responses.

7. Emma says, 'I go to the gym twice a week after school.'
She decides to do a survey to find out what exercise other pupils take outside school.
Write down **two** questions you think she should ask.

8. For each of these survey questions,
   • state why this may not be the best way to ask the question
   • write a better version.
  (i) What is your favourite sport: cricket, tennis or athletics?
 (ii) Do you do lots of exercise each week?
(iii) Don't you think this government should encourage more people to recycle waste?

9. 'The older you get, the less sleep you need.'
Write down three questions and the responses to each question to test the truth or otherwise of this statement.

10. Alan wants to find out what people think of the *Democratic Party*.
He is trying to decide between these two questions for his questionnaire.

A: Do you agree that the *Democratic Party* is the best party?
  Agree ☐   Disagree ☐
B: Do you think the policies of the *Democratic Party* are
  Very good ☐   Good ☐   Fair ☐   Poor ☐   Very poor ☐ ?
Which question should he use?
Explain your answer.

11. Denise wants to find out what people think of their local bus service. Part of the questionnaire she has written is shown.

> **Q1.** What is your address? ....
>
> **Q2.** Don't you agree that waiting times for the next bus are too long?
> Yes ☐   No ☐
>
> **Q3.** How many times did you travel by bus last week?
> Very often ☐   Occasionally ☐   Seldom ☐

  (i) Why should Q1 not be asked?

 (ii) Give a reason why Q2 is unsuitable.

(iii) Explain why Q3 is unsuitable in its present form.
Rewrite the question to make it suitable for a questionnaire.

12. A new variety of soup, 'Cheese and Onion', is to be launched by a leading manufacturer. They wish to know if it will be popular and sell well.
People are asked to try a free sample and comment on their impression.
Write three questions and suitable responses to test people's opinions.

Test yourself 12

1. Which of the following are discrete data and which are continuous?
   (i) The number of pages in a book.
   (ii) The number of goals scored in the Premier League last Saturday.
   (iii) The time it takes you to complete a crossword puzzle.
   (iv) The weight of your schoolbag.
   (v) The number of questions you got correct in your last science test.
   (vi) The mid-day temperature in Rome yesterday.
   (vii) The number of bedrooms in your home.

2. State whether each of the following data is numerical or categorical:
   (i) the colours of the cars in a showroom
   (ii) the number of houses on your street
   (iii) the types of animals on a farm
   (iv) the blood groups of the students in your class
   (v) the number of countries in the EU
   (vi) the different nationalities of Premier League soccer players.

3. Ella wants to buy a new computer.
   She looks on the internet for information to answer the following questions.
   (i) How much is a computer monitor?
   (ii) In what colours are the monitors available?
   (iii) What are the sizes of the monitors?
   (iv) How much is a keyboard?
   For each question, write down if the data required is numerical or categorical.

4. Louise spends her summer holiday working in a shop that hires out hats for weddings and other functions.
   (i) Write down whether the number of hats hired out each day is discrete or continuous.
   (ii) Give one example of categorical data that could be associated with hats.

5. State whether each of the following is primary or secondary data:
   (i) Standing at a supermarket exit door and asking the customers what they thought of the service they had received.
   (ii) Checking garda records to find the number of road-traffic accidents that occurred during the past month.
   (iii) Counting the number of cars that turn left at a particular junction.
   (iv) Checking the internet to find the top ten in the latest chart-toppers list.
   (v) Asking all the students in your class to give the numbers of sisters and brothers they have.

6. Daniel wrote down the number of minutes his phone calls lasted.

| 8 | 10 | 16 | 3 | 1 | 24 | 25 | 30 | 36 | 17 | 19 | 11 |
| 16 | 18 | 4 | 3 | 7 | 2 | 1 | 4 | 17 | 19 | 23 | 26 |

Make a copy of this frequency table.
Fill it in.
What percentage of calls lasted between 11 and 20 minutes inclusive?

Number of minutes	Tally	Frequency
1–10		
11–20		
21–30		
31–40		

7. Karen is doing a survey to find out how often people go to the cinema and how much they spend. She stands outside a cinema and asks people as they go in. Write a reason why this sample could be biased.

8. Here are some questions that are not suitable for a questionnaire.
Why do you think that they are not suitable? Suggest a better question.

Q1. Most people agree that it would be a good thing to lower the drink-drive limit. Do you?
Yes ☐ No ☐ Don't know ☐

Q2. Do you agree that we need a change of National Anthem?
Yes ☐ No ☐ Don't know ☐

Q3. Soccer is more exciting to watch than rugby. Do you agree?
Yes ☐ No ☐ Don't know ☐

9. Jack wants to find out what percentage of adults have cars.
He interviews 100 people in an out-of-town shopping centre to find out if they own a car.
Explain why this sample may be biased.

10. Describe what is meant by **a simple random sample**.

11. A market research company is conducting a survey to find out whether, last year, most people had a holiday in Ireland, elsewhere in Europe or in the rest of the world. It also wants to know if they stayed in self-catering accommodation, hotels or went camping. Design **two** questions and responses that could be used in a questionnaire to find out all this information.

For the problem solver...

1. On one side of a school corridor there are five classrooms numbered 1 to 5.
The classrooms are occupied by the classes 6A, 6B, 6C, 6D and 6E.
6A is not in room 1; 6B is not in room 5;
6C is not in room 1 or room 5;
6D is in a room with a lower number than 6B;
6C is not next to 6B; 6E is not next to 6C.
Which class is in room 1?

2. When the cathedral clock strikes four, it takes 8 seconds between the first and last strokes. How many seconds does it take to strike twelve?

3. The date 8 November 1988 was unusual. If we write it in the form 8/11/88, we have $8 \times 11 = 88$.
How many such dates were there in 1990?

4. I am a 4 digit number. The product of my digits is 4 and the sum of my digits is 6. I am an even number less than 1200. What am I?

5. Villages A, B, C, D, E, F, G, H, I are joined by a network of roads.
The lengths of the roads are in kilometres.

  (i)   Find the shortest route from A to I.
 (ii)   Find the shortest route from B to E.
(iii)   A family on a sight-seeing tour wish to visit all of the villages as they go from A to I. Find the shortest route passing through all the villages.

6. In the sequence which begins 2, 3, 5, 10, ... each number after the second is the sum of all the previous numbers in the sequence. What is the 10th number in the sequence?

Key words

grid   location   plane   coordinates   axes   origin

x-axis   *y*-axis   four quadrants   Cartesian plane   midpoint

Section 13.1 Grids

The sketch of the wall of a room is 13 cm across and 9 cm up.

To mark the position of a light switch we need two measurements.

If we start from the corner marked O, the light switch is 8 cm **across** and 4 cm **up**.

These measurements give us the location of a point on the flat surface (or **plane**).

The location 8 across and 4 up is written as (8, 4).

(8, 4) are called the **coordinates** of the point.

Every point on a flat surface can be found using a grid.

For example, the lock L has coordinates (9, 3).

The socket P has coordinates (2, 2).

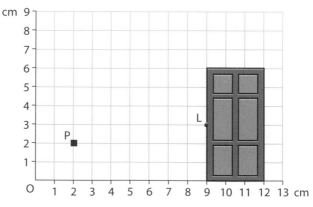

To make a grid we draw two lines, a horizontal line and a vertical line. These are called **axes**.

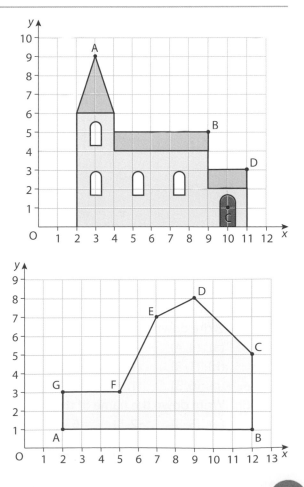

The horizontal line is called the **x-axis**. The vertical line is called the **y-axis**.

The point P has coordinates (3, 2).

The first number is the **x-coordinate**. The second number is the **y-coordinate**.

The point O is called the **origin**. The point Q has coordinates (1, 3).

Exercise 13.1

1. Write the coordinates of the points marked A, B, C and D in the given figure.

2. From the given grid, write down the coordinates of the points marked A, B, C, D, E, F and G.

3. Write down the coordinates of the points marked A to L in the given figure.

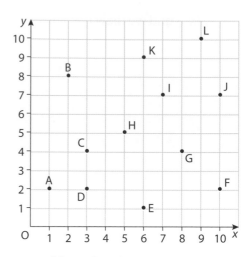

4. Draw a grid on squared paper from 0 to 10 across and from 0 to 8 up.
Mark these points on the grid and join them in the order given.

(i) (1, 1), (1, 3), (3, 3), (3, 1), (1, 1)   (ii) (2, 4), (2, 7), (5, 7), (5, 4), (2, 4)

Describe the figure made in each case.

5. In the figure below each letter represents a pair of coordinates.

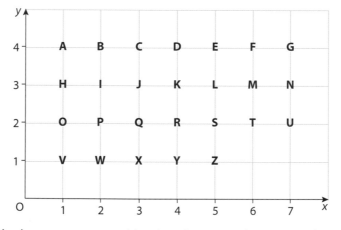

By writing the letter represented by the given coordinates, work out each of the following:

(i) Write down the name of the animal given by each of these coordinates:

   (a) (4, 4)   (1, 2)   (7, 4)

   (b) (1, 3)   (1, 2)   (4, 2)   (5, 2)   (5, 4)

   (c) (6, 3)   (1, 2)   (7, 3)   (4, 3)   (5, 4)   (4, 1)

(ii) Write down the name of the river given by each of these coordinates:

   (a) (5, 3)   (2, 3)   (6, 4)   (6, 4)   (5, 4)   (4, 1)

   (b) (2, 4)   (1, 2)   (4, 1)   (7, 3)   (5, 4)

   (c) (5, 2)   (5, 3)   (1, 4)   (7, 3)   (5, 4)   (4, 1)

6. (i) Write down the coordinates of these places on the given map:

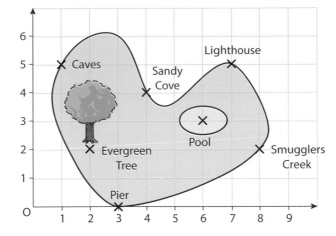

(a) Smuggler's Creek   (b) Lighthouse   (c) Sandy Cove

(ii) Write down the names of the places on the map with these coordinates:

(a) (1, 5)   (b) (6, 3)   (c) (3, 0)   (d) (2, 2)

7. On which axis do these points lie?

(4, 0)   (2, 0)   (3, 0)   (6, 0)

8. Name four points on the *y*-axis.

9. This grid shows the map of a village.

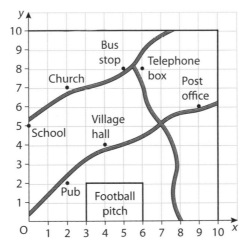

(i) Write down the coordinates of these:

(a) the church   (b) the post office   (c) the village hall   (d) the school

(ii) What is at the point (6, 8)?

(iii) Which two locations have the same *x*-coordinate?

(iv) Which two locations have the same *y*-coordinate?

(v) Write down the coordinates of the corners of the football pitch.

Section 13.2 The four quadrants ——————————

In the previous section all the points that were plotted had positive numbers only.

If we extend the grid to include negative numbers, we can then describe the location of any point in the plane.

In the diagram opposite we have a horizontal line and a vertical line meeting at the point O. It is called the **coordinated plane** or the **Cartesian Plane** in honour of the French mathematician, René Descartes, who lived in the sixteenth century.

The coordinates of the **origin** O are (0, 0).

The coordinates of A are (3, 2).

The coordinates of B are (−2, 2).

The coordinates of C are (−3, −2).

The coordinates of D are (4, −3).

The diagram on the right shows that the x-axis and y-axis divide the plane into four quarters.

Each of these is called a **quadrant**.

Exercise 13.2 ——————————

1. Write down the coordinates of the points marked on the diagram below:

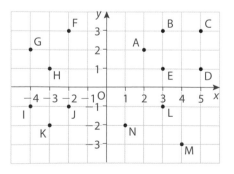

2. Draw a pair of axes, as in Question 1 above, and mark in the following points:

A(2, 3),   B(3, 5),   C(−2, 1),   D(−3, 2)

E(4, 0),   F(−4, −1),   G(2, −3),   H(−1, −3)

3. Write down the coordinates of the fourth vertex in each of the figures given below:
   (i) ABCD is a square   (ii) PQRS is a rectangle.

           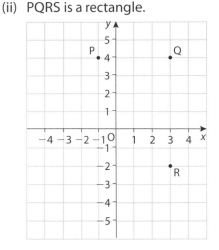

4. In the given figure, write down the
   letters and coordinates of each
   of these:
   (i)   two points in the first quadrant
   (ii) two points in the third quadrant
   (iii) two points in the fourth quadrant
   (iv) two points on the x-axis
   (v)   two points on the y-axis.

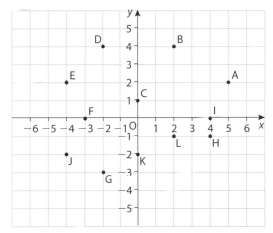

5. In which quadrant does each of the following points lie?
   A(2, 3),   B(4, −1),   C(−3, −1),   D(−2, −4)

6. On which axis is each of the following points?
   (i) (2, 0)   (ii) (0, 3)   (iii) (−3, 0)   (iv) (0, −2)   (v) (0, 0)

7. Draw x and y axes from 0 to 5.
   (i)   Plot the points (2, 1), (5, 1) and (5, 4). These are three corners of a square.
   (ii) What are the coordinates of the fourth corner of the square?

8. Draw x and y axes from −2 to 4.
   (i)   Plot the points A(3, 2), B(3, −1) and C(−1, −1).
   (ii) Points A, B and C are three corners of a rectangle.
         Point D is the fourth corner of the rectangle. Plot point D on your diagram.
   (iii) What are the coordinates of point D?

9. Look for a pattern in these coordinates.
   Use the pattern to find the missing coordinates.

   (i) (3, 5)   (5, 6)   (7, 7)   (9, 8)   (…, …)   (…, …)

   (ii) (3, 0)   (5, 2)   (7, 4)   (9, 6)   (…, …)   (…, …)

   (iii) (4, 6)   (5, 4)   (6, 2)   (7, 0)   (…, …)   (…, …)

   (iv) (0, 6)   (−2, 3)   (−4, 0)   (−6, −3)   (…, …)   (…, …)

10. Look at these coordinates: (2, 6) (4, 4) (5, 3) (8, 0).

    (i) Describe a pattern in these.

    (ii) Use the pattern to fill in the missing numbers in these coordinates

            (7, …)   (0, …)   (−2, …)

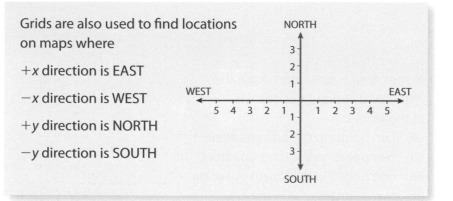

Grids are also used to find locations on maps where

+x direction is EAST

−x direction is WEST

+y direction is NORTH

−y direction is SOUTH

11. Draw a grid on squared paper as shown and mark the following points on it.

    A. (5 km East, 3 km South)
    B. (3 km West, 3 km South)
    C. (2 km West, 3 km North)
    D. 3 km East
    E. 2 km South

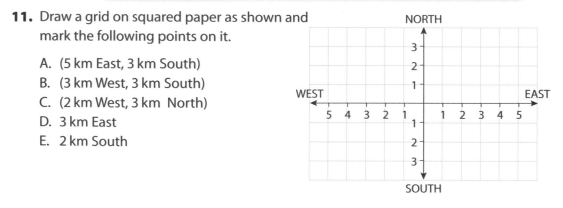

12. Draw a grid from −2 to 8 on the x-axis and from 8 to −4 on the y-axis.
    A girl starts at the origin and cycles to her friend A (3 km EAST, 2 km NORTH).
    From there she cycles to her friend B (4 km EAST, 5 km SOUTH).
    Mark A and B on your grid.

13. Mark leaves his house at the origin and travels (3 km EAST, 4 km SOUTH).
    From there he travels (5 km WEST, 2 km SOUTH).
    His brother Sean is back at the origin.
    What is Mark's location relative to Sean's location?

14. Here are some tiles in the shape of a parallelogram.

Each tile has a corner marked with an *.
The coordinates of the first corner are (3, 2).

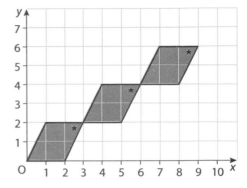

(i) Write down the coordinates of the second and third corners that you see.

(ii) You cannot see the fourth corner which has an *.
By following the pattern, write down the coordinates of this fourth corner.

(iii) Can you now find the coordinates of the fifth corner that has an *?

Section 13.3 Midpoint of a line segment

The given diagram shows the points A(2, 1) and B(6, 5).

If we join A to B we get the line segment [AB].

M is the midpoint of [AB].

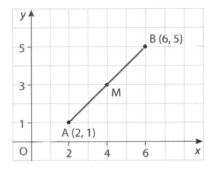

From the grid we can see that the coordinates of M are (4, 3).

Notice that the x-coordinate 4 is halfway between the x-coordinates of A and B, i.e. 2 and 6.

Similarly, the y-coordinate of M, 3, is halfway between 1 and 5.

Thus $M = \left(\dfrac{2+6}{2}, \dfrac{1+5}{2}\right) = (4, 3)$.

> To find the midpoint of a line segment, add the two x-values and divide by 2 and add the two y-values and divide by 2.

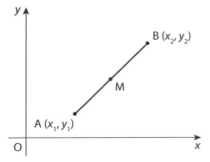

Formula for midpoint

> The midpoint, M, of the line segment joining $A(x_1, y_1)$ and $B(x_2, y_2)$ is
>
> $$M = \left(\frac{x_1 + x_2}{2}, \frac{y_1 + y_2}{2}\right).$$

Example 1

Find the midpoint of the line segment joining A(-3, 4) and B(1, 2).

Midpoint $= \left(\dfrac{x_1 + x_2}{2}, \dfrac{y_1 + y_2}{2}\right)$

$= \left(\dfrac{-3 + 1}{2}, \dfrac{4 + 2}{2}\right)$

$= \left(\dfrac{-2}{2}, \dfrac{6}{2}\right) = (-1, 3)$

Exercise 13.3

1. The given grid shows four points A, B, C and D.

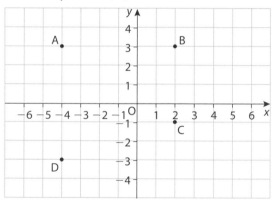

   (i) Write down the coordinates of each of these points.
   (ii) Use the grid to write down the coordinates of the midpoint of
      (a) [AB]   (b) [BC]   (c) [AD].

2. (i) Write down the coordinates of A, B and C in the given grid.
   (ii) Write down the coordinates of the midpoint of
      (a) [AB]   (b) [BC]
   (iii) If ABCD is a rectangle, find the coordinates of D.

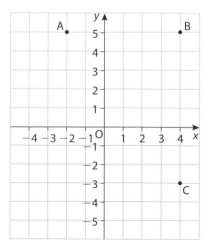

3. In the given grid, M is the midpoint of the line segment [AB].

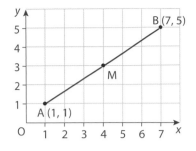

(i) Use the grid to write down the coordinates of M.

(ii) Is there another way to find the coordinate of M? Use it to show that your answer in (i) above is correct.

4. Find the coordinates of the midpoint of the line segment joining the following pairs of points:

(i) (2, 1) and (4, 3)   (ii) (1, 1) and (5, 5)   (iii) (1, 3) and (3, 5)

(iv) (4, 3) and (6, 1)   (v) (0, 4) and (6, 2)   (vi) (5, −2) and (1, 4)

5. A(1, 1), B(5, 1), C(5, 4) and D(1, 4) are four points in the plane.

(i) Find the coordinates of M, the midpoint of [AC].

(ii) Show that M is also the midpoint of [BD].

6. Use the formula $\left(\dfrac{x_1 + x_2}{2}, \dfrac{y_1 + y_2}{2}\right)$ to find the midpoint of the line segment joining these pairs of points:

(i) (3, 5) and (1, 3)   (ii) (7, 4) and (1, 2)   (iii) (6, 2) and (−2, 0)

(iv) (0, 7) and (4, 3)   (v) (1, −3) and (3, 5)   (vi) (4, −3) and (2, −3)

7. Find the midpoint of the line segment joining A(−3, 6) and B(5, −6). On which axis does the midpoint lie?

8. Work out the coordinates of the midpoint of each of these line segments:

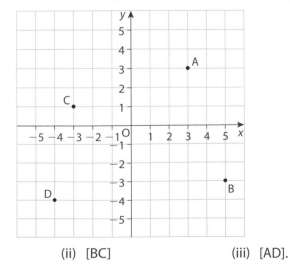

(i) [AB]   (ii) [BC]   (iii) [AD].

9. A, B, C and D are the vertices of a rectangle

    (i) Find the coordinates of the midpoint of [AC].

    (ii) Investigate if this is also the midpoint of [BD].

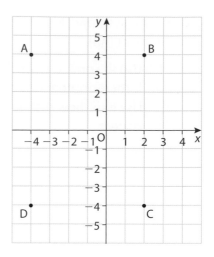

10. Show that the midpoint of the line segment joining P(5, −3) and Q(−5, 7) is on the y-axis.

11. The points C(8, 6) and D(2, 2) are the endpoints of the diameter of a circle k. Find the coordinates of the centre, O, of the circle.

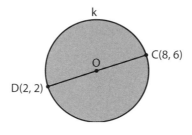

Test yourself 13

1. (i) Write down the coordinates of the points marked A to G in the given figure.
   (ii) Write down the coordinates of the four corners of the door.

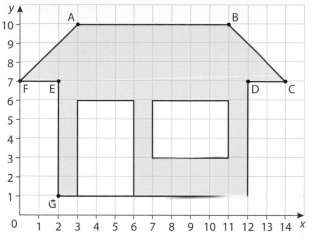

2. A number of places are shown on the given graph.
   (i) Write down the coordinates of
      (a) the playground
      (b) home
      (c) the post office
      (d) granny
   (ii) One day Paula left home and travelled to $(-3, -1)$; then onto $(1, 0)$ and then to $(3, -1)$.
      Write down the places she visited.

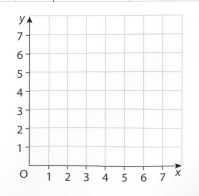

3. Make a copy of this grid.

   Plot the points A(1, 5), B(4, 7), C(7, 5).
   If D has coordinates (7, 1), what shape is ABCD?

4. Write down the coordinates of each
   labelled point:

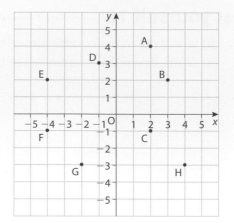

5. (i) Write down the coordinates of the given
   points A, B and C.

   (ii) If ABCD is a rectangle, find the
   coordinates of D.

   (iii) Find the coordinates of the midpoints of
   (a) [AB]　　(b) [BC]　　(c) [AC].

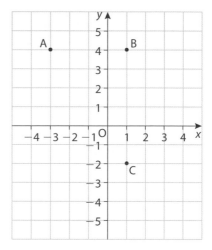

6. Work out the coordinates of the midpoint of each of these line segments:

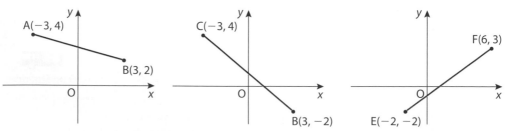

7. The given diagram shows a line ℓ.
   (i) If (2, a) is on the line, find the value of a.
   (ii) If (−3, b) is on the line, find the value of b.
   (iii) Find a point on ℓ such that the y-coordinate
   is twice the value of the x-coordinate.

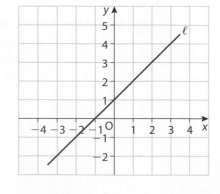

For the problem solver...

1. Use a copy of this grid.

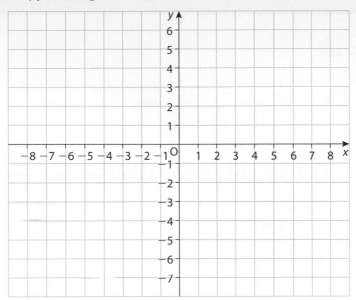

   Plot these points and join them in order.

   $(-7, 4)$, $(-3, 6)$, $(-1, 4)$, $(-1, 0)$, $(-2, -1)$, $(7, -1)$, $(2, -4)$,
   $(4, -6)$, $(-2, -6)$, $(-5, -4)$, $(-5, 0)$, $(-3, 2)$, $(-3, 4)$, $(-7, 4)$.

   Put a large dot at $(-3.5, 4.5)$. What picture did you get?

2. Points P and Q have coordinates $(1, 4)$ and $(1, -2)$ respectively.
   For which of the following possible coordinates of point R would
   triangle PQR **not** be isosceles?
   A $(-5, 4)$ B $(7, 1)$ C $(-6, 1)$ D $(-6, -2)$ E $(7, -2)$

3. Which of the following points is *not* at a distance of 1 unit from the
   origin?
   A $(0, 1)$ B $(1, 0)$ C $(0, -1)$ D $(-1, 0)$ E $(1, 1)$

14 Solving Equations

Key words

equation	equate	solve	symbol	balancing
solution	mystery number		perimeter	expression

Section 14.1 The idea of an equation

In Chapter 6 we used symbols such as $\square$, $\blacktriangle$ and $\maltese$ to represent unknown numbers.

Here are some examples:

$$\square + 6 = 10 \qquad \blacktriangledown \times 4 = 20 \qquad \maltese - 9 = 3$$

In each of these examples we can write down the value of the mystery number without too much difficulty.

An example such as $\square + 6 = 10$ is called an **equation**.

It is called an equation because $\square + 6$ is **equal to** 10.

When we find the mystery number, we say that we have **solved** the equation.

Exercise 14.1

Find the missing number to make each of the following equations true:

1. $\square + 6 = 8$ **2.** $4 + \square = 11$ **3.** $\square + 8 = 19$

4. $\square - 3 = 9$ **5.** $14 - \square = 1$ **6.** $3 \times \square = 36$

7. $\square \times 5 = 60$ **8.** $4 \times \square + 3 = 27$ **9.** $\square \times 5 - 3 = 27$

10. $6 \times \square - 6 = 30$ **11.** $30 \div 3 - \square = 6$ **12.** $\square \div 5 = 7$

13. $72 \div \square = 9$ **14.** $\dfrac{\square}{4} = 6$ **15.** $4 + 4 + \dfrac{\square}{4} = 9$

The mass (in grams) of one shape is given in each of the following diagrams.
Find the mass of the other shape.

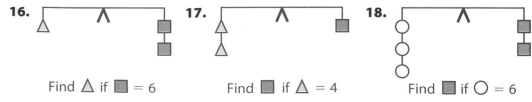

16. Find $\triangle$ if $\blacksquare = 6$ **17.** Find $\blacksquare$ if $\triangle = 4$ **18.** Find $\blacksquare$ if $\bigcirc = 6$

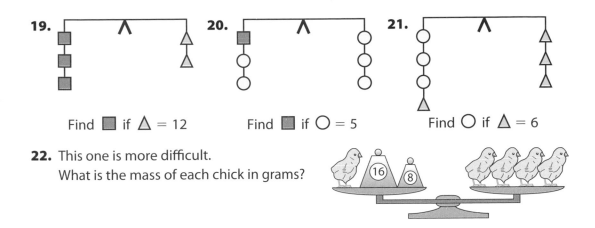

19. Find ■ if △ = 12

20. Find ■ if ◯ = 5

21. Find ◯ if △ = 6

22. This one is more difficult.
   What is the mass of each chick in grams?

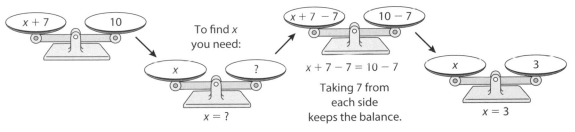

Section 14.2 Solving equations

In question 22 of the previous section we saw that 4 chicks 'balanced' with 1 chick and 24 grams.

Equations are all about balancing the two sides of the equation.

The four diagrams below show that balancing can be used to solve the equation $x + 7 = 10$.

To find x you need:

$x + 7 - 7 = 10 - 7$

Taking 7 from each side keeps the balance.

$x = ?$

$x = 3$

We say $x = 3$ is the **solution** to the equation.

The 'balancing' method for solving equations can be used in a more structured way as shown in the following two examples. These examples illustrate that whatever operation is performed on one side of an equation, the same operation must be performed on the other side.

> **Example 1**
>
> Solve the equation $\quad x + 7 = 16$
>
> $$x + 7 = 16$$
> Take 7 from both sides: $\quad x + 7 - 7 = 16 - 7$
> $$\therefore \quad x = 9$$

Example 2

Solve the equation $3x - 5 = 16$

$$3x - 5 = 16$$
Add 5 to both sides: $3x - 5 + 5 = 16 + 5$
$$3x = 21$$
Divide both sides by 3: $x = 7$

Exercise 14.2

1. Write down the mass, in grams, of each object if the scales are balanced in each diagram:

   (i)   (ii)

Solve each of the following equations:

2. $x + 4 = 10$ **3.** $x + 6 = 18$ **4.** $x + 7 = 12$ **5.** $x + 3 = 11$

6. $x - 4 = 7$ **7.** $x - 6 = 4$ **8.** $x - 7 = 1$ **9.** $x - 9 = 2$

10. $x + 6 = 14$ **11.** $2x = 8$ **12.** $3x = 15$ **13.** $4x = 12$

14. $5x = 25$ **15.** $6x = 30$ **16.** $7x = 28$ **17.** $9x = 18$

18. $x + 9 = 14$ **19.** $7x = 14$ **20.** $x + 7 = 11$ **21.** $x - 5 = 6$

22. $5x = 35$ **23.** $2x + 1 = 9$ **24.** $3x + 2 = 14$ **25.** $2x - 3 = 7$

26. $3x - 1 = 8$ **27.** $5x + 2 = 12$ **28.** $4x + 2 = 14$ **29.** $3x - 5 = 16$

30. $2x - 7 = 5$ **31.** $2x + 3 = 11$ **32.** $3x + 6 = 9$ **33.** $7x + 2 = 30$

34. $3x - 12 = 18$

Work out what x stands for in each of the following diagrams.

35.

36.

37.

38.

39. In the given diagram, the number in each box is found by adding the two numbers above it. Find the value of *x*.

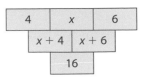

40. Write an equation in *x* and solve it in each of the following:

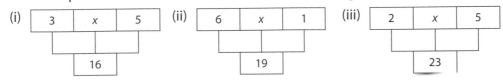

Section 14.3 Equations with letters on both sides

Consider the equation $5x + 1 = 2x + 10$.

This equation has letters on both sides.

Here we take $2x$ from each side to get rid of the *x*s on the right-hand side.

Again $5x + 1 = 2x + 10$

$\quad\quad 5x + 1 - 2x = 2x - 2x + 10$ … take 2x from each side

$\quad\quad 3x + 1 = 10$

$\quad\quad 3x + 1 - 1 = 10 - 1$ … take 1 from each side

$\quad\quad 3x = 9$

$\quad\quad x = 3$ … divide both sides by 3

> **Example 1**
>
> Solve the equation $\quad x - 15 = 9 - 2x$
>
> In this equation we will add $2x$ to both sides to get rid of the letter term on the right-hand side.
>
> Add 2x to each side: $\quad\quad x - 15 + \mathbf{2x} = 9 - 2x + \mathbf{2x}$
>
> $\quad\quad\quad \therefore \quad\quad 3x - 15 = 9$
>
> Add 15 to each side: $\quad 3x - 15 + \mathbf{15} = 9 + \mathbf{15}$
>
> $\quad\quad\quad\quad\quad\quad\quad 3x = 24$
>
> Divide both sides by 3: $\quad\quad\quad x = 8$

Exercise 14.3

1. The scales on the right are balanced.
If x is the weight of 1 cake in grams, use the
diagram to write down an equation in x.
Now solve the equation to find the value of x.

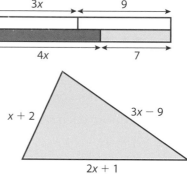

Solve the following equations:

2. $3x + 3 = 2x + 7$ **3.** $8x + 5 = 7x + 10$ **4.** $5x + 2 = 4x + 8$

5. $7x + 3 = 5x + 9$ **6.** $5x + 1 = 3x + 11$ **7.** $6x + 2 = 3x + 5$

8. $6x - 2 = 4x + 10$ **9.** $7x - 9 = 3x + 11$ **10.** $9x - 15 = 3x + 3$

11. $x + 7 = 2x - 1$ **12.** $2x + 6 = 4x - 6$ **13.** $3x + 1 = 5x - 13$

14. $5x - 2 = 40 - x$ **15.** $3x + 7 = 32 - 2x$ **16.** $6 + 2x = 33 - x$

17. Work out the value of x in each of these diagrams:

(i)

(ii)

18. The perimeter of the given triangle is 36 cm.
Find the value of x.

19. What is the sum of the three angles of a triangle?
Now write an equation and solve it to find the value for x in each of these triangles:

(i)
$2x + 5°$
$2x°$
$x°$

(ii)
$x + 20°$
$x°$
$3x + 10°$

(iii)
$x + 40°$
$x - 10°$
$x°$

20. The solution to each equation below stands for a letter.
Use the table on the right to find the letters.
Rearrange them into the name of an animal.

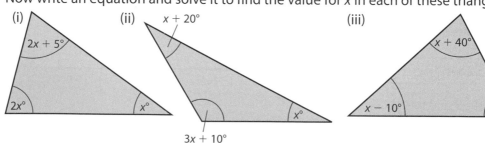

$3x + 6 = 12$ $16 - 2x = 6$

$21 - 3x = 2x + 11$ $4x + 4 = 16$

$6x - 2 = 4$ $6x - 9 = 5x$

1	T
2	B
3	A
4	B
5	R
6	G
7	E
8	S
9	I

Section 14.4 Equations with brackets

In chapter 6 you learned how to remove the brackets in an expression.

For example $3(2x - 1) = 6x - 3$.

When solving equations involving brackets, we first remove the brackets as shown in the following example.

Example 1

Solve the equation: $4(2x - 3) = 2(3x - 5)$.

In this type of equation we first remove the brackets:

$$4(2x - 3) = 2(3x - 5)$$

Remove the brackets: $\quad\quad 8x - 12 = 6x - 10$

Add 12 to both sides: $\quad 8x - 12 + 12 = 6x - 10 + 12$

$$\therefore \quad\quad 8x = 6x + 2$$

Take $6x$ from both sides: $\quad 8x - 6x = 6x + 2 - 6x$

$$2x = 2$$

Divide both sides by 2: $\quad\quad x = 1$

Exercise 14.4

Solve the following equations:

1. $2(x + 3) = 12$

2. $2(x - 1) = 6$

3. $3(x + 4) = 18$

4. $5(x - 1) = 10$

5. $3(2x + 1) = 33$

6. $4(2x - 3) = 36$

7. $3(2x + 1) = 2x + 11$

8. $5x + 5 = 2(2x + 5)$

9. $3(2x - 10) = 2x + 10$

10. $5(2x - 1) = 8x + 7$

11. $4(2x - 3) = 2(3x - 5)$

12. $3(2x - 6) = 2(2x + 1)$

13. $3(5x - 2) = 4(3x + 6)$

14. $5(3x - 2) = 7(2x - 1)$

15. $5(x + 4) - 3(x - 2) = 32$

16. $5(2x - 4) = 3(2x - 1) - 1$

17. $6(1 + 2x) = 5(3x - 1) - 4$

18. $2(x + 2) - 3(x - 3) = x + 7$

19. Use the given diagram to write down an equation in x.
Now solve the equation to find the value of x.

20. By forming an equation, find the value of x in the given diagram.

Section 14.5 Forming simple equations

Consider this problem:

> I think of a number and take 6 away from it. If the result is 12, find the number.

> Of course the mystery number is 18.

If we let x stand for the number, we could write the problem as follows:

$x - 6 = 12$

We have changed the word problem into an equation.

If we solve the equation, we find the mystery number.

> Another word for an equation is a mathematical sentence.

The equation is: $x - 6 = 12$

Add 6 to both sides: $x - 6 + 6 = 12 + 6$

$\therefore \quad x = 18$ ... the required number.

Here are some examples of information changed to mathematical sentences:

> When 5 is added to a certain number, the result is 8.
>
> **Equation:** $x + 5 = 8$

> When 3 is taken from twice a certain number, the result is 10.
>
> **Equation:** $2x - 3 = 10$

Exercise 14.5

1. I think of a number and call it x. What number is

(i) 2 bigger than x

(ii) 4 bigger than x

(iii) 3 less than x

(iv) 10 less than x

(v) 14 more than x

(vi) twice x

(vii) five times x

(viii) 2 greater than twice x?

2. Write an equation for each of the following. Use x as the unknown number.

(i) I think of a number.
I add 6.
The result is 12.

(ii) I think of a number.
I subtract 7.
The result is 10.

(iii) I think of a number.
I double it.
The result is 14.

(iv) I think of a number.
I double it and then add 5.
The result is 19.

(v) I think of a number.
I treble it and subtract 6.
The result is 15.

(vi) I think of a number.
I add 2 to it.
I multiply my answer by 4.
The result is 28.

3. Write an equation for each of the following. Use n as the unknown number.

(i) I think of a number.
I multiply it by 3.
I then add 7.
The result is 19.

(ii) I think of a number.
I multiply it by 4.
I then subtract 5.
The result is 17.

(iii) I think of a number.
I add 3 to it.
I multiply the result by 4.
The result is 28.

(iv) I think of a number.
I subtract 2 from it.
I multiply the result by 3.
The result is 9.

4. Construct a series of short sentences which would result in the following equations. Start with 'I think of a number and call it x'.

(i) $x + 4 = 9$ (ii) $x - 8 = 4$ (iii) $2x = 14$

(iv) $3x = 27$ (v) $2x + 3 = 13$ (vi) $3x - 1 = 14$

(vii) $5x + 1 = 31$ (viii) $4x - 3 = 25$ (ix) $2(x + 3) = 10$

Section 14.6 Writing and solving equations

In the previous section we learned how to change statements into equations.

In this section we will continue with this process and then solve the equation.

Example 1

When 3 is taken from five times a certain number, the result is the same as adding 6 to twice the number. Find this number.

Equation: $\qquad 5x - 3 = 2x + 6$

Add 3 to each side: $\qquad 5x - 3 + 3 = 2x + 6 + 3$

$\therefore \qquad 5x = 2x + 9$

Take $2x$ from each side: $\qquad 5x - 2x = 2x + 9 - 2x$

$\therefore \qquad 3x = 9$

$\therefore \qquad x = 3$

The required number is 3.

Example 2

One number exceeds another number by 6. When 4 is added to three times the smaller number, the result is the same as twice the larger number. Find the numbers.

Let x and $(x + 6)$ be the numbers ...... [$(x + 6)$ is the larger]

Equation:
$$3x + 4 = 2(x + 6)$$
$$3x + 4 = 2x + 12$$

Take 4 from both sides: $3x + 4 - 4 = 2x + 12 - 4$
$$3x = 2x + 8$$

Take $2x$ from both sides: $3x - 2x = 2x + 8 - 2x$
$$\therefore \quad x = 8$$

The first number, x, is 8.
The second number, $(x + 6)$, is $8 + 6 = 14$
$\therefore$ the numbers are 8 and 14.

Exercise 14.6

Write each of the following statements as equations and then solve the equation.

1. I think of a number, add 8 to it and the result is 14. Find the number.

2. I think of a number, double it and then add 5.
   If the result is 19, find the number.

3. I think of a number, treble it and take 6 from my answer.
   If the result is 18, find the number.

4. To four times a certain number I add 16 and the result is 28. Find this number.

5. If I multiply a number by 3 and then subtract 4, the result is the same as twice the number. Find this number.

6. When 3 is taken from five times a certain number, the result is the same as adding 6 to twice the number. Find this number.

7. One number is 5 greater than another number.
   If the sum of the two numbers is 59, find the numbers.

8. When 3 is taken from twice a certain number, the result is the same as adding 3 to the number. Find this number.

9. One number is 5 greater than another number. If twice the smaller number is added to the larger one, the result is 26. Find the two numbers.

10. Write an equation for each of these shapes.
   Solve it to find the value of a.

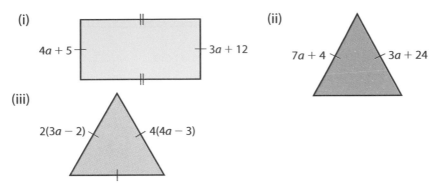

(i) $4a + 5$ $3a + 12$

(ii) $7a + 4$ $3a + 24$

(iii) $2(3a - 2)$ $4(4a - 3)$

11. Write an equation and solve It to find the value of x in the given figure.

$2x$ 1 $4x$

25

12. When a number is increased by 4 and the result is doubled, the answer is 22. Find the number.

13. One number exceeds another number by 6.
   Write these two numbers in terms of x.
   When twice the larger number is added to three times the smaller number, the result is 32.
   Find the two numbers.

14. Ann is 5 years older than Mary.
   If the sum of their ages is 51, find the age of each.

15. Write and solve an equation to find the value of n.
   Use this to find the missing numbers.
   Part (i) has been started for you.

   The number in each box is the sum of the two numbers above it.

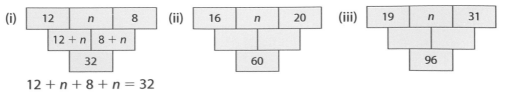

(i)

12	n	8

$12 + n$	$8 + n$

32

$12 + n + 8 + n = 32$

(ii)

16	n	20

60

(iii)

19	n	31

96

16. In each of these problems, use angle facts to form an equation.
Solve it to find the unknown. The angles are measured in degrees.

(i)

(ii)

17. Alan is x years of age and his father is three times as old.
If the sum of their ages is 64 years, find Alan's age.

18. This is an isosceles triangle where equal sides are marked.
If the perimeter of the triangle is 76 cm,
  (i) write down an equation in a
  (ii) solve the equation to find the value of a
  (iii) find the length of the equal sides.

$3(a + 5)$

$4(2a + 1)$

19. Jack is seven years older than Conor.
  (i) If Jack's age is x years, what is Conor's age?
  (ii) Write down an expression for the sum of their ages.
  (iii) If twice the sum of their ages is 66 years, find Conor's age.

Test yourself 14

1. Solve each of these equations:
   (i) $2x + 5 = 9$
   (ii) $3x + 2 = x + 4$
   (iii) $6x - 2 = x + 8$

2. The given scales are balanced.
   If x units is the weight of each cat,
   write an equation in x and solve it to
   find the value of x.

3. Write an equation and solve it to find the value of x in each of the figures below:
   (i)
   (ii)

4. Solve each of these equations:
   (i) $7x = 21$
   (ii) $5x + 3 = x + 27$
   (iii) $2(x - 3) = 4(x - 4)$

5. When 4 is taken from three times a certain number, the result is the same as adding 5 to twice the number. Find the number.

6. The perimeter of the given rectangle is 22 cm.
   Form an equation and solve it to find the value of x.

7. Solve these equations:
   (i) $3x - 12 = 6$
   (ii) $5(x - 3) = 3x - 3$
   (iii) $3(2x - 1) = 15$

8. The lengths of the sides of the given triangle are in centimetres.
   If the perimeter is 26 cm, find the value of x.

   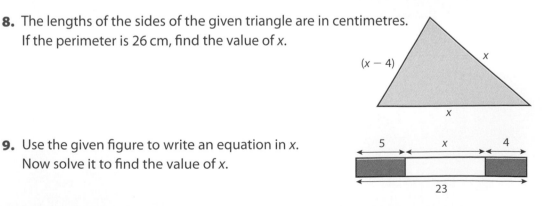

9. Use the given figure to write an equation in x.
   Now solve it to find the value of x.

10. Solve each of these equations:
    (i) $2x - 9 = x - 5$
    (ii) $4(x - 2) + 2 = 3(x - 2)$

11. I think of a number.
When I add 2 to the number and multiply my answer by 4, the result is 20.
What is the number?

12. The given rectangle measures $(3x - 7)$ cm by $(x + 5)$ cm.

Find the value of x if the rectangle is a square.

$(3x - 7)$ cm

$(x + 5)$ cm

13. The number in each box is the sum of the numbers in the two boxes above it.
For each diagram, form an equation in n and solve it to find its value.

(i) | 2 | 7 | n |

27

(ii) | 3 | n | 5 |

20

14. Write down two expressions for the length of the given figure.
By equating the lengths, solve the equation to find the value of x.

$7x$ 9

$5x$ 3 $4x$

For the problem solver...

1. I am thinking of a rule that converts the number 6 into the number 20.
   Which of the following could *not* be my rule?
   A add 14   *B* take half then add 17   *C* treble then add 2
   D add 4 then square   *E* subtract 2 then multiply by 5

2. A child's box of bricks contains cubes, cones and spheres. Two cones and a sphere on one side of a pair of scales will just balance a cube on the other side; and a sphere and a cube together will just balance three cones. How many spheres will just balance a single cone?
   A 1   *B* 2   *C* 3   *D* 4   *E* 5

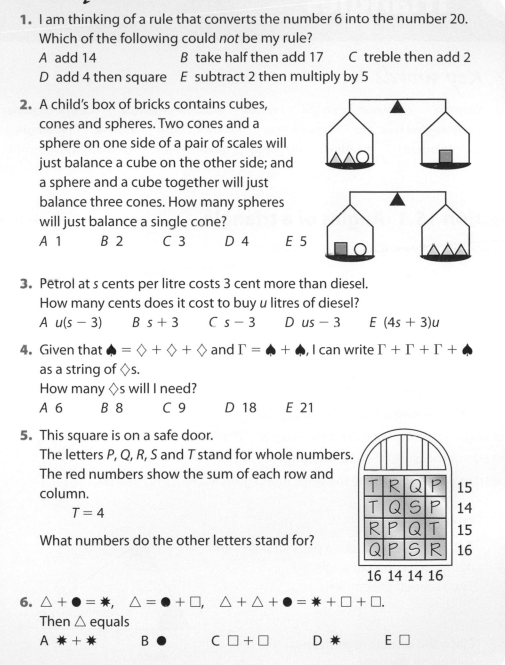

3. Petrol at *s* cents per litre costs 3 cent more than diesel.
   How many cents does it cost to buy *u* litres of diesel?
   A $u(s - 3)$ *B* $s + 3$ *C* $s - 3$ *D* $us - 3$ *E* $(4s + 3)u$

4. Given that ♠ = ◇ + ◇ + ◇ and Γ = ♠ + ♠, I can write Γ + Γ + Γ + ♠ as a string of ◇s.
   How many ◇s will I need?
   A 6   *B* 8   *C* 9   *D* 18   *E* 21

5. This square is on a safe door.
   The letters *P*, *Q*, *R*, *S* and *T* stand for whole numbers.
   The red numbers show the sum of each row and column.

   $T = 4$

   What numbers do the other letters stand for?

T	R	Q	P	15
T	Q	S	P	14
R	P	Q	T	15
Q	P	S	R	16

   16 14 14 16

6. △ + ● = ✱,   △ = ● + □,   △ + △ + ● = ✱ + □ + □.
   Then △ equals
   A ✱ + ✱   *B* ●   *C* □ + □   *D* ✱   *E* □

chapter

15 Geometry 2 – Triangles

Key words

triangle   equilateral triangle   vertex   isosceles triangle   scalene triangle
right-angled triangle   hypotenuse   exterior angle   square   rectangle
parallelogram   rhombus   diagonal   quadrilateral   perpendicular height

Section 15.1 Angles of a triangle

A triangle has three sides and three angles.

Each corner of the triangle is called a **vertex** (plural **vertices**).
The triangle above is called the triangle ABC or △ABC.
It could also be named as △BAC or △CBA.
The angle at the vertex B can be written as ∠B or ∠ABC.
The size or measure of ∠ABC is written as |∠ABC|.
The triangle is enclosed by the three line segments [AB], [AC] and [BC].

Discovery

Cut out a triangle from a piece of paper and
mark each corner or angle.
Then tear off the corners.

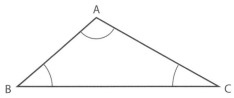

Place the corners together as
shown on the right.
You will notice that the three
angles will form a straight line,
that is, they make an angle of 180°.

$\angle a + \angle b + \angle c = 180°$

Example 1

Find the sizes of the angles marked with
letters in the given diagram.

Angles in a straight line add
up to 180°.

$$|\angle E| + 55° = 180°$$
$$|\angle E| = 180° - 55°$$
$$|\angle E| = 125°$$

Angles in a triangle add up to 180°.

$$|\angle A| + 55° + 84° = 180°$$
$$|\angle A| + 139° = 180°$$
$$|\angle A| = 180° - 139°$$
$$|\angle A| = 41°$$

Exercise 15.1

1. For the given triangle, write down

    (i) $|\angle ABC|$ (ii) $|\angle ACB|$

   (iii) $|\angle BAC|$ (iv) $|AB|$

    (v) $|AC|$ (vi) $|BC|$

2. Copy the given triangle and mark these measurements on
your sketch.

      $|XY| = 3, |XZ| = 4.2, |YZ| = 5$

      $|\angle XYZ| = 68°$ and $|\angle YXZ| = 80°$

   Find $|\angle XZY|$.

3. Draw any triangle and use your protractor to verify that the three angles of a
triangle add up to 180°.

4. If the symbol ⌐ denotes a right angle (90°), find the size of the angle marked with a
letter in each of these triangles:

5. Find the size of the angle marked with a letter in each of the following triangles:

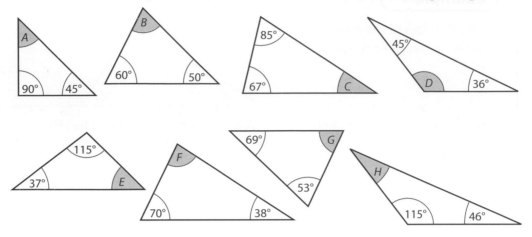

6. Remembering that a straight angle is 180°, find the size of the angle marked with a letter in each of the following triangles:

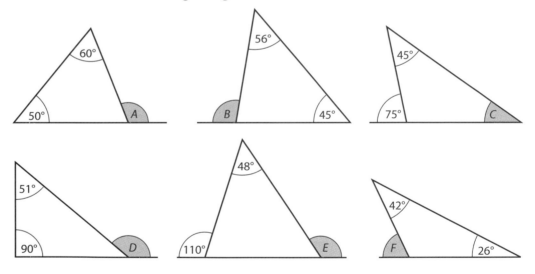

7. Find the values of *a* and *b* in each of these diagrams:

(i)   (ii)   (iii)

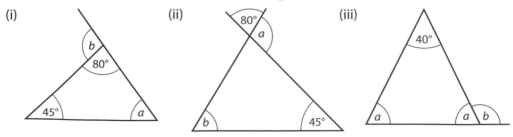

8. Find the values of *x* and *y* in the given diagram.

9. Find the angles marked with letters in this diagram.
Explain your answers by using one of the explanations on the right below.

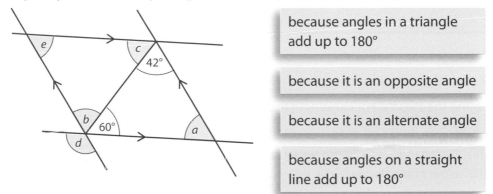

> because angles in a triangle add up to 180°

> because it is an opposite angle

> because it is an alternate angle

> because angles on a straight line add up to 180°

10. Explain why a triangle can never have a reflex angle within it.

Section 15.2 Exterior angle of a triangle

In the given diagram one side of the triangle is extended or produced.

The shaded angle is called an **exterior angle** because it is outside the triangle.

The angles marked 1 and 2 are called **interior remote angles** relative to the shaded angle.

> The shaded exterior angle is equal in size to the sum of the interior remote angles.

Here's why!

The given triangle contains the angles *A*, *B* and *C* and an exterior angle *D*.

$$|\angle D| + |\angle C| = 180° \text{ ... straight angle}$$
$$\text{Also} \quad |\angle A| + |\angle B| + |\angle C| = 180° \text{ ... angles in a triangle}$$
$$\therefore \quad |\angle D| + |\angle C| = |\angle A| + |\angle B| + |\angle C|$$
$$|\angle D| = |\angle A| + |\angle B| \text{ ... take } \angle C \text{ from both sides}$$

Example 1

Find the value of the angle marked x in the given triangle.

$\angle x = 84° + 72°$ ... exterior angle

$\therefore \quad \angle x = 156°$

Exercise 15.2

1. Name the two exterior angles in the given triangle.

(i) Name the angle that is equal to $1 + 3$.
(ii) Name the angle that is equal to $1 + 2$.
(iii) How many degrees in $1 + 2 + 3$?

2. Find the value of the angle marked with a letter in each of the following triangles:

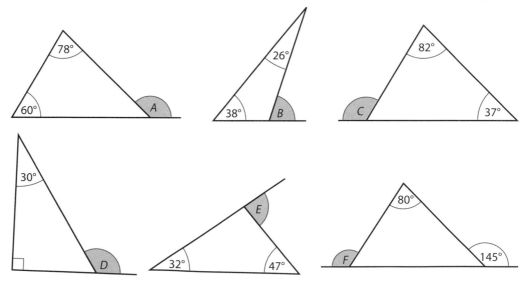

3. Find the value of x in each of these triangles:

(i)   (ii)   (iii)

4. Find the value of *x* and *y* in each of these figures:

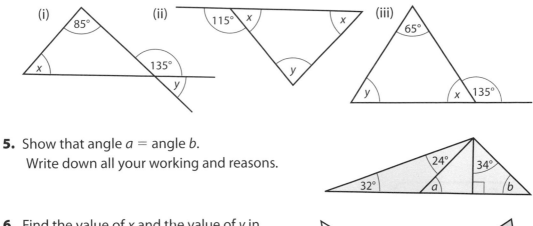

5. Show that angle *a* = angle *b*.
Write down all your working and reasons.

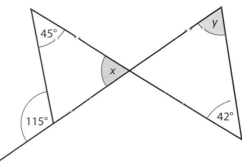

6. Find the value of *x* and the value of *y* in
the given figure.

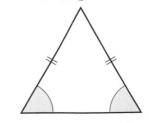

Section 15.3 Special triangles

1. Equilateral triangle

> All three sides are the same length.
> All three angles are the same size.
All are equal to 60°.

2. Isosceles triangle

> Two sides equal in length.
> The angles opposite the equal
sides are equal.

Similar symbols on lines show that sides are equal in length.

3. Right-angled triangle

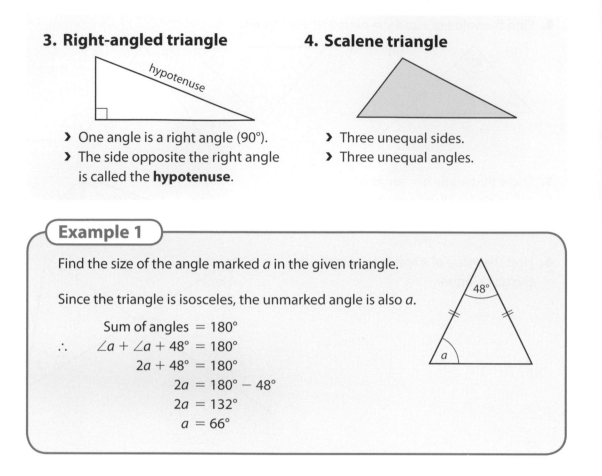

> One angle is a right angle (90°).
> The side opposite the right angle is called the **hypotenuse**.

4. Scalene triangle

> Three unequal sides.
> Three unequal angles.

Example 1

Find the size of the angle marked *a* in the given triangle.

Since the triangle is isosceles, the unmarked angle is also *a*.

$$\text{Sum of angles} = 180°$$
$$\therefore \quad \angle a + \angle a + 48° = 180°$$
$$2a + 48° = 180°$$
$$2a = 180° - 48°$$
$$2a = 132°$$
$$a = 66°$$

Exercise 15.3

1. Name three different triangles in this diagram.

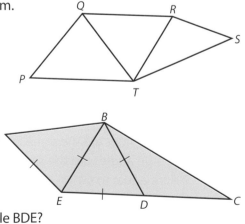

2. In the given diagram,
$$|AE| = |BE| = |BD| = |DE|$$
and CDE is a straight line.
  (i) What special name is given to the triangle ABE?
  (ii) What special name is given to the triangle BDE?
  (iii) The triangle BDC is scalene.
        Name another scalene triangle in the diagram.

3. Pick the best label for each of the following triangles from the ones given below.

(i) (ii) (iii)

Right-angled isosceles

Right-angled

Scalene

(iv) 45° (v)

Equilateral

Isosceles

30°

32°

85°

4. Name the equal angles in each of the following isosceles triangles:

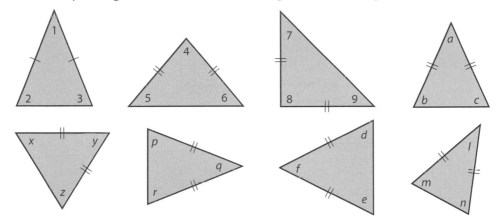

5. Calculate the measure of the angle marked with a letter in each of the following triangles:

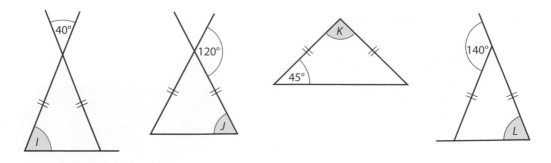

6. In the diagram $|AD| = |DB| = |BC| = |CD|$.

   (i) What type of triangle is BCD?
   (ii) What is the size of angle BDC?
   (iii) Work out the size of angle ABC.

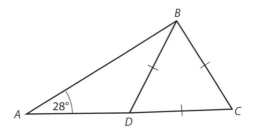

7. Find the value of x in each of the following diagrams:

(i)   (ii)   (iii)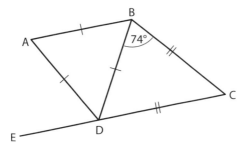

8. In the diagram $|AB| = |BD| = |DA|$ and $|BC| = |CD|$.
CD is extended to E.

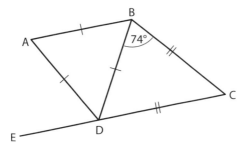

   (i) What type of triangle is BCD?
   (ii) What is the size of angle BDC?
   (iii) What is the size of angle DAB?
   (iv) Work out the size of angle ADE.

9. In each of the following diagrams the arrows indicate that the lines are parallel. Find the value of *x* in each diagram.

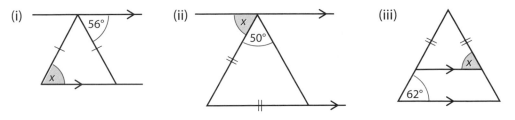

(i)   56°   *x*

(ii)   *x*   50°

(iii)   *x*   62°

10. In the given diagram equal sides are marked.
Find the size of the angles marked *c* and *d*.

c   *d*   58°

Construction challenge

11. Draw four rough copies of this square.
Using straight lines, can you divide the square into
   (i)   two right-angled triangles
   (ii) three right-angled triangles
   (iii) four right-angled triangles
   (iv) an isosceles triangle and two right-angled triangles?

12. (i) Draw two equilateral triangles by using just five lines.
   (ii) Draw two equilateral triangles by using just four lines.

Test yourself 15

1. Find the missing angles in these triangles.

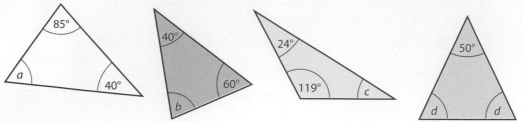

2. Find the size of the angle marked with a letter in each of these triangles:

3. Calculate the size of each angle marked with a letter.
Give reasons for your answers.

4. Find the size of the angles marked
A and B in the given triangle.

5. Find the size of angle C.
Triangle ABC is equilateral.
Explain why.

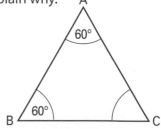

6. Say whether each of these statements is true or false:
   (i)   A triangle can have two right angles.
  (ii)   A triangle can have a right angle and two acute angles.
 (iii)   A triangle can have an acute angle and two obtuse angles.
 (iv)   A triangle can contain a right angle and an obtuse angle.
  (v)   An equilateral triangle could contain a right angle.

For the problem solver...

1. The diagram shows two rectangles which enclose five regions.
   Now draw two intersecting rectangles which
   enclose nine regions.

2. In the diagram $|PQ| = |PR| = |RS|$.
   What is the size of angle x?

   A 54°   B 72°   C 90°

   D 108°   E 144°

3. The diagram shows three squares of
   the same size.
   What is the value of x?

   A 105   B 120   C 135

   D 150   E 165

4. The diagram shows a square drawn inside
   an equilateral triangle.
   What is the size of angle JMC?

   A 90°   B 60°   C 45°

   D 30°   E 15°

5. In the diagram, $|\angle RPM| = 20°$ and
   $|\angle QMP| = 70°$.
   What is the size of $\angle PRS$?

   A 90°   B 110°   C 120°

   D 130°   E 140°

6. What is the value of $a + b + c + d + e + f$?

   A 360   B 540   C 720

   D 900   E it depends on the triangle

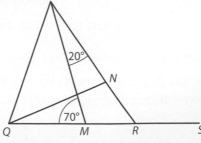

16 Presenting Data

Key words

line plots   bar charts   stem-and-leaf   key   frequency

Section 16.1 Line plots

Twenty five pupils in a class were asked to write down the number of children in their families.

The results are given in the table below:

Number of children per family	1	2	3	4	5	6
Number of families	4	6	7	5	2	1

We will now show this information on a line plot.

On the horizontal line we show the number of children per family.

Each child is represented by a dot (●) as shown below.

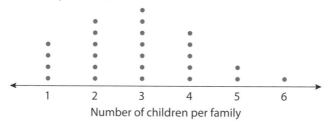

Number of children per family

From the line plot it is easy to see that there are seven families that have three children.

Exercise 16.1

1. The line plot below shows the number of goals scored per match on a Saturday afternoon in a football league.

Number of goals scored

(i) What does each dot represent?

(ii) How many matches were played on that Saturday?

   (iii) In how many matches were 3 goals scored?

   (iv) In how many matches was an even number of goals scored?

   (v) How many matches ended in 0-0 draws?

   (vi) What is the greatest number of matches that could have ended 2-2?

2. The table below gives the different ways that the pupils in a first-year class travel to school.

Way of travel	Walk	Bicycle	Bus	Car	Train
Number of pupils	7	3	8	4	3

   (i) Draw a line plot to illustrate this data.

   (ii) How many pupils are there in the class?

   (iii) What was the most frequently used method of travelling to school?

   (iv) What percentage of pupils travelled by bus?

3. The colours of cars in a car-park are listed below:

white	red	blue	green	blue	red	silver
blue	silver	white	silver	blue	red	green
silver	blue	red	blue	silver	green	white

Represent this data on a line plot.

4. The frequency table below shows the numbers of text messages received by a group of students on a particular day:

No. of messages	1	2	3	4	5	6	7
Frequency	2	4	4	7	5	4	2

   (i) Represent this data using a line plot.

   (ii) How many students were in the group?

   (iii) How many students received 5 text messages or more?

   (iv) What percentage of the group received 4 text messages?

Section 16.2 Bar charts

Bar charts are a simple but effective way of displaying data.

A bar chart consists of a series of bars of the same width, drawn either vertically or horizontally.

The bars are generally separated by narrow gaps of equal width, which make the chart easier to read.

Both axes must be clearly labelled.

The height of each bar gives the frequency.

The bar chart below shows how 60 first-year students generally travel to school.

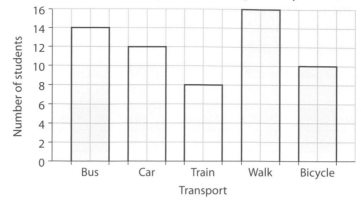

It can be seen from the bar chart that 14 travel by bus, 12 by car, 8 by train, 16 walk and 10 cycle.

Notice that the numbers of students who travel by the different methods are shown on the vertical line (or axis).

Bar charts are particularly suitable for making comparisons. It is clear from the given bar chart that the most common way of travelling to school is by walking, while the least common way is by train.

Example 1

The table below gives the make of 120 cars in a car park.

Make of car	Ford	VW	Toyota	Fiat	Nissan	Opel	Others
Number of cars	32	16	24	8	12	20	8

(i) Draw a vertical bar chart to show this information.

(ii) What percentage of the cars are Nissan?

(i)

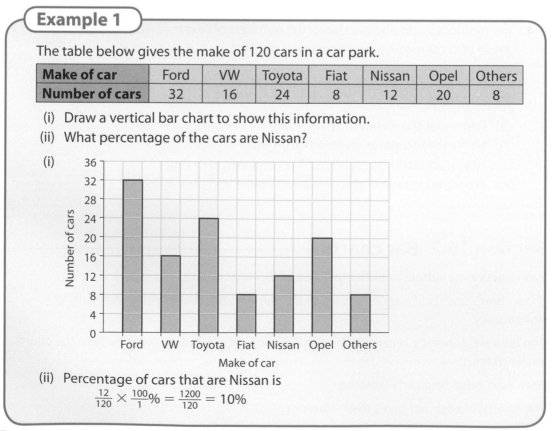

(ii) Percentage of cars that are Nissan is

$$\frac{12}{120} \times \frac{100}{1}\% = \frac{1200}{120} = 10\%$$

Exercise 16.2

1. The bar chart below shows the colours of cars in a car park.

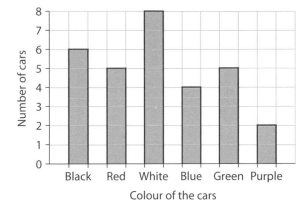

(i) How many red cars were in the car park?

(ii) What was the most popular colour of car in the car park?

(iii) Find the total number of cars in the car park.

(iv) What fraction of the cars were red?

(v) What percentage of the cars were black?

2. The bar chart below shows the type of pet kept by members of a youth club. No member kept more than one type of pet.

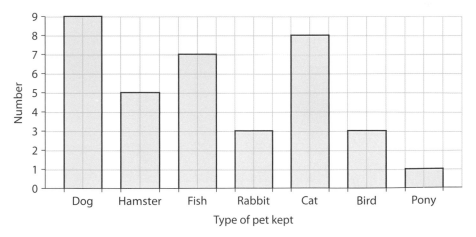

(i) Which was the most popular pet?

(ii) How many members kept a pet?

(iii) What percentage of the pets were dogs?

(iv) Which was the third most popular pet?

(v) What fraction of the pets were rabbits?

3. The students of first-year carried
   out a traffic survey by standing
   outside the school gates for half
   an hour one morning. Their results
   are illustrated by the bar chart
   opposite.

   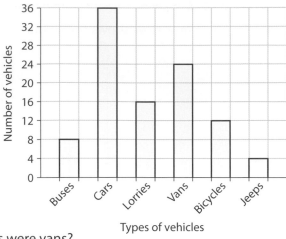

   (i) How many lorries passed
       during the survey?
   (ii) Find the total number of
        vehicles which passed.
   (iii) What fraction of the vehicles
         were buses?
   (iv) What percentage of the vehicles were vans?
   (v) How many more lorries than jeeps passed?

4. This bar chart gives the number of students in each of the first four year-groups of a
   school.

   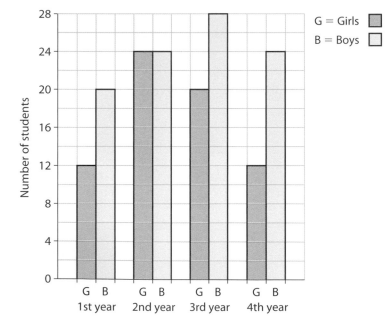

   (i) Find the number of students in each of the four years.
   (ii) In which year is the number of boys the same as the number of girls?
   (iii) In which year is the number of boys twice the number of girls?
   (iv) In which years are there 8 more boys than girls?
   (v) Which year has the least number of students?
   (vi) What fraction of first-year students are girls?

5. The bar chart below gives the favourite subject chosen by each pupil in a class of 30.

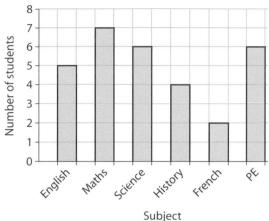

  (i)   How many students chose Maths?
 (ii)   What subject was chosen by four students as their favourite subject?
(iii)   How many subjects were more popular than English?
 (iv)   What percentage of students chose PE?
  (v)   One subject was $2\frac{1}{2}$ times more popular than another subject.
         Name these two subjects.

6. The following table gives the shoe sizes for a class of 30 first-year students:

Size of shoe	4	5	6	7	8
Number of students	4	8	10	6	2

Draw a vertical bar chart to represent this information.
Mark the shoe size on the horizontal axis and the number of students on the vertical axis.

7. The table below gives the number of children per household on a certain street.

Number of children per household	0	1	2	3	4	5	6
Number of households	12	6	10	14	8	6	4

Draw a bar chart to illustrate this information.

  (i)   How many households were in the street?
 (ii)   How many households had four children or more?
(iii)   What fraction of the households had no children?
 (iv)   What percentage of the households had 2 or 3 children?
  (v)   What was the third most common number of children per household?

8. The following bar chart represents the marks scored by a class of 30 pupils in a test:

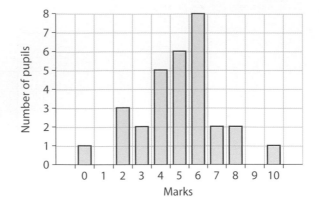

  (i) How many pupils scored 7 marks or more?

 (ii) Which mark was scored most frequently?

(iii) What percentage of the pupils got less than 4 marks?

(iv) Which mark was scored by exactly 3 students?

9. For her survey on fitness, Doreen asked a sample of people, as they left a sports centre, which activity they had taken part in. She then drew a bar chart to show her data.

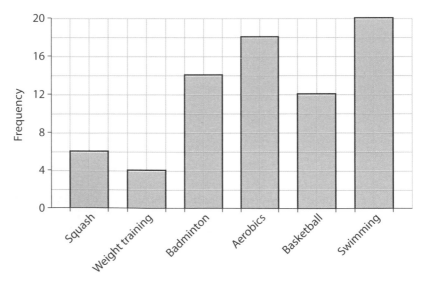

  (i) Which was the most popular activity?

 (ii) How many people took part in Doreen's survey?

(iii) Give a probable reason why fewer people took part in weight training.

(iv) Is a sports centre a good place in which to do a survey on fitness?
Explain why.

10. The bar chart on the right shows the amount of money raised for new computers by the five year-groups in a school.

Does year 1 have fewer pupils than year 3?

Select one of these answers.

      1. Yes   2. No   3. Can't tell

Explain your selection.

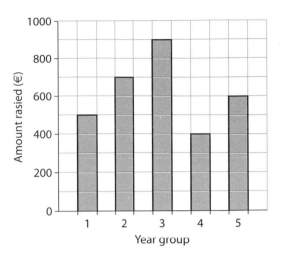

11. These graphs show the temperatures for three weeks of the year. Match these sentences to the bar charts.

   (i) It was very warm at first, then suddenly it got much colder.

  (ii) Every day was colder than the day before.

 (iii) Every day was hotter than the day before.

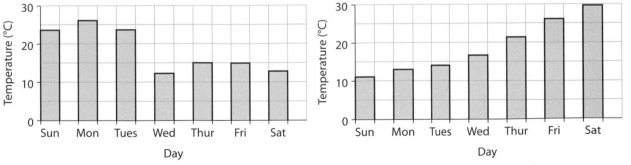

Section 16.3 Stem and leaf plots

A **stem and leaf plot** is a very useful way of presenting data.
It is useful because it shows all the original data and gives you an overall picture that shows the shape of the data.

It is similar to a horizontal bar chart, with the numbers themselves forming the bars. Stem and leaf plots are suitable only for small amounts of data.

A stem and leaf plot is made by splitting the number into two parts.

If the numbers consist of two digits, e.g. 34, 46, 57, ..., the stem will represent the tens and the leaf will represent the units.

Here is a typical stem and leaf plot:

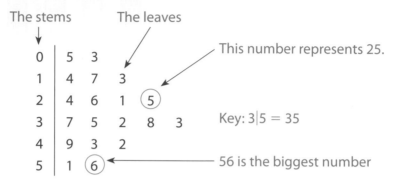

The stems   The leaves

```
0 | 5 3                This number represents 25.
1 | 4 7 3
2 | 4 6 1 (5)
3 | 7 5 2 8 3          Key: 3|5 = 35
4 | 9 3 2
5 | 1 (6)              56 is the biggest number
```

You must always add a **key** to show how the stem and leaf combine.

The data or numbers represented above are:

     5, 3, 14, 17, 13, 24, 26, 21, 25, 37, 35, 32, 38, 33, 49, 43, 42, 51, 56

We will now redraw the stem and leaf plot above, putting the numbers in **order of size**.

This is shown on the right.

```
0 | 3 5
1 | 3 4 7
2 | 1 4 5 6
3 | 2 3 5 7 8
4 | 2 3 9
5 | 1 6            Key: 2|1 = 21
```

Example 1

The times, in seconds, taken by 20 students to complete a puzzle are shown below.

     17,   9, 23, 28, 14, 12, 26, 32, 23, 19,
     34, 13,   8, 28, 42, 36, 23, 33, 11, 44

Construct a stem and leaf plot to represent this information.

The smallest number is 8 and the largest is 44.
The stem of the diagram will be in tens starting with 0 and finishing with 4.

Now work through the numbers and put the second digit in the appropriate row.

```
0 | 9  8
1 | 7  4  2  9  3  1
2 | 3  8  6  3  8  3
3 | 2  4  6  3
4 | 2  4
```

We now rewrite the diagram with all the leaves in order, with the smallest nearest to the stem.

```
0 | 8  9
1 | 1  2  3  4  7  9
2 | 3  3  3  6  8  8
3 | 2  3  4  6
4 | 2  4                   Key: 2|6 = 26
```

Exercise 16.3

1. The stem and leaf plot below shows the marks obtained by students in a maths test.

```
4 | 1  5  7
5 | 0  3  5  9
6 | 2  3  4  7  8
7 | 1  4  7  8
8 | 2  5  8
9 | 3                  Key: 6|2 = 62
```

  (i) How many students took the test?

 (ii) What was the highest mark achieved?

(iii) How many students got between 60 and 70 marks?

 (iv) How many students got 80 marks or more?

  (v) If an A-grade is 85 marks or more, how many students got an A-grade?

2. The stem and leaf plot below shows the ages of the first 25 customers to enter a shop one morning.

```
0 | 7  9
1 | 5  7  8  9
2 | 0  2  3  5  6  8  9
3 | 2  4  7  8  9
4 | 1  3  6  8
5 | 2  4  5
```
                                                    Key: 1|8 = 18

   (i)   What age was the youngest customer?
  (ii)   How many customers were aged between 20 and 30 years inclusive?
 (iii)   What fraction of customers were aged between 30 and 40 years?
 (iv)   How many customers were in their teens?
  (v)   How many were younger than the oldest customer?

3. The stem and leaf plot below shows the times, in seconds, taken by a group of first-year pupils to complete a 200-metre race.

```
2 | 6  8  9
3 | 1  5  6  8  9
4 | 0  2  5  5  8  9
5 | 1  3  6  7
6 | 2  5  7  8
7 | 0  1
```
                                        Key: 4|0 = 40 seconds

   (i)   What was the fastest time recorded?
  (ii)   How many pupils ran the race in less than 40 seconds?
 (iii)   How many pupils took part in the race?
 (iv)   What was the time of the 8th fastest pupil?
  (v)   What was the time of the 3rd slowest pupil?
 (vi)   What was the difference between the times of the fastest and slowest pupils?
(vii)   If a time of 40 seconds or less qualifies a pupil for a further race, how many pupils qualified?

4. Twenty pupils were asked how many DVDs they had in their collection. The results are shown below:

       6, 14, 8, 11, 15, 24, 17, 25, 23, 6, 9, 15, 19, 21, 28, 32, 10, 34, 12, 23

   (i)   Draw a stem and leaf plot to show this information.   0 |
       (The stems are done for you.)   1 |
  (ii)   How many students had more than 20 DVDs?   2 |
 (iii)   How many students had 15 or less DVDs?   3 |
 (iv)   What was the difference between the highest and lowest numbers of DVDs in the collections?

5. The number of points gained by the teams in a football league at the end of the season are as follows:

38 62 33 46 24 53 47 66 41 62
38 80 46 45 51 54 39 52 62 34

 (i) Draw a stem and leaf plot to represent this data.
 (ii) How many teams got 60 or more points?
 (iii) What was the difference between the highest and lowest number of points?
 (iv) What percentage of the teams scored between 40 and 50 points?

6. Here are the marks, out of 50, scored by pupils in a Science test:

32, 36, 41, 14, 23, 27, 34, 11, 21, 28, 9, 32, 46, 24, 31, 43, 36, 27, 34, 36

 (i) Draw a stem and leaf plot to represent this data.
 (ii) How many pupils scored more than 30 marks?
 (iii) What was the difference between the highest and lowest mark?
 (iv) Marks between 30 and 39 inclusive got grade B.
     How many pupils achieved grade B?
 (v) What was the mark that was scored most frequently?

7. The stem and leaf plot below shows the length of time it takes members of a class to complete one length of a swimming pool.

```
17 | 3  5  8
18 | 2  6  7  8  9
19 | 0  1  6  7  7  7  9
20 | 2  5  6  9  9
21 | 1  3  7
22 | 2  5            Key 20|2 = 20.2 seconds
```

 (i) What was the time of the slowest swimmer?
 (ii) How many members had a time of 20 seconds or more?
 (iii) How many members had times of less than 19 seconds?
 (iv) What was the difference in times between the fastest and slowest swimmers?
 (v) What percentage of the members took 21 seconds or more?

8. One Saturday, Conor recorded the ages of the first 30 customers at a supermarket. The ages are shown below.

24 32 18 45 34 27 16 41 36 8 21 39 19 22 31
35 28 17 24 35 15 26 34 34 24 48 27 34 43 14

 (i) Construct a stem and leaf plot to represent this data.
 (ii) What was the age of the third youngest person?
 (iii) How many customers were aged between 20 and 30 years?
 (iv) What was the most frequently recorded age?

9. The stem and leaf diagram opposite shows the ages, in years, of 26 people who wished to enter a 10-km walking race.

stem	leaf
0	8 9
1	4 4 6 9
2	1 3 6 6 6 8
3	3 5 5 7 9
4	0 2 3 3 7 7
5	1 2 4

Key: 1|4 = 14 years old

  (i) How many people were less than 20 years old?

 (ii) Write down the most frequently recorded age.

(iii) Exactly half the people entering the walk are more than a certain age. What is that age?

(iv) Shauna says that two people will not be allowed to enter.

     Using the information in the stem and leaf diagram, suggest a possible reason for this.

10. The weights, in grams, of 20 cherry tomatoes are shown.

    5.4 4.6 6.7 3.9 4.2 5.0 6.3 5.4 4.8 3.5

    4.6 5.6 5.8 6.0 2.8 4.4 4.7 5.6 5.1 4.6

  (i) Draw a stem and leaf diagram to represent this information.

 (ii) What is the difference between the highest and lowest weight?

(iii) How many tomatoes weighed 5 grams or more?

(iv) What was the most frequently recorded weight?

11. These are the numbers of visits to the library by women members in one year.

    12 43 24   0 37 32   8 15 14 21 36 14

    23 33 15   0 34 13 13   3 16   3 38 29

    22 16 44 12 41 18 26   8 12 15

  (i) Record this data in a stem and leaf diagram like this one. Put the leaves in order.

 (ii) Use your stem and leaf diagram to find

    (a) the difference between the highest and lowest number of visits

    (b) the number of members who made 30 or more visits to the library.

Library visits by women

0	
1	
2	
3	
4	

12. These are the numbers of library visits made by the men in one year.

  (i) Write down the lowest and highest numbers of visits made by these men.

 (ii) Make two statements about the differences between the numbers of visits made to the library by men and women (in Q11 above).

Library visits by men

0	0 0 2 4 5 5 5 7 8 8 9
1	2 2 4 4 6 6 7 7 8
2	0 1 2 5 7 8
3	1 5

Key: 2|1 = 21 visits

Test yourself 16

1. The bar chart below shows information about the sales of fresh and frozen poultry at a butcher's shop on a particular Saturday.

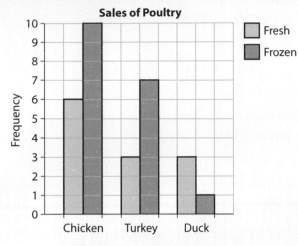

Sales of Poultry

Fresh
Frozen

(i)   How many frozen chickens were sold?
(ii) How many fresh turkeys were sold?
(iii) How many ducks were sold altogether?
(iv) What fraction of the turkeys sold were frozen?
(v) What percentage of the ducks sold were fresh?

2. The result of throwing a dice 30 times is shown.

Score	Tally	Frequency
1		
2		
3		
4		
5		
6		

```
1   2   3   3   5   2   1   6   5   4
2   4   5   3   2   3   1   4   2   6
6   3   6   5   3   1   3   4   6   5
```

(i) Copy and complete the frequency table for these scores.
(ii) Draw a bar chart to show the data. Which score occurs most often?

3. The table below gives the shoe sizes of third-year pupils in a school.

Shoe size	3	4	5	6	7	8	9
Number of pupils	2	6	9	7	6	4	1

(i)   Which is the most common shoe size?
(ii) How many pupils took part in the survey?
(iii) What fraction of the pupils wore size 7 or size 8?
(iv) Draw a line plot to show this data.
(v) Name another diagram that could be used to represent this data.

4. These bar charts show the number of hours of TV watched by four boys one week.

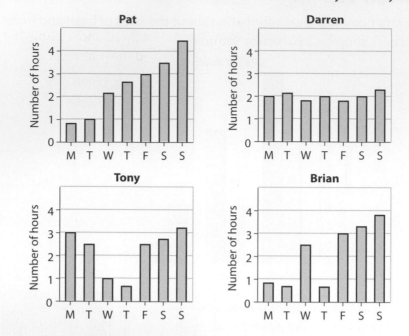

Whose graph matches these comments?
(i) I watched most TV at the beginning and end of the week.
(ii) I watched about the same amount of TV each day.
(iii) I watched quite a lot of TV on four days and not much on the other three days.
(iv) Each day I watched more TV than on the day before.

5. Here are the marks of 20 students in a science test displayed in a stem and leaf diagram.

(i) What is the lowest mark?
(ii) What is the difference between the lowest and highest marks?
(iii) If marks between 40 and 60 inclusive achieve grade C, how many got this grade?
(iv) What percentage of the students got a mark between 50 and 60?

stem	leaf
2	6 8
3	3 7 9
4	0 5 7 8
5	3 5 7 9
6	1 2 4 8
7	1 3 5

Key: 5|3 = 53

For the problem solver...

1. Referring to the rectangles below, the largest is red and the smallest is blue. Orange is the same size as yellow and not next to blue. Which is orange?

2. Which of the following bar charts could represent the data from the pie chart on the right?

3. The number 2002 is a palindrome, since it reads the same forwards and backwards. For how many other years this century will the number of the year be a palindrome?

4. At half time in a netball match, Jokers were leading Jesters by 3 goals to 2. Seven goals were scored in the second half. Which of the following could *not* have been the result of the match?
   A   The match was drawn   B   Jesters won by 2 goals
   C   Jesters won by 4 goals   D   Jokers won by 2 goals
   E   Jokers won by 3 goals

5. Write the numbers 21, 23, 25 and 27 using the digits 3, 4, and 5 once only in each number. You can use the signs $+, -, \times, \div, \sqrt{}$ and brackets.

6. On my clock's display, the time has just changed to 02:31.
   How many minutes will it be until all the digits 0, 1, 2, 3 next appear together again?
   A   1   B   41   C   50   D   60   E   61

277

Measure

17

Key words

metric system	metre (m)	centimetre (cm)	millimetre (mm)	gram (g)
milligram (mg)	kilogram (kg)	capacity	litre (ℓ)	millilitre (ml)

Section 17.1 The metric system – Units of length

Down through the ages different civilisations have used various ways to measure length and distances.

The ancient Egyptians used a **cubit** to measure length. One cubit was the length between a person's elbow and the tips of his fingers.

In the twelfth century, King Henry I of England made a law that the **yard** was to be the length from the tip of his nose to the end of his thumb when his arm was outstretched. (1 yard = 3 feet)

The most commonly used system of measurement throughout the world today is known as the **metric system**. The standard unit of length in the metric system is the **metre**. The door of a typical house is about 2 metres in height.

The part of the ruler shown below is 10 cm in length. Each **centimetre** is divided into 10 units called **millimetres**. There are 100 centimetres in a metre.

This pencil is 7 cm and 8 mm in length.

We use the **kilometre** (1000 metres) to measure long distances.

The distance between Dublin and Cork is about 260 kilometres.

The main units of length and their abbreviations are given in the table below:

1000 metres = 1 kilometre   1000 m = 1 km
1 metre = 100 centimetres   1 m = 100 cm
1 metre = 1000 millimetres   1 m = 1000 mm
1 centimetre = 10 millimetres 1 cm = 10 mm

When converting from one metric unit to another, the following two rules should prove useful.

Rules for converting

1. When changing to a larger unit, you will have fewer of them, so divide.
2. When changing to a smaller unit, you will have more of them, so multiply.

Example 1

Convert   (i) 37 mm to cm   (ii) 420 cm to m   (iii) 3.8 km to m.

(i) 10 mm = 1 cm, so to convert mm to cm, divide by 10.
    ∴   37 mm = 37 ÷ 10 cm = 3.7 cm
(ii) 100 cm = 1 m, so to convert cm to m, divide by 100.
    ∴   420 cm = 420 ÷ 100 m = 4.2 m
(iii) 1 km = 1000 m, so to convert km to m, multiply by 1000.
    ∴   3.8 km = 3.8 × 1000 m = 3800 m.

Exercise 17.1

1. Which unit would you use to measure each of these lengths?
   Choose from millimetres, centimetres or metres.
   (i) the length of a pen
   (ii) the length of a football pitch
   (iii) the thickness of a bathroom tile
   (iv) the height of a giraffe
   (v) the thickness of an exercise book
   (vi) the perimeter of a basketball court.

2. Measure the lengths of these lines and give your answer in centimetres and millimetres:
   (i) _____
   (ii) _____

3. Use a ruler to draw lines of lengths:
   (i) 6 cm   (ii) 75 mm   (iii) 6.4 cm   (iv) 6 cm 8 mm   (v) 84 mm

4. What reading, in mm, is given by each pointer?

5. Copy and complete each of the following:
   (i) 5 cm = ☐ mm   (ii) 6.8 cm = ☐ mm   (iii) 40 mm = ☐ cm
   (iv) 200 mm = ☐ cm   (v) 145 mm = ☐ cm   (vi) 16.4 cm = ☐ mm

6. Maria only had a broken ruler. Find the length of this strip in centimetres and millimetres.

7. Copy and complete each of the following:
   (i) 100 cm = 1 ☐   (ii) 1 km = ☐ m   (iii) 2.5 km = ☐ m
   (iv) 300 cm = ☐ m   (v) 850 cm = ☐ m   (vi) 55 m = ☐ cm

8. What length does the pointer show
   (i) in metres
   (ii) metres and centimetres?

9. Express each of the following in metres:
   (i) 600 cm   (ii) 8 km   (iii) 2.8 km   (iv) 480 cm   (v) 3.28 km

10. Express each of these in centimetres:
   (i) 15 m   (ii) 2.8 m   (iii) 40 mm   (iv) 124 mm   (v) 8 m 64 cm

11. Convert each of the following to kilometres:
   (i) 4000 m   (ii) 12800 m   (iii) 750 m   (iv) 3 km 450 m   (v) 90 m

12. Change each of the following to metres:
   (i) $\frac{3}{5}$ km   (ii) 0.63 km   (iii) 60 m 90 cm   (iv) 6500 cm

13. What are the readings on the scale below
   (i) in cm
   (ii) in mm?

14. Which of the following is most likely to be the length of a biro?

    (i) 30 mm   (ii) 13 cm   (iii) 1.3 m   (iv) 0.8 m

15. Write these lengths in order of size, starting with the shortest:

      12 cm   80 mm   10.8 cm   1.2 m   0.8 m

16. The Eiffel Tower is about 300 metres in height. How long would it take a lift travelling at 120 cm per second to reach the top?

17. A tortoise moves 8 mm every second. How many metres will it travel in one hour?

18. Susan's bedroom wall is 3 metres long. Can she fit all of these units along the wall? Give a reason for your answer.

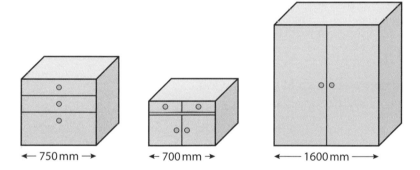

← 750 mm →   ← 700 mm →   ←——— 1600 mm ———→

Section 17.2 Units of mass (weight)

The basic unit of mass (or weight) is the **gram**.
The gram is defined to be the weight of 1 cm^3 of water.

The most commonly-used units of mass are shown below

1 gram = 1000 milligrams	1 g = 1000 mg
1000 grams = 1 kilogram	1000 g = 1 kg
1000 kilograms = 1 tonne	1000 kg = 1 tonne **kilo** means 1000 times

The smallest unit of mass is the **milligram**.
It is generally used by pharmacists when weighing medicines.

Here are some weights you should know:

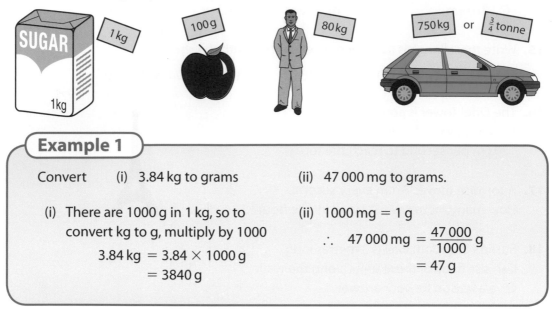

Example 1

Convert (i) 3.84 kg to grams (ii) 47 000 mg to grams.

(i) There are 1000 g in 1 kg, so to
convert kg to g, multiply by 1000

$3.84 \text{ kg} = 3.84 \times 1000 \text{ g}$
$= 3840 \text{ g}$

(ii) 1000 mg = 1 g

$\therefore \quad 47\,000 \text{ mg} = \frac{47\,000}{1000} \text{ g}$
$= 47 \text{ g}$

Exercise 17.2

1. Copy and complete each of the following:
   (i) 3 kg = ☐ g
   (ii) 2.8 kg = ☐ g
   (iii) 3000 g = ☐ kg
   (iv) 6500 g = ☐ kg
   (v) 3 kg 100 g = ☐ g
   (vi) 2 kg 90 g = ☐ g

2. Copy and complete each of the following:
   (i) 3 g = ☐ mg
   (ii) 8.6 g = ☐ mg
   (iii) 0.8 g = ☐ mg
   (iv) 4000 mg = ☐ g
   (v) 6400 mg = ☐ g
   (vi) 900 mg = ☐ g

   1 g = 1000 mg

3. How many of each of these packets would be needed to make 1 kg?

4. What unit of mass, kg, g or mg, would be most suitable to weigh the following?
   (i) a tea bag
   (ii) a bag of potatoes
   (iii) a medical tablet
   (iv) a ship
   (v) a person
   (vi) a leaf of a tree
   (vii) a lorry full of sand
   (viii) a packet of sweets

5. Express in kilograms and grams each of the weights indicated below:
   (i)   (ii)   (iii)

6. A 5 cent coin weighs 4.5 grams.
   Find the weight of coins in a bag
   which contains €50 in 5 cent coins.
   Give your answer in kg.

7. Below is a kitchen scales with markings up to 2 kg.
   Write down the weight each arrow is pointing to.

8. A recipe for 12 biscuits uses 240 g of flour.
   Adam has 2.4 kg of flour.
   How many biscuits can he make?

9. Copy and complete this table:

g	3000	4500				750
kg			2	0.5	1.4	

10. A packet of detergent weighs 1.5 kg. If each wash in a washing machine takes
    75 grams, how many washes can be got from a packet?

11. Find the cost of the cheese on this scale if the
    marked price is

    50 g for €1.20.

12. How many packets, each containing 320 grams, can be filled from a quantity weighing 9.6 kg?

13. Find the cost of 1 tonne of coal at €10.15 per 25 kg bag.

14. The weight of a parcel is shown by the dial on the weighing scales shown.
Find the cost of posting this parcel if each 50 grams cost 40c.

15. Measure the length of the lorry below in mm.

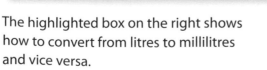

If each mm in length represents 85 kg in mass, calculate the mass of the lorry in tonnes, correct to 1 decimal place.

Section 17.3 Capacity – the litre

The capacity of a container is the amount of liquid it can hold.

The most commonly-used metric measure of capacity is the **litre**.

Milk is generally sold in 1-litre cartons.

The most common domestic central heating oil tank has a capacity of about 1350 litres.

A cube with edge of length 10 cm contains 1 litre.

$$\therefore \quad 1000 \text{ cm}^3 = 1 \text{ litre}$$

Very small amounts of liquid are measured in **millilitres (ml)**.
1 litre = 1000 ml

| 1 litre = 1000 cm³   and   1 litre = 1000 ml |

The highlighted box on the right shows how to convert from litres to millilitres and vice versa.

  (i)   1.4 litres = 1.4 × 1000 = 1400 ml

  (ii)   2600 ml = 2600 ÷ 1000 = 2.600 = 2.6 litres.

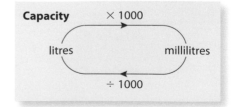

Exercise 17.3

1. Copy and complete the following:

    (i) 2 litres = ☐ ml   (ii) $3\frac{1}{2}$ litres = ☐ ml   (iii) 1.8 litres = ☐ ml

    (iv) 5000 ml = ☐ litres   (v) 4500 ml = ☐ litres   (vi) 500 ml = ☐ litres

2. Write each of these in millilitres:

    (i) 4 litres   (ii) $1\frac{1}{2}$ litres   (iii) $\frac{1}{4}$ litre   (iv) $1\frac{3}{4}$ litres

3. On the right is a 1-litre jug.
How many ml will it contain if

    (i) it is $\frac{1}{2}$ full   (ii) it is $\frac{3}{4}$ full

    (iii) it is $\frac{3}{5}$ full   (iv) it is $\frac{7}{10}$ full?

4. Write down the number of millilitres indicated by the arrows in the given containers:

5. Express each of the following in litres:

    (i) 5000 ml   (ii) 6500 ml   (iii) 1200 ml   (iv) 400 ml

6. Write these quantities in order, starting with the smallest:

    600 ml   0.5 litres   70 ml   1500 ml   0.7 litres

7. Express, in litres, the sum of the four quantities shown:

8. Andy takes two 5 ml doses of medicine four times a day for 5 days.
   If the bottle contained $\frac{1}{4}$ litre of medicine before he started, how many millilitres
   were left after the 5 days?

9. How many 75 ml glasses can be filled from a bottle containing $2\frac{1}{2}$ litres of water.

10. How much liquid do you need to add to this
    container to make 2 litres?

    Give your answer in
    (i) litres
    (ii) millilitres.

11. A tube of toothpaste holds 75 ml.
    How many tubes can be filled from a container which holds $2\frac{1}{4}$ litres?

12. While metric measure is now generally used to measure liquid, we still see
    reference to the **pint** which has been used for generations.
    The graph below can be used to convert between
    litres and pints.

    1 pint is about 570 ml.

    (i) Use the graph to find
       each of these
       (a) the number of pints
          equivalent to 80 litres
       (b) the number of litres
          equivalent to
          120 pints
       (c) the number of pints
          equivalent to 35 litres
       (d) the number of litres
          equivalent to
          100 pints.
    (ii) Is 100 litres more or less
       than 180 pints?
       Explain your answer.
    (iii) If a tank holds 11 000 litres,
       use the graph to express this in pints.

Conversion graph for litres and pints

Test yourself 17

1. Express each of the following in centimetres:
   (i) 50 mm   (ii) 240 mm   (iii) 2 m   (iv) 3.5 m   (v) 0.8 m

2. Change each of these to metres:
   (i) 2 km   (ii) 3.5 km   (iii) 1.8 km   (iv) 300 cm   (v) 480 cm

3. Use the table on the right to fill in the correct number in each of the boxes below:

   | 1 g = 1000 mg |
   | 1000 g = 1 kg |
   | 1000 kg = 1 tonne |

   (i) 4000 g = ☐ kg   (ii) 3 kg = ☐ g
   (iii) 8 g = ☐ mg   (iv) 6000 mg = ☐ g
   (v) 7500 g = ☐ kg   (vi) 8000 kg = ☐ tonnes

4. Express the measurements marked A, B and C in kilograms and grams.

5. What is the cost of 400 g of cheese if 3 kg costs €28.95?

6. What is the most appropriate unit for these measurements?
   (i) The length of a bus
   (ii) The weight of a mouse
   (iii) The thickness of a pane of glass
   (iv) The length of your classroom
   (v) The distance from Cork to Killarney
   (vi) The weight of a fully-loaded truck
   (vii) The amount of petrol in a car's petrol tank
   (viii) The amount of liquid in an average-sized cup
   (ix) The weight of a sack of onions.

7. Copy and complete the following:
   (i) 3 litres = ☐ ml   (ii) 6.4 litres = ☐ ml   (iii) 4500 ml = ☐ litres

8. Write these quantities in order, starting with the smallest:
   800 ml   0.7 litres   85 ml   840 ml   0.85 litres

9. Find the cost of posting this parcel if each 200 g costs 90 cent.

10. Put these weights in order, smallest first:

    0.5 kg   300 g   520 g   0.7 kg   0.68 kg   78 g $\frac{3}{4}$ kg

11. By how many centimetres is 2.82 m longer than 2790 mm?

12. Jill's medicine is in the container shown.
    She takes 15 ml of this medicine twice a day.
    How long will the medicine last?

13. This graph can be used to convert between miles and kilometres.
    (i) Use the graph to write down
        (a) the number of kilometres equivalent to 100 miles
        (b) the number of miles equivalent to 80 km
        (c) the number of kilometres equivalent to 75 miles
        (d) the number of miles equivalent to 130 km.

Conversion graph for miles and kilometres

    (ii) Use the graph to write these in order of increasing length:

         50 miles   75 km   80 miles   140 km   70 miles   120 km

For the problem solver...

1. Jack and Jill went up the hill to fetch exactly 4 litres of water from a well. They had only a 5-litre and 3-litre bucket. How did they succeed in their mission?

2. Lisa's bucket does not have a hole in it and weighs 21 kg when full of water. After she pours out half the water from the bucket, it weighs 12 kg. What is the weight of the empty bucket?
   A 1 kg   B 2 kg   C 3 kg   D 4 kg   E 5 kg

3. A bottle contains 750 ml of mineral water. Rachel drinks 50% more than Ross, and these two friends finish the bottle between them. How much does Rachel drink?
   A 250 ml   B 375 ml   C 400 ml   D 450 ml   E 500 ml

4. Four lamp posts are in a straight line.
   The distance from each post to the next is 25 metres.
   What is the distance from the first post to the last?

5. Tick's watch runs 2 minutes per hour too slow. Tock's watch runs 1 minute per hour too fast. They set them to the same time at noon on Sunday. The next time they met, one of the watches was one hour ahead of the other. What was the earliest time this could have been?
   A 8 a.m. on Monday   B 7:20 p.m. on Monday
   C 4 a.m. on Tuesday   D midnight on Wednesday
   E 10 p.m. on Saturday

6. Which of the following could have a length of 2010 mm?
   A a table   B an oil tanker   C a teaspoon
   D a school hall   E a hen's egg

7. On a digital clock displaying hours, minutes and seconds, how many times in each 24-hour period do all six digits change simultaneously?

   $$18{:}45{:}29$$

   A 0   B 1   C 2   D 3   E 24

8. Write the numbers 3, 4 and 5 using the digit 2 five times and the usual mathematical symbols, $+$, $-$, $\times$, $\div$ and brackets.
   (For example, $6 = 2 + 2 + 2 + 2 - 2$.)

9. The time shown on a digital clock is 5:55. How many minutes will pass before the clock next shows a time for which all the digits are the same?
   A 71   B 255   C 316   D 377   E 436

Transformation Geometry – Constructions

Key words

(object   image   translation   reflection   axial symmetry
  mirror line   central symmetry   centre of symmetry   construct)

Section 18.1 Transformations

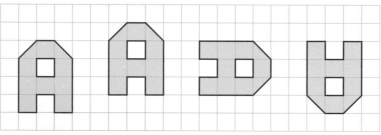

The letter A on the left above has been moved to three other positions in the plane.
The three As on the right are called **images** of the first A.
The shapes and sizes of these images do not change but two of them look different because one is on its side and the other is upside down.
These are examples of what we call **transformations**.
The original figure is called the **object**.
The new position of the figure is called the **image**.
In this chapter we will consider three transformations.

These are
1. **Translations**
2. **Axial symmetry**
3. **Central symmetry**

1. Translations

The illustrations below show the movement of a man on an escalator. He is standing upright in both illustrations but has moved or 'glided' from one position to another.

In Mathematics, movement in a straight line is called a **translation**.

When a shape is moved in a straight line
  (i) the shape and size of the object do not change
 (ii) the object does not turn or rotate.

We use a line segment with an arrow like that
shown on the right to illustrate the direction
and distance in which an object is moved.

The translation AB is written as $\overrightarrow{AB}$.

In this diagram, shape A is mapped to shape B
by a **translation**.
The red arrow shows the distance and direction
of the movement.
The translation may be described as a
movement of 4 places to the right and
2 places up.

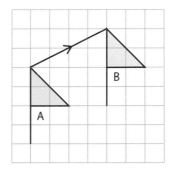

Constructing the image of a figure under a translation

On the right we have a translation $\overrightarrow{AB}$ and a point X.
To find the image of X under the translation $\overrightarrow{AB}$, we move
X along a line parallel to AB so that $|XX'| = |AB|$.
We use a set square and ruler to do this.
X′ is the image of X under $\overrightarrow{AB}$.

On the right we have a line segment [XY] and a
translation $\overrightarrow{AB}$.
To find the image of [XY] under $\overrightarrow{AB}$, we find
the image of X under $\overrightarrow{AB}$ and then find the
image of Y under $\overrightarrow{AB}$.
Call these images X′ and Y′.
The line segment [X′Y′] is the image of [XY]
under the translation $\overrightarrow{AB}$.

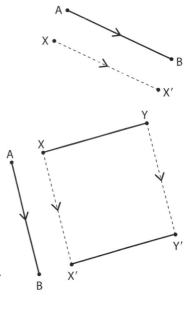

The diagram on the right shows how
to find the image of the blue
letter F under the translation $\overrightarrow{XY}$.

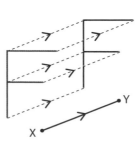

Exercise 18.1

1. Copy the diagrams below and then find the image of the point X under the translation $\overrightarrow{AB}$ in each of them:

2. Find the image of the line segment [XY] under the translation $\overrightarrow{AB}$ in each of the following two diagrams:

3. Draw a sketch of the image of each of the letters shown below under the given translation:

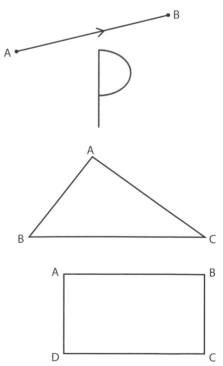

4. Draw the triangle ABC twice and then construct its image under

    (i) $\overrightarrow{BC}$ (ii) $\overrightarrow{AB}$.

5. Copy the rectangle ABCD, as shown. Now construct the image of ABCD under the translation $\overrightarrow{AB}$.

6. Draw a rectangle similar to that shown in Question 5 and then construct its image under the translation $\overrightarrow{DB}$.

7. ABCD is a parallelogram with the diagonals intersecting at the point O.

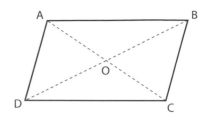

(i)   What is the image of D under $\overrightarrow{DC}$?

(ii) What is the image of A under $\overrightarrow{DC}$?

(iii) What is the image of B under $\overrightarrow{AD}$?

(iv) What is the image of the line segment [AD] under $\overrightarrow{AB}$?

8. In the given diagram, the figure PQRS is mapped to the figure P′Q′R′S′.

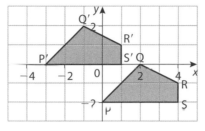

Copy and complete this sentence:

'The image figure P′Q′R′S′ is found by moving the original figure PQRS ... squares to the left and then up ... squares.'

Now describe how you could move P′Q′R′S′ back to PQRS.

9. Which shape is reached after these translations?

(i)   Shape 3 by 6 right and 1 up

(ii) Shape 1 by 4 left and 2 up

(iii) Shape 2 by 7 left and 6 down.

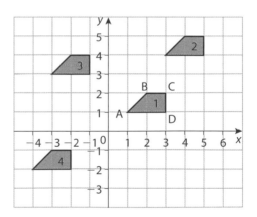

10. Describe the translations which take

(i)   shape 1 to shape 2

(ii) shape 3 to shape 1

(iii) shape 1 to shape 4.

11. ABCD and ABEC are parallelograms.

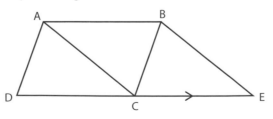

Under the translation $\overrightarrow{CE}$, write down the image of

(i) the point A   (ii) [AD]   (iii) △ADC   (iv) [AC]

12. In the given diagram the square GFEB is the image
of the square ABCD under the translation $\overrightarrow{DB}$.

   (i) What is the image of B under $\overrightarrow{DB}$?

  (ii) What is the image of [AD] under $\overrightarrow{DB}$?

 (iii) What is the image of △BDC under $\overrightarrow{DB}$?

 (iv) What is the image of [AB] under $\overrightarrow{FE}$?

  (v) What is the image of [GF] under $\overrightarrow{AD}$?

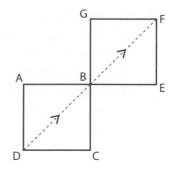

Section 18.2 Symmetrical shapes – Axial symmetry

When each of the shapes shown below is folded along the broken line, one half of the figure fits exactly over the other half. These shapes are said to be **symmetrical**.

The fold line is called the **axis of symmetry**.

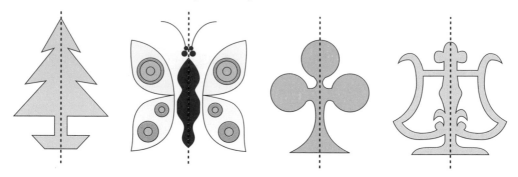

Each of the figures above has only one axis of symmetry.

Some figures have two or more axes of symmetry.

Examples of such figures are shown below.

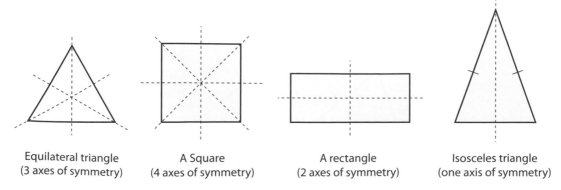

| Equilateral triangle | A Square | A rectangle | Isosceles triangle |
| (3 axes of symmetry) | (4 axes of symmetry) | (2 axes of symmetry) | (one axis of symmetry) |

Note: The diagonals of a rectangle with unequal sides are not axes of symmetry.

Axial symmetry

The diagram on the right shows a blue paper shape and the line *m*.

If we fold the paper along the line *m*, we get the green shape.

Notice that the image is 'flipped over' or 'back-to-front' relative to the given shape.

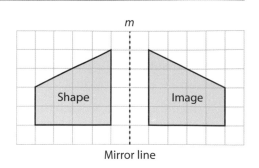

Mirror line

The process of finding the image of a figure (or point) by folding along a line is known as **reflection in a line** or **axial symmetry**.

The reflection line is also known as the **mirror line**.

In the diagrams below, the blue figures are the images of the green figures under axial symmetry in the given line, *m*.

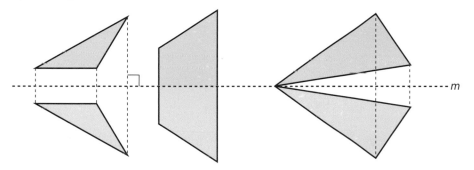

Note: If a point is on the mirror line, its image is the point itself.

Example 1

The diagram on the right shows the square EFGH, the image of the square ABCD under axial symmetry in the line *m*.
Find the image of each of the following under S*m*, axial symmetry in the line *m*.

(i) [AD]   (ii) [AB]   (iii) [AC]   (iv) △BOC   (v) △AOB.

(i) The image of [AD] is [FG].   (ii) The image of [AB] is [EF].
(iii) The image of [AC] is [FH].   (iv) The image of △BOC is △EKH.
(v) The image of △AOB is △FKE.

Finding images under axial symmetry

On the right is a line ℓ and a point X.

To find the image of X under reflection in the line ℓ, we use a set square, as shown, and draw a broken line perpendicular to ℓ, through X.

We produce this line to X′ such that M is the midpoint of [XX′].

X′ is the image of X under S_ℓ, where S_ℓ is reflection in ℓ.

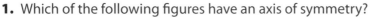

Exercise 18.2

1. Which of the following figures have an axis of symmetry?

(i) (ii) (iii) (iv)

2. How many axes of symmetry has each of the following figures?

(i) (ii) (iii)

(iv) (v) (vi)

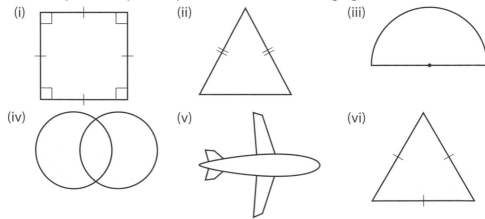

3. How many axes of symmetry (if any) has each of the letters shown below?

ABCDEFGH
NPRSTXZ

4. Draw a parallelogram similar to that shown on the right. Cut out the figure and by folding along the diagonals verify that it has no axis of symmetry.

5. Make a copy of the rectangle shown and then draw in the axes of symmetry.

6. How many axes of symmetry has this figure?

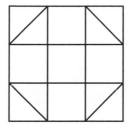

7. Use a set square and ruler to construct the image of X by S_ℓ, axial symmetry in the line ℓ, in each of the following diagrams:

8. Draw a freehand sketch of the image of each of the following line segments under S_ℓ, axial symmetry in the line ℓ.

9. Some letters look the same after reflection in a vertical mirror line.
   (i) What do these three letters have in common?
   (ii) Can you draw any other capital letters that look the same when reflected in a vertical mirror line? (Exclude O.)

   M ┊ M
   A ┊ A
   H ┊ H

10. These letters look the same when reflected in a horizontal mirror line.
   (i) What do these letters have in common?
   (ii) Can you draw any other capital letters that look the same when reflected in a horizontal mirror line? (Exclude O.)
   (iii) Can you draw a capital letter that looks the same when reflected in both a horizontal and vertical mirror line? (Exclude O.)

   E B C

   E B C

11. Use a set square or ruler to draw a rough sketch of the image of each of these shaded triangles under reflection in the mirror line *m*.

12. Construct the image of the given square ABCD under axial symmetry in the line BC.

13. The diagram on the right shows the image of ABCD under an axial symmetry in the line ℓ.
Write down the image of each of the following under S_ℓ, axial symmetry in the line ℓ:

(i) the point A   (ii) the point C
(iii) [DC]   (iv) [DA]
(v) [BD].

14. In the given diagram, BEFC is the image of ABCD under axial symmetry in the line *m*.
Write down the image of each of the following under axial symmetry in the line *m*:

(i) D   (ii) [AD]
(iii) [DC]   (iv) [BD]
(v) [AC].

15. ABCD is a rectangle with the diagonals intersecting at the point O.
The line ℓ is perpendicular to DC.
Find the image of each of the following under reflection in the mirror line ℓ:

(i) D   (ii) [AD]   (iii) [AO]
(iv) [OC]   (v) △AOE   (vi) △AOD
(vii) △COF   (viii) the figure EBCO.

16. On the right is the reflection of a clock in a mirror.
What time does the clock actually show?

17. Rachel put these two shapes together, edge to edge.

Her new shape had just 1 line of symmetry.
Show two ways Rachel might have done this.

18. Show how you can put these shapes together to make a single shape with a mirror line.

19. In the diagram on the right, we have the word THE and a
mirror line.
Which of the following is the image of THE under a reflection
in this mirror line?

A	B	C	D	E
THE	⊥H∃	TH∃	∃HⱢ	∃HT

Section 18.3 Central symmetry

The diagram on the right shows two points A and X.

We join A to X and continue the line to A′ such
that $|XA'| = |AX|$.

The point A′ is called the image of A under a
reflection in the point X.

Another name for reflection in a point is **central symmetry**.
Instead of using A′ we will use the notation $S_X(A)$ to denote the
image of A under a central symmetry in the point X.

This notation is used in the given diagram to represent the images of A, B and C under S_X, reflection in the point X.

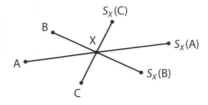

Finding the image of any figure under a central symmetry

The following diagrams illustrate how to find the images of

  (i) a line segment [AB]   (ii) the capital letter *T*

under S_X, central symmetry in the point X.

In each case the red figure is the image of the blue figure.

The diagram on the right shows the letter F and its image under S_X. Notice that the red image appears upside down and back-to-front in relation to the given blue figure.

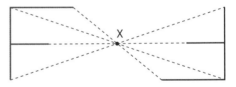

Centre of symmetry

All the figures shown below are mapped onto themselves under central symmetry in the point X.

   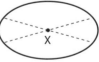

In each figure X is the **centre of symmetry**.

Every point in each figure is mapped onto another point in the figure under reflection in the point X.

Not every figure has a centre of symmetry.

For example, no triangle has a centre of symmetry.

Exercise 18.3

1. The given diagram shows three points.
Describe in words the meaning of $S_X(A)$.

2. Copy the given three points and construct the image of A and B under S_X, central symmetry in the point X.

3. Construct the image of the given line segment under central symmetry in the point X in each of the following:

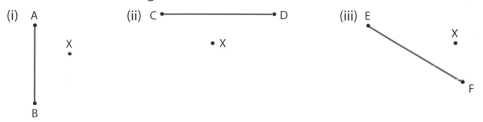

If you have done the constructions correctly you will notice that each line segment is mapped onto a parallel line segment.

4. Sketch the image of the triangle ABC under S_C, central symmetry in the point C in each of the following:

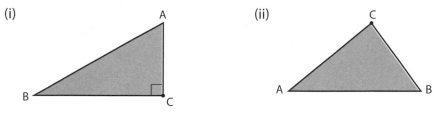

5. Draw a rough sketch of the image of each of the following letters under central symmetry in the point X:

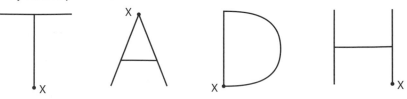

Describe how each image appears in relation to the given figure.

6. Which of the following figures have O as the centre of symmetry?

(i)   (ii)   (iii)

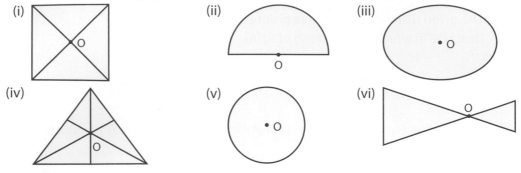

(iv)   (v)   (vi)

7. Draw the image of ABCD under S_D, central symmetry in the point D.

8. ABCD is a square with the diagonals intersecting at the point O. Write down the image of each of the following under central symmetry in the point O.

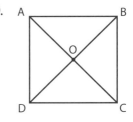

  (i)   A   (ii)   D   (iii)   [AB]
(iv)   [BC]   (v)   [AO]   (vi)   △AOD
(vii)   △AOB   (viii)   △ABD.

9. Examine the diagram on the right and now name the transformation that maps

  (i) F_1 onto F_2
 (ii) F_2 onto F_3
(iii) F_3 onto F_4
(iv) F_1 onto F_3.

10. The diagonals of the given parallelogram intersect at the point M.

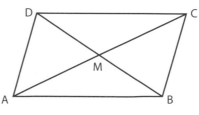

Write down the answers to each of the following:
  (i) $S_M(D)$ (ii) $S_M[AD]$ (iii) $S_M[AB]$
(iv) $S_M(△DCM)$ (v) $S_M(△AMB)$ (vi) $S_M(△CAB)$.

11. Examine the two words shown on the right. You should eventually be able to see the word *upside-down*.

Turn the page upside down.

What do you see now?

Does the figure have

   (i) an axis of symmetry

   (ii) a centre of symmetry?

12. Name the transformation that will map

   (i) A to D   (ii) D to C

 (iii) A to B   (iv) A to C

  (v) D to E   (vi) C to B.

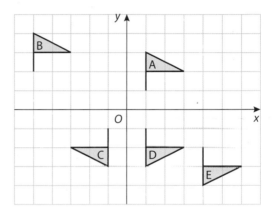

Section 18.4 Constructions

1. Bisector of a given angle using only compass and straight edge

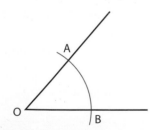

To bisect the given angle place the point of the compass at O and draw an arc to cut both arms of the angle at A and B.

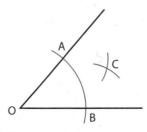

With the point of the compass at A, and keeping the same radius, draw an arc between the arms of the angle. Repeat at B, cutting the first arc at C.

Join the point O to C. OC is the bisector of the angle AOB.

2. How to construct the perpendicular bisector of a line segment

Set your compass to over half the length of [AB]. With A as centre, draw an arc above and below the line.

Keep your compass with the same radius. With B as centre, draw two more arcs. These arcs intersect the first two arcs at P and Q.

Join P and Q.
PQ is the perpendicular bisector of [AB].
M is the midpoint of [AB].

3. Line perpendicular to a given line ℓ, passing through a given point on ℓ

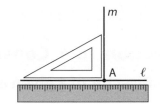

Given a line ℓ and the point A on ℓ.

Place the ruler along the line ℓ and place the set square on the ruler.

Move the set square along the ruler until it reaches the point A. Draw the line m through A.
m is perpendicular to ℓ.

4. How to draw a line parallel to a given line, through a given point

Given a line ℓ and a point P.	Place one side of the set square along the line ℓ. Place the ruler along the other side and hold firmly.	Slide the set square along the ruler up to the point P. Draw a line *m* through P. The line *m* is parallel to ℓ.

5. Division of a line segment into three equal parts

  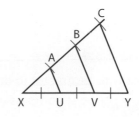

Draw a line segment [XY]. Draw a line through X making an acute angle with [XY].	Use a compass with X as centre and draw an arc crossing the line at A. With A as centre and with the same radius, draw another arc crossing the line. Mark this point B. Repeat the process at point B and mark the new point C.	Join C to Y. Using a set square and ruler draw lines through A and B parallel to CY. These lines meet [XY] at the points U and V. U and V divide [XY] into three equal parts.

6. How to draw a line segment of a given length on a given ray

[AB is a given ray.
We will now construct a line segment 6 cm in length on the given ray.

Use your ruler and compass to find a length of 6 cm.

Place the point of the compass on the point A and draw an arc intersecting the ray at the point X. The required line segment is [AX].

Exercise 18.4

1. Use your protractor to draw an angle of 70°.
Now use your compass and ruler to construct the bisector of the angle.

2. Use your set square to draw a right angle.
Now use your compass and ruler to divide the angle into two equal parts.
Use your protractor to verify that each part is 45°.

3. Draw a line segment 6 cm in length.
Use your compass to construct the perpendicular bisector of this line segment.
Verify that each half is 3 cm in length.

4. Draw a line segment 7 cm in length.
Bisect the line and verify that both halves are equal in length.

5. The diagram below shows a line segment [AB] and a line AY in which |AX| = |XY|.
Use your set square and ruler to draw XM parallel to YB.
Verify that M is the midpoint of [AB].

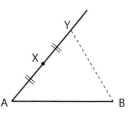

6. Draw a line segment 9 cm in length.
Now use your compass, ruler and set square to divide the line into 3 equal parts.
Use your ruler to verify that each part is 3 cm in length.

7. Draw a triangle ABC having the same measurements as those shown on the right.
Use your compass to bisect the three sides of the triangle.
If your drawing is accurate, the three lines should intersect at the same point.
Now use this point as the centre to draw a circle through A, B and C.
This circle is called the **circumcircle** of the triangle.

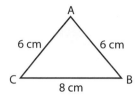

8. Draw a triangle with base 7 cm and other sides of length 5 cm and 6 cm.
Bisect the three angles using a compass and ruler.
The three bisectors should meet at the one point.
Using this point as centre, draw a circle which touches the three sides of the triangle.
This circle is called the **incircle** of the triangle.

Test yourself 18

1. (i) Name the transformation that maps

    (a) F_1 onto F_2

    (b) F_2 onto F_3

    (c) F_1 onto F_3.

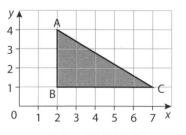

  (ii) Make two drawings of the rectangle ABCD.
Now construct the image of ABCD under

    (a) the translation $\overrightarrow{AB}$

    (b) central symmetry in the point D.

2. (i) Say if each of the following figures could be its own image under a central symmetry:

  (ii) The diagram shows a triangle ABC.
A′B′C′ is the image of the triangle ABC
under an axial symmetry in the y-axis.

    (a) Write down the coordinates of A, B and C.

    (b) Write down the coordinates of A′, B′ and C′.

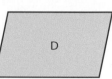

3. (i) How many axes of symmetry has each of the following figures?

    (a)   (b)   (c)

(ii) ABCD is a rectangle.

The diagonals intersect at the point O.

(a) What is the image of D under the translation $\overrightarrow{AB}$?

(b) What is the image of △DOC under central symmetry in the point O?

(c) What is the image of [AB] under the translation $\overrightarrow{BC}$?

4. (i) Draw a sketch of the given triangle ABC.

Now draw the image of the △ABC under a central symmetry in the point C.

(ii) Which of the transformations A, B or C below will map

(a) K to L

(b) L to M

(c) L to N, where

A: Translation

B: Reflection in a line

C: Central symmetry?

5. (i) How many axes of symmetry does this figure have?

(ii) The parallelogram ZPQT is the image of the parallelogram XYZR under the translation $\overrightarrow{XZ}$.

(a) What translation is the same as $\overrightarrow{XR}$?

(b) What is the image of X under $\overrightarrow{TQ}$?

(c) What is the image of △XRZ under $\overrightarrow{XZ}$?

(d) What is the image of [TQ] under central symmetry in Z?

For the problem solver...

1. If you looked in a mirror at an accurate clock at 1:30 pm, which of the following would you see?

2. The diagram shows a pattern made from matchsticks stuck to a piece of card. What is the smallest number of matchsticks that need to be added so that the resulting pattern has a line of symmetry?

   A 0   B 1   C 2   D 3   E 4

3. Beatrix takes a sheet of paper (shown on the near right), folds the sheet in half 4 times and punches a hole all the way through the folded sheet, as shown on the far right.

   She then unfolds the sheet. How many holes are there now in the unfolded sheet?

   A 4   B 6   C 8   D 12   E 16

4. Sam has six plain-coloured plates hanging on her lounge wall, in the formation shown.
   What is the smallest number of plates that need to be moved to turn this formation upside down?

   A 1   B 2   C 3   D 4   E 5

5. The figure shows an equilateral triangle divided into small equilateral triangles, all equal. What is the lowest number of small triangles which must now be shaded to produce a figure which has a line of symmetry?

   A 2   B 3   C 4   D 5   E 6

6. Humpty Dumpty sat on a wall, admiring his new digital watch which displayed hours and minutes only. He noticed that is was 15:21 when Jack and Jill set off up the hill, but that when they later came tumbling down again his watch showed only 10:51. At that point Humpty realised that he'd had his watch on upside down all the time! How long did Jack and Jill take to go up the hill and down?

   A   40 min   B   2 hr 10 min   C   2 hr 20 min
   D   3 hr 10 min   E   4 hr 30 min

Answers

Chapter 1: Natural Numbers

Exercise 1.1

1. (i) T (ii) F (iii) F (iv) T (v) F
2. (i) 8, 10, 12, 14 (ii) 1, 3, 5, 7, 9, 11
    (iii) 1, 2, 3, 4 (iv) 7, 8, 9, 10
    (v) 5, 7, 9, 11, 13
3. (i) the first five natural numbers
    (ii) the first five odd natural numbers
    (iii) the first three even natural numbers
    (iv) four consecutive even natural numbers
    beginning with 6
    (v) consecutive odd natural numbers
    beginning with 9
    (vi) consecutive odd natural numbers
    beginning with 101
4. (i) 4 (ii) 400 (iii) 200
    (iv) 4000 (v) 40
5. 822, 3759, 61 208
7. (i) 7431 (ii) 1347
8. 3960
9. 30 303
10. 7173
11. (i) 709 (ii) 2309 (iii) 6004
    (iv) 20 402 (v) 90 090 (vi) 302 045
    (vii) 1 030 000
12. 931, 2988, 3079, 3098, 3190, 3297
13. (i) 10 D 800 (ii) 11 KE 1020
    (iii)12 KY 8000
14. (i) 863 221 (ii) 122 368

Exercise 1.2

1. (ii) F (iii) T; $9 \times 2 = 18$
    (iv) T; $5 \times 7 = 35$ (v) F
    (vi) T; $12 \times 5 = 60$ (vii) F
    (viii) T; $16 \times 3 = 48$
2. (i) $18 \times 1, 9 \times 2, 6 \times 3$
    (ii) $30 \times 1, 15 \times 2, 10 \times 3, 6 \times 5$
    (iii) $36 \times 1, 18 \times 2, 12 \times 3, 9 \times 4, 6 \times 6$
    (iv) $40 \times 1, 20 \times 2, 10 \times 4, 8 \times 5$
3. 5
4. (i) 1, 2, 3, 6 (ii) 1, 2, 4, 8
    (iii) 1, 3, 5, 15 (iv) 1, 2, 3, 4, 6, 8, 12, 24
    (v) 1, 2, 4, 7, 14, 28 (vi) 1, 5, 7, 35
    (vii) 1, 2, 3, 4, 6, 7, 12, 14, 21, 28, 42, 84
    (viii) 1, 2, 3, 4, 6, 9, 12, 18, 27, 36, 54, 108

5. 1, 2, 4, 7, 14 = 28
6. (i) Y (ii) N (iii) Y (iv) Y
7. (i) Y (ii) Y (iii) N (iv) Y
8. (i) 1, 2, 3, 6, 9, 18 (ii) 1, 2, 3, 4, 6, 8, 12, 24
    (iii) 1, 2, 3, 6 (iv) 6
9. (i) 5 (ii) 7 (iii) 14
    (iv) 14 (v) 9 (vi) 9
10. (i) 9 (ii) 14 (iii) 13
11. (i) 2, 3, 5, 7, 9, 11, 13, 15
12. 19 + 7; 23 + 3; 13 + 13
13. (i), (ii), (iv)
14. … 18, 24, 30, 36, 42, 48;
    … 11, 13, 17 19, 23, 25, 29, 31, 35, 37, 41, 43, 47,
    49; 25, 35, 49
15. (i) 2 + 11 + 17 (ii) $2 \times 3 \times 5$
16. (i) F; 2 is a prime number
    (ii) T
    (iii) F, 9 is not a prime number
    (iv) F, there are four
17. 1, 2, 3, 4, 6, 8, 12, 16, 24, 48; two of them are
    prime numbers
18. 13, 17, 37
19. (i) $2 \times 2 \times 3$ (ii) $2 \times 3 \times 5$
    (iii) $3 \times 3 \times 5$ (iv) $2 \times 2 \times 3 \times 7$
    (v) $2 \times 2 \times 3 \times 3 \times 3$
20. (i) 5 + 7 (ii) 5 + 11
    (iii) 5 + 19 (iv) 3 + 29
21. 5 + 7, 11 + 13, 17 + 19
22. Always a prime number
23. 17 + 29
24. (i) 3, 5 (ii) 3, 5, 10, 15, 30
    (iii) 12, 18, 30 (iv) four

Exercise 1.3

1. (i) 3 (ii) 21, 24
    (iii) 27 (iv) 300
2. (i) 7, 14, 21, 28, 35, 42
    (ii) Yes (iii) 147, 154
3. 9, 18, 27, 36, 45, 54, 63, 72
4. (i) 4, 8, 12, 16, 20, 24 (ii) 6, 12, 18, 24, 30, 36
    (iii) 12 and 24 (iv) 12
5. (i) 10 (ii) 24 (iii) 28
    (iv) 60 (v) 56
6. (i) 8 (ii) 12
    (iii) 30 (iv) 24
7. (i) 6, 8 etc. (ii) 3, 6, 8 etc.

8. (i) 3, 9, 12   (ii) 3, 5, 9

9. 24

10. (i)

12	24	36	48	60	72		
15	30	45	60	75	90	→	60

  (ii) 3, 4   (iii) 6, 7

11. (i) T   (ii) F   (iii) F   (iv) T

12. (ii) Line 3: multiples of 4;
       Line 4: multiples of 14
  (iii) Multiples of 10

13. 150 seconds

Exercise 1.4

1. (i) 16   (ii) 36   (iii) 144
  (iv) 196   (v) 25   (vi) 53
  (vii) 106   (viii) 36

2. (i) 16   (ii) 72   (iii) 400
  (iv) 98   (v) 32   (vi) 9
  (vii) 27   (viii) 92

3. (i) 36   (ii) 41   (iii) 15   (iv) 34

4. 36, 49, 64, 81

5. (i) 16   (ii) 36   (iii) 81   (iv) 121

6. (i) All square numbers
  (ii) Same

7. (i) 2^3 (ii) 3^3 (iii) 6^4 (iv) 2^5

8. (i) T   (ii) T   (iii) F

9. (i) 4^2 or 2^4 (ii) 2^3 (iii) 3^3
  (iv) 10^3 (v) 5^3 (vi) 11^2

10. (i) 3   (ii) 5   (iii) 8   (iv) 12   (v) 20

11. (i) 7   (ii) 81   (iii) 144
  (iv) 81   (v) 64   (vi) 1

12. (i) 100   (ii) 18   (iii) 2   (iv) 3

13. (ii)

14. (ii)

15. (i) 5 + 11   (ii) 7 + 29
  (iii) 2 + 47   (iv) 3 + 97

16. (i) 2, 3   (ii) 5, 6   (iii) 6, 7

17. (i) 13   (ii) 15   (iii) 21
  (iv) 26   (v) 31

18. (i) 2   (ii) 3   (iii) 2   (iv) 4

19.
$$10 \times 10 \times 10 = 10^3$$
$$10 \times 10 \times 10 \times 10 = 10^4$$
$$10 \times 10 \times 10 \times 10 \times 10 = 10^5$$
$$10^6$$
  (i) Multiples of 10   (ii) Increase by 1

Exercise 1.5

1. 17   **2.** 17   **3.** 28
4. 2   **5.** 13   **6.** 39
7. 29   **8.** 21   **9.** 26
10. 27   **11.** 46   **12.** 18
13. 26   **14.** 45   **15.** 32

16. (i) +   (ii) ÷   (iii) ÷
  (iv) +   (v) ×   (vi) ÷, ×

17. (i) 44   (ii) 28   (iii) 54
  (iv) 22   (v) 12   (vi) 30
  (vii) 17   (viii) 3

18. (i) 34   (ii) 31   (iii) 17
  (iv) 32   (v) 10   (vi) 50

19. (i) 5   (ii) 2   (iii) 10
  (iv) 4   (v) 21   (vi) 6

20. (i) 29   (ii) 64   (iii) 22
  (iv) 26   (v) 50   (vi) 5

21. (i) 7   (ii) 24   (iii) 48
  (iv) 38   (v) 92   (vi) 41

22. (i) 8   (ii) 1   (iii) 2

23. (i) 5   (ii) 31

24. (i) $5 \times (4 + 3) = 35$
  (ii) $20 - (3 + 8) = 9$
  (iii) $(8 + 10) \div 2 = 9$
  (iv) $48 \div (16 - 4) = 4$
  (v) $(11 - 6) \times 2 = 10$
  (vi) $(5 + 3) \times 4 - 2 = 30$

25. D; 36   **26.** E   **27.** (i)

Exercise 1.6

1. (i) 622   (ii) 1399   (iii) 8423   (iv) 3428

2. (i) 604   (ii) 486   (iii) 384
  (iv) 216   (v) 524

3. (i) 178   (ii) 919   (iii) 1065
  (iv) 6056   (v) 249   (vi) 1023

4. (i) 50   (ii) 50   (iii) 90
  (iv) 130   (v) 80   (vi) 160

5. (i) 120   (ii) 450   (iii) 1500
  (iv) 2400   (v) 400   (vi) 800
  (vii) 2000   (viii) 2400   (ix) 4800
  (x) 8100

6. (i) 6   (ii) 60   (iii) 40
  (iv) 70   (v) 70

7. (i) 423   (ii) 4686   (iii) 1780
  (iv) 8400   (v) 5208   (vi) 13 770
  (vii) 8742   (viii) 9796

8. €640

9. (i) 576   (ii) 458

10. (i) 561   (ii) 23   (iii) 6   (iv) 1683

11. (i)   5   (ii)   7
       55   20   35   63
    11   44   4   5   45   9
  (iii)   6
       54   48
    9   72   8

12. 2 AD, 11 AD, 20 AD, 101 AD, 110 AD, 200 AD, 1001 AD, 1010 AD, 1100 AD

13. (i) 90   (ii) 19 each

14. (i) T   (ii) F   (iii) F   (iv) F
    (v) F   (vi) T
15. (i) C   (ii) B   (iii) D   (iv) A
16. (i) T   (ii) F   (iii) T   (iv) F
17. (i) D   (ii) A   (iii) B   (iv) A
18. 55

Exercise 1.7

1. (i) 630   (ii) 620   (iii) 640
   (iv) 600   (v) 600   (vi) 650
   (vii) 610   (viii) 650
2. 605, 615, 625, 635, 645
3. (i) 140   (ii) 80   (iii) 680
   (iv) 1760   (v) 3790
4. (i) 800   (ii) 300   (iii) 2200
   (iv) 3100   (v) 3700
5. (i) 3000   (ii) 6000   (iii) 8000
   (iv) 10 000   (v) 11 000
6. (i) 82 400   (ii) 82 000
7. (i) 28 500   (ii) 28 000   (iii) 30 000
8. (i) 849   (ii) 750
9. (i) 38 499   (ii) 37 500
10. (i) nearest 1000   (ii) nearest 10 000
11. (I) 2000   (ii) 1500
   (iii) 2100   (iv) 2900
12. (i) 60   (ii) 355   (iii) 225
13. (i) 23 650   (ii) 23 749
14.

	Greece	Italy	Netherlands
(i)	132 000 km²	301 000 km²	33 800 km²
(ii)	11 000 000	57 000 000	16 000 000
	Germany	**Ireland**	
(i)	357 000 km²	70 300 km²	
(ii)	83 000 000	3 900 000	

   (iii) Italy (Netherlands)

Test yourself 1

1. (i) 492   (ii) 7
2. (i) 8   (ii) 18
3. (i) 2, 5, 11, 19
   (ii) 1, 2, 4, 7, 14, 28; $2 \times 2 \times 7$
4. A – 28, B –43, C – 280, D – 460
5. (i) 11   (ii) 5   (iii) 30
   (iv) 24   (v) 32   (vi) 18
6. 376
7. (i) 1459   (ii) 9541
   (iii) $\boxed{5} + \boxed{9} = \boxed{1}\,\boxed{4}$
8. (i) 3, 13, 23   (ii) 28
   (iii) 3, 4, 15   (iv) 4, 9, 25, 64
9. (i) 120   (ii) 400   (iii) 800
10. (i) 44   (ii) 4

11. 264
12. 4, 6, 7, 8, 9, 12
13. (i) B – 31 000, L – 3000, S – 505 000,
     P – 92 000, F – 547 000
   (ii) Luxembourg
   (iii) Portugal and France
   (iv) Belgium and Portugal
14. (i) 38   (ii) 57
15. (i) T
   (ii) F (8 is not a factor of 4)
   (iii) F (4 = 1, 2, 4)
   (iv) F ($7 \neq 5$)
   (v) F (there are four)

For the problem solver... (1)

1. 169 (i.e. $234 - 65$)
2. 1331
3. 6 (2 big + 4 small)
4. $(4 + 4 + 4) \div 4$; $4(4 - 4) + 4$;
   $[(4 \times 4) + 4] \div 4$; $\frac{4 + 4}{4} + 4$; $(4 + 4) - \frac{4}{4}$;
   $4 + 4 + (4 - 4)$; $(4 + 4) + \frac{4}{4}$; $(44 - 4) \div 4$
5. 320
6. $n = 11$
7. 39 days

Chapter 2: Integers

Exercise 2.1

1. (i) $0, -2, -4$ (ii) $-1, -3, -5$
   (iii) $-4, -8, -12$ (iv) 3, 5, 7
   (v) 2, 4, 6   (vi) $2, -1, -7$
2. (i) 10°C   (ii) 5°C   (iii) 0°C
   (iv) −5°C   (v) −6°C   (vi) −8°C
3. (i) 10°C   (ii) 3°C   (iii) −3°C
   (iv) −7°C   (v) −6°C   (vi) 0°C
4. (i) $-4, -3, 0, 1, 3, 6$
   (ii) $-8, -5, -2, 0, 4, 6$
   (iii) $-8, -5, -2, 1, 3, 9$
   (iv) $-7, -4, -3, -1, 0, 3, 5$
5. (i) 11°C   (ii) 18°C   (iii) 11°C
6. 32°C
7. (i) 3, 4, 5, 6
   (ii) $-2, -3, -4, -5$
   (iii) $-6, -5, -4, -3$
8. (i) T   (ii) T   (iii) F   (iv) F
   (v) T   (vi) F   (vii) F   (viii) T
9. 23°C
10. (i) Moscow   (ii) Moscow   (iii) Rome
11. (i) $<$ (ii) $>$ (iii) $<$ (iv) $>$
   (v) $<$ (vi) $>$ (vii) $<$ (viii) $<$

Exercise 2.2

1. (i) -2 (ii) -4 (iii) -3 (iv) -3
   (v) 3 (vi) 5 (vii) -4 (viii) -6
2. (i) $-2+4$ (ii) $2-4$
   (iii) $-6+5$ (iv) $4-5$
3. (i) 10 (ii) 2 (iii) 7 (iv) -2
   (v) -7 (vi) -6 (vii) -5 (viii) -4
4. (i) -3 (ii) -6 (iii) -6 (iv) -7
   (v) -11 (vi) 10 (vii) -15 (viii) -50
5. 8 6. 8 7. 9 8. 8
9. 7 10. 5 11. -5 12. 3
13. 9 14. 4 15. 9 16. 2
17. (i) 3 (ii) 11 (iii) -9
    (iv) 3 (v) -20 (vi) -9
19. (i)

		-12		
	-3		-9	
1		-4		-5
-2	3	-7	2	

(ii)

		-17		
	-5		-12	
2		-7		-5
6	-4	-3	-2	

20. (i)

-8	-1	-6
-3	-5	-7
-4	-9	-2

(ii)

2	1	-3
-5	0	5
3	-1	-2

(iii)

0	-14	-1
-6	-5	-4
-9	4	-10

21. $-8°C$ 22. €200

Exercise 2.3

1. (i) 24 (ii) -20 (iii) -56
   (iv) -45 (v) -54 (vi) 36
   (vii) 48 (viii) -70 (ix) -72
   (x) 66 (xi) -80 (xii) -54
2. (i) -6 (ii) -9 (iii) -4
   (iv) 3 (v) 3 (vi) -3
3. (i) 8 (ii) -2 (iii) -9
   (iv) -5 (v) 6 (vi) -5
   (vii) -9 (viii) 6 (ix) -9
   (x) -5
4. (i) -8 (ii) -6 (iii) 8
   (iv) 5 (v) -4 (vi) 21
5. -50
7. (i) -36 (ii) 24 (iii) 90
   (iv) 60 (v) 96 (vi) -42
8. (i) -2 (ii) -5 (iii) -6
   (iv) -6 (v) 27 (vi) -12
9. (i) 21, -7 (ii) $-7, -2$ (iii) -2
   (iv) 10, -2 (v) $-10, -2$ (vi) 21, -3

10. (i) 9 (ii) 36 (iii) 49
    (iv) -8
11. (i) -21 (ii) -6 (iii) -14
    (iv) -45 (v) 14 (vi) 38
12. (i) $-5, -2$ (ii) $-10, -3$ (iii) $-3, -2$
    (iv) 6, -1 (v) $-6, -2$ (vi) $-5, 3$
13. (i) 50 (ii) 29
    (iii) 9 correct, 1 wrong

Test yourself 2

1. (i) 2 (ii) -2 (iii) -10 (iv) -7
   (v) -15 (vi) 18 (vii) -3 (viii) 2
2. (i) $-12, -3, -1, 0, 4, 6, 9$
   (ii) $-9, -4, -3, 2, 7, 14$
3. (i) $-6°C$ (ii) $-3°C$ (iii) $5°C$ (iv) $24°C$
4. (i) $>$ (ii) $<$ (iii) $>$ (iv) $>$
5. (i) $-8, 2$ (ii) $-5, 3$
   (iii) $-8, -5$ (iv) $-8, -5$
6. -54
7. (i) -7 (ii) 13 (iii) 60
9. (i) $-9°C$ (ii) $-7°C$
   (iii) $-12°C$ (iv) $-25°C$
10. (i) -15 (ii) M
    (iii) (a) FIND (b) PLAN (c) MILK
12. $-4°C$
13. AUCKLAND
14. 7

For the problem solver... (2)

1. D 2. 5 4. E 5. E
6. $9 \times 9 - \sqrt{9}$

Chapter 3: Fractions

Exercise 3.1

1. (i) $\frac{1}{2}$ (ii) $\frac{1}{4}$ (iii) $\frac{1}{3}$ (iv) $\frac{3}{5}$
   (v) $\frac{1}{8}$ (vi) $\frac{5}{6}$ (vii) $\frac{2}{3}$ (viii) $\frac{5}{8}$
2. (i) $\frac{1}{2}$ (ii) $\frac{3}{4}$ (iii) $\frac{2}{3}$ (iv) $\frac{2}{5}$
   (v) $\frac{7}{8}$ (vi) $\frac{1}{6}$ (vii) $\frac{1}{3}$ (viii) $\frac{3}{8}$
3. $\frac{4}{6}, \frac{2}{3}$; equivalent fractions
4. (i) $\frac{1}{7}$ (ii) $\frac{1}{4}$ (iii) $\frac{3}{4}$ (iv) $\frac{1}{3}$
5. (i) 8 (ii) 4
6. (i) $\frac{1}{2}$ (ii) $\frac{3}{4}$ (iii) $\frac{2}{3}$ (iv) $\frac{2}{3}$
   (v) $\frac{3}{4}$ (vi) $\frac{3}{5}$ (vii) $\frac{2}{3}$ (viii) $\frac{14}{21}$
7. (i) $\frac{1}{2}$ (ii) $\frac{1}{3}$ (iii) $\frac{1}{3}$ (iv) $\frac{1}{3}$
   (v) $\frac{1}{6}$ (vi) $\frac{1}{3}$ (vii) $\frac{2}{3}$ (viii) $\frac{3}{5}$
   (ix) $\frac{2}{3}$ (x) $\frac{3}{5}$

8. $\frac{3}{4}$

9. (i) $\frac{1}{4}$ (ii) $\frac{1}{2}$ (iii) $\frac{1}{5}$ (iv) $\frac{1}{4}$
(v) $\frac{1}{3}$ (vi) $\frac{3}{10}$ (vii) $\frac{1}{5}$ (viii) $\frac{4}{9}$

10. (i) $\frac{12}{24}$ (ii) $\frac{18}{24}$ (iii) $\frac{16}{24}$
(iv) $\frac{15}{24}$ (v) $\frac{22}{24}$;
(a) $\frac{2}{3}$ (b) $\frac{3}{4}$ (c) $\frac{11}{12}$

11. $a = \frac{4}{5}$, $b = \frac{2}{5}$, $c = \frac{2}{5}$, $d = \frac{9}{10}$, $e = 3\frac{7}{10}$, $f = 1\frac{1}{3}$

12. (i) $<$ (ii) $>$ (iii) $<$ (iv) $<$ (v) $<$ (vi) $>$

Exercise 3.2

1. (i) P (ii) I (iii) P
(iv) I (v) I

2. (i) $1\frac{1}{5}$ (ii) $2\frac{2}{3}$ (iii) $5\frac{1}{2}$ (iv) $2\frac{3}{4}$
(v) $5\frac{1}{3}$ (vi) $4\frac{1}{6}$ (vii) $9\frac{2}{3}$ (viii) $4\frac{3}{11}$
(ix) $6\frac{3}{10}$ (x) $5\frac{3}{8}$

3. (i) $\frac{5}{3}$ (ii) $\frac{12}{5}$ (iii) $\frac{19}{8}$ (iv) $\frac{15}{4}$
(v) $\frac{19}{5}$ (vi) $\frac{14}{3}$ (vii) $\frac{20}{3}$ (viii) $\frac{47}{9}$
(ix) $\frac{37}{10}$ (x) $\frac{49}{9}$

4. (i) $\frac{2}{3}$ (ii) $\frac{3}{4}$ (iii) $\frac{3}{7}$ (iv) $\frac{3}{4}$
(v) $\frac{3}{5}$ (vi) $\frac{4}{5}$ (vii) $\frac{2}{9}$ (viii) $\frac{3}{4}$

5. (i) 6 (ii) 27 (iii) 26
(iv) 24 (v) 28 (vi) 280

6. (i) 30 km (ii) €72 (iii) 63 litres
(iv) 115 cm (v) €75 (vi) 138 m

7. (i) 24 (ii) 8 (iii) 4
(iv) 3 (v) 3 (vi) 3

8. (i) $\frac{3}{4}$ of 8 = 6 (ii) $\frac{2}{3}$ of 9 = 6
(iii) $\frac{3}{5}$ of 25 = 15

9. 69

10. Ham = 140, Salad = 224, Tuna = 70, Cheese = 126

11. (i) CAVE (ii) POLITICS

12. (i) (ii) 12

Exercise 3.3

1. (i) $\frac{3}{5} + \frac{1}{5} = \frac{4}{5}$ (ii) $\frac{1}{7} + \frac{4}{7} = \frac{5}{7}$
(iii) $\frac{3}{8} + \frac{3}{8} = \frac{6}{8} = \frac{3}{4}$ (iv) $\frac{5}{12} + \frac{4}{12} = \frac{9}{12} = \frac{3}{4}$

2. (i) $\frac{3}{5}$ (ii) $\frac{5}{7}$ (iii) $\frac{7}{9}$
(iv) $\frac{7}{11}$ (v) $\frac{2}{3}$ (vi) $\frac{1}{2}$
(vii) $\frac{3}{7}$ (viii) $\frac{11}{13}$ (ix) $\frac{9}{8}$

3. (i) $\frac{5}{8}$ (ii) $\frac{7}{10}$ (iii) $1\frac{1}{2}$
(iv) $\frac{1}{2}$ (v) $1\frac{1}{6}$ (vi) $\frac{1}{3}$
(vii) $\frac{5}{12}$ (viii) $\frac{1}{2}$ (ix) $\frac{7}{20}$

4. (i) $\frac{4}{5}$ (ii) $1\frac{5}{24}$ (iii) $1\frac{1}{2}$
(iv) $\frac{13}{18}$ (v) $\frac{11}{12}$ (vi) $\frac{13}{24}$

5. (i) $3\frac{1}{2}$ (ii) $3\frac{7}{12}$ (iii) $6\frac{1}{10}$
(iv) $5\frac{1}{10}$ (v) $4\frac{1}{6}$ (vi) $5\frac{8}{15}$
(vii) $4\frac{3}{10}$ (viii) $5\frac{13}{15}$ (ix) $1\frac{1}{6}$

6. A = R, B = P, C = S, D = Q, E = U, F = T

7. (i) $1\frac{5}{8}$ (ii) $1\frac{5}{12}$ (iii) $\frac{1}{3}$
(iv) $2\frac{1}{4}$ (v) $1\frac{1}{8}$ (vi) $2\frac{5}{12}$

8. (i) $3\frac{5}{12}$ (ii) $1\frac{9}{10}$ (iii) $8\frac{5}{9}$
(iv) $8\frac{5}{8}$ (v) $1\frac{4}{5}$ (vi) $2\frac{5}{24}$

9.

$5\frac{1}{3}$	2	$2\frac{2}{3}$
$\frac{2}{3}$	$3\frac{1}{3}$	6
4	$4\frac{2}{3}$	$1\frac{1}{3}$

Exercise 3.4

1. $\frac{3}{8}$ **2.** $\frac{3}{20}$ **3.** $\frac{9}{20}$
4. $\frac{8}{15}$ **5.** $\frac{8}{21}$ **6.** $\frac{2}{3}$
7. $\frac{3}{5}$ **8.** $\frac{4}{15}$ **9.** $\frac{1}{14}$
10. $\frac{1}{9}$ **11.** $\frac{3}{10}$ **12.** $\frac{1}{6}$
13. $\frac{3}{7}$ **14.** 1 **15.** $\frac{1}{4}$
16. $3\frac{1}{3}$ **17.** 3 **18.** $4\frac{1}{5}$
19. $5\frac{1}{4}$ **20.** 3 **21.** $4\frac{1}{2}$
22. 23 **23.** 15 **24.** 14
25. 52 **26.** 68 **27.** $3\frac{1}{3}$
28. (i) DESK (ii) STOOL (iii) BENCH
29. (i) $\frac{5}{14}$ (ii) $\frac{3}{10}$ (iii) 12
(iv) $\frac{3}{4}$ (v) 9 (vi) 14

Exercise 3.5

1. $\frac{2}{5}$

2. (i) $1\frac{1}{2}$ (ii) $1\frac{1}{4}$ (iii) $\frac{4}{9}$ (iv) $\frac{7}{2}$
(v) 8 (vi) 27 (vii) 18 (viii) 36

3. (i) 10 (ii) $3\frac{1}{2}$ (iii) $3\frac{1}{2}$ (iv) 6
(v) $\frac{1}{2}$ (vi) 6 (vii) $\frac{9}{10}$ (viii) $\frac{5}{6}$

4. C

5. (i) $3\frac{4}{5}$ (ii) $3\frac{1}{3}$ (iii) $2\frac{8}{11}$ (iv) $\frac{2}{3}$

6. A = M, B = L, C = Q, D = P

7. (i) 2 (ii) $\frac{4}{5}$ (iii) 6

8. $\frac{1}{9}$

9. $C + D\left(\frac{5}{12}\right)$, $B + E\left(\frac{5}{18}\right)$, $F + G\left(\frac{5}{24}\right)$, $A + H\left(\frac{1}{12}\right)$

10. (i) $1\frac{2}{5}$ (ii) $\frac{2}{3}$ (iii) $\frac{5}{18}$

11. (i) ROME (ii) PARIS (iii) MADRID

Exercise 3.6

1. (i) $\frac{2}{3}$ (ii) $\frac{3}{7}$ (iii) $\frac{1}{5}$
(iv) $\frac{1}{5}$ (v) $\frac{2}{5}$ (vi) $\frac{1}{9}$

2. $\frac{2}{15}$

3. (i) TRICKS (ii) PRECIOUS
(iii) DISAPPEAR

4. $4\frac{3}{20}$ km **5.** €216

6. 26 **7.** 5 mins

8. (i) 9 (ii) 36

9. €117 **10.** 32 **11.** 48

12. 29 300 **13.** 18 **14.** 16

15. d

16. (i) $\frac{3}{10}$ (ii) 12

Test yourself 3

1. (i) $\frac{1}{3}$ (ii) $\frac{3}{4}$ (iii) $\frac{2}{3}$
(iv) $\frac{3}{5}$ (v) $\frac{3}{4}$

2. (i) $\frac{3}{2}$ (ii) $\frac{9}{4}$ (iii) $\frac{11}{3}$
(iv) $\frac{19}{4}$ (v) $\frac{14}{5}$

3. (i) $\frac{2}{12}$ (ii) $\frac{6}{15}$ (iii) $\frac{12}{21}$

4. (i) $\frac{5}{6}$ (ii) $1\frac{3}{8}$ (iii) $1\frac{1}{2}$ (iv) $\frac{13}{14}$
(v) $\frac{1}{6}$ (vi) $\frac{1}{12}$ (vii) $\frac{1}{12}$ (viii) $\frac{1}{3}$

5. $a = \frac{3}{4}$, $b = \frac{5}{6}$, $c = 1\frac{3}{8}$, $d = \frac{2}{5}$, $e = \frac{4}{5}$, $f = \frac{2}{5}$

6. (i) $\frac{3}{4}\left(\frac{9}{12}\right)$ (ii) $\frac{2}{5}\left(\frac{6}{15}\right)$
(iii) $\frac{2}{3}\left(\frac{8}{12}\right)$ (iv) $\frac{3}{4}\left(\frac{15}{20}\right)$

7. (i) $\frac{3}{10}$ (ii) 2 (iii) $1\frac{5}{8}$ (iv) 3
(v) $1\frac{1}{2}$ (vi) $\frac{5}{6}$ (vii) $\frac{2}{3}$ (viii) 4

8. (i) FISH (ii) BREAD (iii) PASTA

9. (i) $1\frac{5}{9}$ (ii) $1\frac{3}{10}$ (iii) 6 (iv) 4

10. $3\frac{5}{8}$ km

11. €14

12. 42

13. (i) $\frac{5}{12}$ (ii) 4

14. 60 cows

15. (i) $\frac{4}{9}$ (ii) 23 (iii) $2\frac{2}{3}$

16. (i) $\frac{3}{5}$ (ii) B = 150, C = 300

For the problem solver... (3)

1. 81 cm **2.** 8.15 am, 9.15 am

3. Tuesday **4.** $\frac{1}{3}$

5. $\frac{2}{3}$ **7.** $\frac{1}{5}$

Chapter 4: Decimals

Exercise 4.1

1. (i) $\frac{7}{10}$ (ii) $\frac{6}{100}$ (iii) $\frac{2}{10}$ (iv) $\frac{7}{1000}$
(v) $\frac{7}{100}$ (vi) $\frac{9}{1000}$ (vii) 30 (viii) $\frac{7}{1000}$

2. (i) twenty units (ii) five tenths
(iii) six hundredths (iv) four thousandths

3. (i) 4.3 (ii) 16.07 (iii) 0.17
(iv) 6.03 (v) 12.028

4. (i) $\frac{1}{10}$ (ii) $\frac{3}{10}$ (iii) $\frac{1}{2}$
(iv) $\frac{4}{5}$ (v) $\frac{3}{5}$

5. (i) $\frac{1}{4}$ (ii) $\frac{3}{4}$ (iii) $\frac{7}{25}$
(iv) $\frac{1}{20}$ (v) $\frac{2}{25}$

6. (i) 0.9 (ii) 0.1 (iii) 0.5 (iv) 0.8
(v) 0.7 (vi) 0.16 (vii) 0.28 (viii) 0.25
(ix) 0.75 (x) 0.09

7. A = 0.3, B = 0.8, C = 1.8, D = 8.1, E = 9.2,
F = 9.7, G = 4.3, H = 4.6, I = 4.9, J = 0.25,
K = 0.75, L = 1.5

8. (i) 33.36 (ii) 22.368
(iii) 28.426 (iv) 5.332

9. (i) 14.6 (ii) 12.43 (iii) 9.28
(iv) 25.112 (v) 3.16 (vi) 2.026

10. (i) 18.93 (ii) 136.15
(iii) 46.309 (iv) 49.564

11. (i) 2.57 (ii) 14.7 (iii) 85.4
(iv) 62.53 (v) 2.146 (vi) 0.014

12. (i) 0.4 (ii) 0.4

13. (i) 0.55 (ii) 3.45 (iii) 4.65
(iv) 7.8 (v) 2.465 (vi) 0.05

14. (i) 0.08, 0.3, 0.36, 0.4, 0.45, 0.5
(ii) 1.96, 2.09, 2.17, 2.4, 2.52, 2.73

15. (i) 3 (ii) 8 (iii) 1
(iv) 2 (v) 7

16. (i) 860.5 (ii) 5.068

17. 14.42

Exercise 4.2

1. (i) 720   (ii) 1200   (iii) 4000
    (iv) 16   (v) 134   (vi) 1480
    (vii) 2136   (viii) 4850   (ix) 740
2. (i) 17.4   (ii) 1.84   (iii) 0.174
    (iv) 3.87   (v) 0.128   (vi) 0.018
    (vii) 0.387   (viii) 0.0146   (ix) 0.0089
3. (i) 230   (ii) 674   (iii) 0.86
    (iv) 34   (v) 0.0328   (vi) 0.04
    (vii) 4.7   (viii) 1.58
4. (i) 4.8   (ii) 15.5   (iii) 0.96
    (iv) 0.48   (v) 0.66   (vi) 0.69
    (vii) 0.16   (viii) 0.084
5. (i) 36.8   (ii) 49.36   (iii) 20.24
    (iv) 0.72   (v) 11.84   (vi) 76.2
    (vii) 2.55   (viii) 0.336
6. (i) 0.3   (ii) 5   (iii) 0.4
    (iv) 0.4   (v) 0.4   (vi) 0.5
7. (i) 6.4   (ii) 32.1
    (iii) 1.36   (iv) 11.23
8. (i) 4   (ii) 7   (iii) 27.7
    (iv) 15.35   (v) 60   (vi) 510
    (vii) 2.3   (viii) 36
9. (i) (1.2×4) (ii) (0.5×60)
    (iii) (3×0.9) (iv) (1.2×0.2)
    (v) (3×0.2) (vi) (0.8×0.2)
    (vii) (0.5×0.2) (viii) (1.2×0.9)
10. (i) 52.8   (ii) 52.8   (iii) 5.28
    (iv) 0.528   (v) 0.0528
11. (i) 1.6   (ii) 40
    (iii) 0.9   (iv) 0.06
12. (i) 264 m   (ii) 1320 m   (iii) 3168 m
13. (i) 26   (ii) 26   (iii) 2600
    (iv) 260   (v) 26 000
14. 9.13 kg   15. €69.20
16. 32   17. 88
18. 54   19. B
20. (iv)

Exercise 4.3

1. (i) 39   (ii) 12   (iii) 4
    (iv) 16   (v) 24
2. (i) 1.9   (ii) 13.7   (iii) 0.4
    (iv) 3.2   (v) 6.0
3. (i) 8.54   (ii) 0.35   (iii) 0.18
    (iv) 3.01   (v) 9.16
4. (i) 135 km   (ii) 87 km
    (iii) 136 km   (iv) 328 km
5. (i) 1.1   (ii) 0.8   (iii) 12.7
    (iv) 0.1   (v) 1.8
6. (i) CAKE   (ii) CHEESE   (iii) BREAD

7. A & Y, B & X, C & Z
8. (i) 0.5   (ii) 0.25   (iii) 0.75
    (iv) 0.125   (v) 0.375   (vi) 0.625
    (vii) 0.45   (viii) 0.12   (ix) 0.4375
    (x) 0.46875
9. (i) 0.83   (ii) 0.43   (iii) 0.36
    (iv) 0.44   (v) 0.36
10. (i) $\frac{3}{5}$ (ii) $\frac{7}{11}$ (iii) $\frac{7}{12}$ (iv) $\frac{6}{15}$
11. (i) 84   (ii) 12   (iii) 4
    (iv) 7.5   (v) 8   (vi) 24
12. (iv)
13. (i) 31.5, 34.8   (ii) 0.6, 0.6   (iii) 0.1, 0.1
14. (i) €1200
    (ii) Bigger; as each number is rounded up
15. C, A, E, B, D
16. C: 2.34

Test yourself 4

1. (i) 0.3   (ii) 4.7   (iii) 0.15
    (iv) 0.067   (v) 1.03
2. (i) 3.28   (ii) 1.495   (iii) 93.2
    (iv) 0.0328
3. (i) 124   (ii) 1.5   (iii) 12.06
4. (i) 24.6   (ii) 134
    (iii) 1.24   (iv) 4.128
5. (i) 7.53   (ii) 100
    (iii) 0.04563   (iv) 1000
6. $a = 4.2$, $b = 0.24$, $c = 6.375$
7. (i) 726   (ii) 0.726   (iii) 7.26
8. (i) BEAR   (ii) WHALE
    (iii) TIGER   (iv) ELEPHANT
9. (i) 0.72
    (ii) 2; (a) smaller   (b) bigger
10. 4.6125 & 4.61, 4.0613 & 4.06, 4.586 & 4.59,
    4.598 & 4.60, 4.6189 & 4.62
11. (i) $\frac{2}{5}$ (ii) $\frac{1}{4}$ (iii) $\frac{1}{8}$
    (iv) $\frac{2}{25}$ (v) $\frac{4}{25}$
12. €73
13. (i) 9.6   (ii) 4   (iii) 1
14. (i) 0.25×0.8 (0.2)   (ii) 0.8×1.2 (0.96)
    (iii) $12.6 \div 0.25$ (50.4)
15. D

For the problem solver... (4)

1. BURGER   2. 27 minutes
3. 0.42   4. 2.3 (decimal point)
5. (i) CHERRY   (ii) APPLE
    (iii) PEACH   (iv) GRAPE
6. (iv)   7. B

Chapter 5: Sets

Exercise 5.1

1. (i) Y   (ii) Y   (iii) N   (iv) Y
   (v) N   (vi) Y   (vii) N
2. A – days beginning with the letter S
   B – first six natural numbers
   C – summer months
   D – last five letters of the alphabet
   E – counties of Munster
   F – first five even natural numbers
   G – vowels (of the alphabet)
3. A – {a, b, c, d, e}
   B – {3, 5, 7, 9, 11, 13}
   C – {spring, summer, autumn, winter}
   D – {Tuesday, Thursday}
   E – {s, c, i, e, n}
   F – {Cork, Carlow, Cavan, Clare}
   G – {a, e, i}
   H – {red, orange, yellow, green, blue, indigo, violet}
4. (i) Assortment of road signs
   (ii) farm animals

Exercise 5.2

1. (i) T   (ii) F   (iii) T
   (iv) F   (v) F
2. (i) $\notin$ (ii) $\in$ (iii) $\in$
   (iv) $\notin$ (v) $\in$ (vi) $\notin$
   (vii) $\in$ (viii) $\notin$
3. (i) T   (ii) F   (iii) T
   (iv) T   (v) T   (vi) T
   (vii) F   (viii) T
4. A – {Mars, Mercury}; B – {a, e, i, o, u};
   C – {2, 4, 6, 8, 10, 12};
   D – {1, 2, 3, 4, 5, 6, 7, 8, 9, 10, 11, 12};
   E – {p, a, r, l, e}; F – {3, 5, 7, 9, 11, 13}
5. (i) {x|x is a whole number between 1 and 8 inclusive}
   (ii) {x|x is a vowel (of the English language)}
   (iii) {x|x is an even number between 1 and 15}
   (iv) {x|x is a solar system planet beginning with letter M}
   (v) {x|x is a euro currency coin}
6. (i) Y   (ii) N   (iii) Y   (iv) Y
   (v) N   (vi) Y   (vii) N   (viii) N
   (ix) Y   (x) Y
7. Yes (e.g. 10); No

Exercise 5.3

1. They contain exactly the same elements
2. A and D, B and C

3. No
4. $X = \{T, I, L, E\}$, $Y = \{L, I, T, E\}$; Yes
5. $B = \{6, 7, 8, 9\}$; No
6. $X = \{P, A, R, L, E\}$, $Y = \{R, E, P, A, L\}$; equal
7. (i) {10, 11, 12}   (ii) {2, 4, 6, 8, 10, 12}
   (iii) {1, 3, 5}   (iv) {3, 6, 9, 12}
8. (i) T   (ii) F   (iii) T
   (iv) F   (v) T
9. (i) T   (ii) F   (iii) T
   (iv) F   (v) T   (vi) T
10. (i) {a, b, c, d, e}, $\varnothing$
   (ii) {a}, {a, b}, {b, c, d, e} etc.
11. (i) {1}, {2}, {1, 2}, $\varnothing$
   (ii) {x}, {y}, {z}, {x, y}, {x, z}, {y, z}, {x, y, z}, $\varnothing$
12. $C\,\{5, 7, 9\}$
13. (i) T   (ii) F   (iii) T
   (iv) T   (v) T   (vi) F
14. $B = \{a, b, c, d\}$, $C = \{a, b, c\}$, $C = \{a, b\}$ etc.

Exercise 5.4

1. Venn diagram; $A = \{1, 3, 4, 6, 8\}$; $\#A = 5$
2. (i) {3, 4, 6, 8, 9}
   (ii) {3, 5, 7, 9, 10}
   (iii) {3, 9}
   (iv) {3, 4, 5, 6, 7, 8, 9, 10}
3. (i) $A = \{1, 2, 3, 7, 8, 9\}$
   (ii) $B = \{3, 4, 5, 6, 7\}$
   (iii) 4 (or 5 or 6)
   (iv) 10 (or 11)
   (v) 3, 7
4. (i) {3, 6, 7, 8, 9}   (ii) {1, 2, 3, 5, 7, 10}
   (iii) {3, 7}
   (iv) {1, 2, 3, 5, 6, 7, 8, 9, 10}
5. (i) {a, b, c, e}   (ii) {b, d, e, f, g}
   (iii) {b, e}   (iv) {a, b, c, d, e, f, g}
6. (i) T   (ii) T   (iii) F
   (iv) T   (v) T
8. (i) {4, 5, 6}   (ii) {4, 5, 6, 7, 8, 9, 10}
   (iii) {7, 8}   (iv) $\varnothing$
9. (i) {S, C, I, E, N}   (ii) {N, E, A, R}
   (iii) {E, N}   (iv) {S, C, I, E, N, A, R}
10. (i) {1, 2, 3, 4, 7, 8, 9}   (ii) {2, 7, 8}
   (iii) {2, 7, 8}   (iv) {1, 2, 3, 4, 7, 8, 9}
11. (i) {8, 12}
   (ii) {0, 1, 2, 3, 4, 5, 8, 9, 12}
   (iii) {8, 9}
   (iv) {0, 1, 2, 4, 8, 9, 10, 11, 12}
   (v) {1, 3, 5, 8, 9, 10, 11, 12}
   (vi) {1, 8}
12. (i) 7   (ii) 6   (iii) 3   (iv) 10
13. (i) T   (ii) F   (iii) T   (iv) T   (v) F
   (vi) T   (vii) T   (viii) F   (ix) T

Exercise 5.5

1. A'; (i) {1, 3, 4, 5, 6, 7, 9}
 (ii) {1, 3, 4, 7} (iii) {5, 6, 9}
2. (i) {a, d, e, f} (ii) {a, d, e, f, g, h, k}
 (iii) {g, h, k}
3. (i) {3, 4, 5, 6} (ii) {3, 4, 8, 9}
 (iii) {2, 7, 8, 9, 10} (iv) {2, 5, 6, 7, 10}
 (v) {3, 4, 5, 6, 8, 9} (vi) {2, 7, 10}
4. (i) {c, f, g, i, j, k} (ii) {b, c, e, j, k}
 (iii) {a, b, d, e, f, g, i} (iv) {c, j, k}
 (v) {a, d} (vi) {b, c, e, f, g, i, j, k}
5. (i) 5 (ii) 6 (iii) 2 (iv) 6 (v) 3
6. (i) {2, 4, 6, 8, 9, 10} (ii) {1, 2, 7, 8, 9, 10}
 (iii) {1, 3, 4, 5, 6, 7} (iv) {2, 8, 9,10}
8. (i) T (ii) T (iii) F
 (iv) T (v) F (vi) T
 (vii) T (viii) F (ix) F
9. (i) {1, 4, 5, 7, 8, 10} (ii) {1, 3, 5, 6, 7, 9}
 (iii) {3, 4, 6, 8, 9, 10} (iv) {1, 5, 7}
 (v) ∅
10. (i) B' (ii) A'
 (iii) $(A \cup B)'$ (iv) $(A \cap B)'$
11. (i) {1, 4, 6, 8, 9, 10, 12} (ii) {2, 4, 6, 8, 10, 12}
 (iii) {1, 2, 3, 5, 7, 9, 11} (iv) {4, 6, 8, 10, 12}
 (v) {1, 2, 4, 6, 8, 9, 10, 12}; Yes, the same

Test yourself 5

1. (i) {4, 6, 8, 10}
 (ii) {Wicklow, Westmeath, Waterford, Wexford}
 (iii) {C, O, M, I, T, E}
 (iv) {E, I, O}
 (v) {5, 10, 15, 20, 25, 30}
 (vi) {1, 2, 3, 4, 5, 6, 7, 8, 9}
2. (i) (a) {a, e, h, m, s, t, x} (b) {a, m}
 (ii) (a) 2 (b) 8
3. (i) {a, b, c, d, e} (ii) {b, c, e, l, m, n}
 (iii) {b, c, e}
4. (i) {1, 3, 5} (ii) ∅
 (iii) {1, 3, 5, 7, 8, 9, 10}
5. (i) {a, e, i, o, u, t} (ii) {o, p, q, r, s, t, u}
 (iii) {o, u, t} (iv) {a, e, i, o, p, q, r, s, t, u}
6. (i) {3, 4, 5, 7, 9} (ii) {2, 3, 4, 5, 6, 7, 8, 9}
 (iii) {2, 6, 8}
7. (i) {3, 4, 5, 6} (ii) {3, 4, 8, 9}
 (iii) {3, 4} (iv) {2, 3, 4, 5, 6, 7, 8, 9, 10}
 (v) {3, 4, 5, 6, 8, 9} (vi) {2, 7, 10}
8. (i) $A \cap B$ (ii) $A \cup B$
9. (iii) $A = D$
10. 'A is a subset of B';
 (i) ⊂ (ii) ⊂ (iii) ⊄ (iv) ⊄
11. (i) 7 (ii) 6 (iii) 3 (iv) 10
12. (i) T (ii) F (iii) T (iv) F

13. U

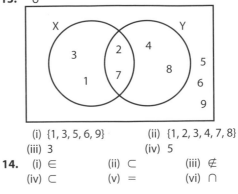

 (i) {1, 3, 5, 6, 9} (ii) {1, 2, 3, 4, 7, 8}
 (iii) 3 (iv) 5
14. (i) ∈ (ii) ⊂ (iii) ∉
 (iv) ⊂ (v) = (vi) ∩

For the problem solver... (5)

1. Straight Curves

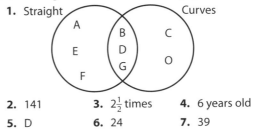

2. 141 **3.** $2\frac{1}{2}$ times **4.** 6 years old
5. D **6.** 24 **7.** 39

Chapter 6: Algebra

Exercise 6.1

1. (i) 2 (ii) 9 (iii) 6
 (iv) 12 (v) 7 (vi) 11
 (vii) 12 (viii) 30
2. (i) 8 (ii) 7 (iii) 10
 (iv) 10 (v) 20 (vi) 4
 (vii) 5 (viii) 30
3. (10 + 2), (9 + 3), (8 + 4) etc.
4. (15 − 6), (14 − 5), (13 − 4) etc.
5. (i) 11 (ii) 15 (iii) 3
 (iv) 10 (v) 15
 (vi) 2 (vii) 6 (viii) 11
6. (i) 24 (ii) 15 (iii) 36
 (iv) 90 (v) 10 (vi) 54
7. (i) 4 (ii) 8 (iii) 7
 (iv) 11 (v) 36 (vi) 12
8. (i) $\triangle + 7$ (ii) $\triangle - 4$ (iii) $2\triangle$
 (iv) $\dfrac{\triangle}{2}$ (v) $\dfrac{\triangle}{3}$ (vi) $\triangle - 6$
9. (i) 21 (ii) Increase by 6
 (iii) 21 (iv) Increase by 5
 (v) $\triangledown + 8$ (vi) ◯ + 17
 (vii) 16 (viii) ▢
 (ix) $\triangle - 36$ (x) Decrease by 9

10. (i) 4 (ii) 9 (iii) 9
(iv) 11 (v) 6 (vi) 8
(vii) 6 (viii) 18 (ix) 4
11. (i) $a + 8$ (ii) $b - 7$
(iii) $2c$ (iv) Increase by 9
(v) Decrease by 10 (vi) $5f$
(vii) Multiply by 3 (viii) Increase by k

Exercise 6.2

1. (i) $5a$ (ii) $4b$ (iii) $8x$
(iv) $12y$ (v) $8c$ (vi) $15a$
(vii) ab (viii) $4ab$
2. (i) $8ab$ (ii) $21xy$ (iii) $3ab$
(iv) abc (v) $6xy$ (vi) abc
(vii) $12xyz$ (viii) $10abc$
3. (i) $3x$ (ii) $6x$ (iii) $3a + 7$
(iv) $7b + 6$ (v) $5x + 10$ (vi) $4x + 3y$
4. (i) $3x$ (ii) $2a$ (iii) $3x$
(iv) $2a + 7$ (v) $7b - 6$ (vi) $5a + 2b$
5. (i) $15a + 6b$ (ii) $7x + 5y + 4$
(iii) $7x + 4$ (iv) $4x + 3$
(v) $8a + 3b + 2$ (vi) $6x + 1$
6. (i) $2ab$ (ii) $5ab$ (iii) $2xy$
(iv) $7cd$ (v) ab (vi) $4xy$
7. (i) $3p - q + r$ (ii) $2k + 5$
(iii) $7ab - 3c$ (iv) $4xy + 11z$
(v) $5ab + 5cd$ (vi) $11x - 8xy$
8. (i) $3y + 9$ (ii) $6x + 4$ (iii) $3a + 7$
9. (i) $a + 2b + c$ (ii) $2x + 6y + z$
(iii) $6a + 3$ (iv) $9x$
10. (i) B and E (ii) B and D (iii) C and D
(iv) D and F (v) $5x + 4$
11. (i) x and y (ii) As their values vary
(iii) 3 (iv) -8 (v) No
12. $4c - 3d + 7$

Exercise 6.3

1. (i) 4 (ii) 6 (iii) 12
(iv) 10 (v) 7 (vi) 12
(vii) 6 (viii) 30
2. (i) 8 (ii) 25 (iii) 25
(iv) 8 (v) 7 (vi) 5
(vii) 5 (viii) -6
3. (i) 2 (ii) 30 (iii) 16
(iv) 8 (v) 40 (vi) 8
(vii) 36 (viii) 38
4. (i) 12 (ii) 18 (iii) 12
(iv) 18 (v) 10 (vi) 60
5. (i) 4 (ii) 3 (iii) 33
(iv) 10 (v) 12 (vi) 26
6. (i) 3 (ii) 7 (iii) 15
(iv) 3 (v) 4 (vi) 2

7. (i) 7 (ii) 5 (iii) 1
(iv) 5 (v) $4\frac{1}{2}$ (vi) 6
8. (i) 2 (ii) -4 (iii) 4
(iv) -8 (v) -8 (vi) 4
(vii) 9 (viii) 10
9. ($p + 5$, 2), ($2p + 2$, -4),
($6 - p$, 9), ($3p$, -9),
($3 + 2p$, -3)
10. FRANCE   **11.** 49
12. England
13. (ii) 47
14. (ii) Yes

Exercise 6.4

1. $4x + 8$ **2.** $3a + 18$
3. $8a + 28$ **4.** $3x + 3y$
5. $10x + 5y$ **6.** $8x + 12y$
7. $12x - 6y$ **8.** $3x + 6y + 3$
9. $12a + 6b + 18$ **10.** $10a + 30$
11. $13x - 2y$ **12.** $9a + 19$
13. $9a + b$ **14.** $2x + 12y$
15. $3a + 7b$ **16.** $9x + y$
17. $-5a + 6$ **18.** $-4b$
19. $-x + 8y$ **20.** $6a - 2$
21. $-3c + 9d$ **22.** $7x + 8y - 3$
23. $6a + 8b + 2$ **24.** $8x - y + 6$
25. $14a - 2b$ **26.** $7x + y$
27. $2a + b$
28. (i) $6x + 10$ (ii) $12h + 20$

Exercise 6.5

1. 5^2 **2.** 4^3
3. a^2 **4.** b^3
5. $2a^2$ **6.** $3x^2$
7. $4b^2$ **8.** a^3
9. x^4 **10.** $4a^3$
11. $6a^2$ **12.** $20x^3$
13. $8x^2 + 23$ **14.** $7x^2 + 18$
15. $3x^2 + 16x$ **16.** $5x^2 + x$
17. $10x^2 - 9x$ **18.** $9a^2 - 13a$
19. $x^2 - 27x$ **20.** $3a^2 - 23a$
21. $-9x$ **22.** $3a^2 + 13a$
23. $5x^2 + 8$ **24.** $14a - 12$
25. (i) 4 (ii) 4 (iii) 8
(iv) 20 (v) 20
26. (i) 13 (ii) 21 (iii) 14
(iv) 22 (v) 35 (vi) 28
(vii) 15 (viii) 22
27. (i) 3 (ii) 15

28. (i) 9   (ii) 16   (iii) 22
    (iv) 6   (v) -12 (vi) -24
    (vii) 36   (viii) 33

29. 24 sq units

30. (i) C   (ii) D   (iii) E
    (iv) B   (v) A

Exercise 6.6

1. $x^2 + 3x + 2$ **2.** $x^2 + 4x + 3$
3. $x^2 + 6x + 8$ **4.** $x^2 + 7x + 10$
5. $x^2 + 7x + 12$ **6.** $2x^2 + 9x + 4$
7. $3x^2 + 20x + 12$ **8.** $2x^2 + 11x + 5$
9. $6x^2 + 11x + 4$ **10.** $x^2 + 2x - 8$
11. $x^2 + 2x - 15$ **12.** $2x^2 - 3x - 2$
13. $3x^2 - 7x - 6$ **14.** $3x^2 + 11x - 4$
15. $5x^2 - 18x - 8$ **16.** $x^2 - 9x + 20$
17. $6x^2 - 7x + 2$ **18.** $8x^2 - 22x + 12$
19. $6x^2 + 7x - 5$ **20.** $20x^2 + 7x - 6$
21. $8x^2 - 8x - 6$ **22.** $6a^2 + 5a - 6$
23. $10a^2 - a - 2$ **24.** $8a^2 - 10a - 3$
25. $ac + ad + bc + bd$ **26.** $xa + xb + ya + yb$
27. $ac + 2ad + 2bc + 4bd$
28. $6ab - 2ad - 9bc + 3cd$
29. $10a^2 - 7ab - 12b^2$ **30.** $x^2 + xy - 6y^2$
31. $x^2 - 4y^2$ **32.** $9x^2 - 4y^2$
33. $4x^2 + 4xy + y^2$ **34.** $x^2 + 6xy + 9y^2$
35. $4a^2 - 4ab + b^2$ **36.** $9x^2 - 12xy + 4y^2$

Test yourself 6

1. (i) $4x$ (ii) $10x + 2$ (iii) $7x^2 - 7x$
    (iv) $4a + b$ (v) $5p + 2q$ (vi) $6a^2 + 2a$

2. (i) 18   (ii) 12
    (iii) 14   (iv) 17

3. (i) $6p + 13q + 11$ (ii) 54

4. (i) a^2 (ii) b^3
    (iii) $a^2 b$ (iv) $4a^3$

5. (i)

$2a + 2b$

    (ii)

	$3m + 3n$	
$2m$		$m + 3n$

    (iii)

	$4a$	
$2a + b$		$2a - b$

6. (i) $10x - 9$ (ii) $16x^2 - 17x$
7. (i) 4   (ii) -30
    (iii) -13 (iv) -22
8. (i) $x + 4$ (ii) $x - 5$
    (iii) $2x + 4$ (iv) $3x + 6$
9. (i) $4m + 2$ (ii) 3
    (iii) $2m$ (iv) $5m + 4$

10. $x - y + 20$
11. (i) $2x^2 + 11x + 12$ (ii) $6x^2 + 13x - 5$
12. (i) PIG   (ii) GOAT   (iii) HORSE

For the problem solver... (6)

1. 12th
2. one
3. $A = 5$, $B = 4$, $C = 6$, $D = 2$
4. $J = 1$, $M = 9$, $C = 8$
5. 3
6. (i) four   (ii) three
7. E ($n = 11$)

Chapter 7: Percentages

Exercise 7.1

1. (i) (a) = 20%,   (b) = 35%,   (c) = 54%
    (ii) (a) = 80%,   (b) = 65%,   (c) = 46%
    (iii) (a) = $\frac{1}{5}$,   (b) = $\frac{7}{20}$,   (c) = $\frac{27}{50}$
    (iv) (a) = 0.2,   (b) = 0.35,   (c) = 0.54

2. (i) 28%   (ii) 54%
    (iii) 15   (iv) $\frac{90}{100} = 90\%$
    (v) $\frac{55}{100} = 55\%$ (vi) $\frac{56}{100} = 56\%$

3. (i) $\frac{1}{5}$ (ii) $\frac{3}{5}$ (iii) $\frac{7}{10}$
    (iv) $\frac{3}{20}$ (v) $\frac{1}{4}$ (vi) $\frac{3}{4}$
    (vii) $\frac{17}{20}$ (viii) $\frac{1}{2}$ (ix) $\frac{1}{50}$
    (x) $\frac{6}{25}$

4. $\frac{15}{200} = \frac{3}{40}$

5. (i) $\frac{1}{3}$ (ii) $\frac{1}{8}$ (iii) $\frac{1}{40}$
    (iv) $\frac{1}{12}$ (v) $\frac{7}{40}$

6. (i) (a) 50%   (b) 20%   (c) 35%
    (d) 80%   (e) 75%
    (ii) (a) 0.2   (b) 0.8   (c) 0.7
    (d) 0.65   (e) 0.95

7. (i) 18%   (ii) 47%   (iii) 30%
    (iv) 70%   (v) 25%   (vi) 40%
    (vii) 75%   (viii) 85%   (xi) 16%
    (x) 38%

8. (i) 0.5   (ii) 0.1   (iii) 0.9
    (iv) 0.35   (v) 0.45   (vi) 0.08
    (vii) 0.125   (viii) 0.24   (ix) 0.01
    (x) 0.245

9. (i) 80%   (ii) 40%   (iii) 75%
    (iv) 45%   (v) 15%   (vi) 7%
    (vii) 1%   (viii) 12.5%   (ix) 34.5%
    (x) 4.5%

10. (i) 36%   (ii) 40%   (iii) 36%

11. $\left(\frac{4}{5}, 80\%, 0.8\right)$; $\left(\frac{3}{4}, 75\%, 0.75\right)$; $\left(\frac{2}{5}, \frac{4}{10}, 40\%\right)$

12. (i) 20%, $\frac{1}{4}$, 0.3, $\frac{2}{5}$, 50%

(ii) $\frac{1}{5}$, $\frac{1}{4}$, $\frac{3}{10}$, 0.45, $\frac{1}{2}$, 60%

13. (i) 0.27   (ii) 0.07   (iii) 0.54

(iv) 0.175   (v) 0.025

14. 25%

15. (i) SATURN   (ii) VENUS   (iii) URANUS

16. (i) 55%   (ii) 32%   (iii) 48%

Exercise 7.2

1. (i) 5   (ii) 8   (iii) 12

(iv) 15   (v) 60   (vi) 48

(vii) 12   (viii) 66

2. (i) 38   (ii) 272   (iii) 504

(iv) €63   (v) €63   (vi) €728

3. 24, 12, 84

4. (i) 18 km   (ii) €101.25   (iii) 300 kg

5. $17\frac{1}{2}$% of €120

6. 58%, 75%, 80%, 68%, 70%, 80%, 58%

7. (i) 25%   (ii) 20%   (iii) 40%

(iv) 5%   (v) 12%   (vi) 15%

(vii) 30%   (viii) 40%   (ix) 8%

8. (i) 30 g   (ii) 30 g   (iii) 96 g

(iv) 35 g   (v) 18 g   (vi) 135 g

9. (i) 0.14   (ii) 0.27   (iii) 0.35

(iv) 0.06   (v) 0.09   (vi) 0.095

(vii) 0.3   (viii) 0.365   (ix) 0.963

(x) 0.203

10. (i) 42   (ii) 40.8   (iii) 5.88

(iv) 182   (v) 207   (vi) 9.75

11. 48% of €55   **12.** €50.15

13. (i) 660   (ii) 198

14. €787.50   **15.** 62%

16. French   **17.** 5%

18. 95%   **19.** 10%

20. (i) 80   (ii) $41\frac{1}{4}$%   (iii) $26\frac{1}{4}$%

21. (i) 15%   (ii) 60 g

Exercise 7.3

1. (i) 99   (ii) 72   (iii) 195

(iv) 36   (v) 96   (vi) 190

2. (i) 160   (ii) 495   (iii) 464

(iv) 322   (v) 504   (vi) €86.40

3. (i) 0.06   (ii) 0.15   (iii) 0.35

(iv) 0.7   (v) 0.075

4. (i) 0.38   (ii) 0.6   (iii) 0.13

(iv) 0.06   (v) 1.2   (vi) 0.125

5. (i) 264   (ii) 210   (iii) €119

(iv) 210 kg   (v) €97.20   (vi) 52 kg

6. (i) 585 g   (ii) 825 g   (iii) $287\frac{1}{2}$ g

7. 700   **8.** €350

9. €18 500   **10.** €1.62

11. €15.46   **12.** €107.20

13. 40%   **14.** €850

15. (i) €20 800   (ii) €17 680

Exercise 7.4

1. €680, €32, €585, €831.25

2. (i) €31.50   (ii) €56

3. €23 375   **4.** €3.20, €320, €320

5. €250

6. (i) €960   (ii) €780

(iii) €483   (iv) €836

7. €690   **8.** €1020

9. €166.50   **10.** €217.80, €847

11. €576   **12.** €696

13. €5082   **14.** €28

15. €240   **16.** €600

17. €620

Exercise 7.5

1. (i) €24   (ii) €40   (iii) €92

(iv) €54   (v) €6.97   (vi) €135

2. (i) 25% (P)   (ii) 20% (P)   (iii) 5% (P)

(iv) 20% (L)   (v) 30% (P)   (vi) 20% (L)

3. 15%

4. A = S; B = R; C = P; D = Q

5. (i) €8   (ii) €8   (iii) €72

(iv) €24   (v) €750

6. €770   **7.** 10%

8. €414   **9.** 25%

10. €1.50, €1.50, €150   **11.** €110

12. (i) €800   (ii) €920

13. (i) 1008   (ii) 26%

14. (i) €1250   (ii) €26

(iii) €310   (iv) 24.8%

15. €60

16. (i) €300   (ii) 2%

17. (i) €1200   (ii) $6\frac{2}{3}$%

Test yourself 7

1. (i) 25%   (ii) 40%   (iii) 34%

(iv) 70%   (v) 90%

2. (i) $\frac{1}{5}$ (ii) $\frac{1}{4}$ (iii) $\frac{9}{20}$

(iv) $\frac{1}{20}$ (v) $\frac{1}{8}$

3. (i) 75%   (ii) 20%   (iii) 25%

(iv) 37.5%

4. (i) 70%   (ii) 50%   (iii) 75%

(iv) 40%   (v) 30%

5. (i) 12   (ii) 43   (iii) 9
(iv) 300   (v) 105   (vi) 1080
(vii) $32\frac{1}{2}$ (viii) 6   (ix) 15

6.

$\frac{3}{4}$	0.75	75%
$\frac{3}{5}$	0.6	60%
$\frac{7}{10}$	0.7	70%
$\frac{2}{5}$	0.4	40%
$\frac{9}{10}$	0.9	90%

7. (i) 60%   (ii) 75%   (iii) 48%
8. (i) 120   (ii) 54
9. $87\frac{1}{2}$%, 85%, 80%, 90%, $87\frac{1}{2}$%
10. (i) 10%, 20%, $\frac{1}{4}$, 0.3, $\frac{2}{5}$ (ii) 40%, $\frac{1}{2}$, $\frac{3}{5}$, $\frac{3}{4}$, 0.78
11. (i) LION   (ii) TIGER
12. (i) 240   (ii) 7.5%
13. (i) €632.50   (ii) €148
14. 26%

For the problem solver... (7)

2. 1800 ml   **3.** D   **4.** A (5%)
5. 20%   **6.** E (410)

Chapter 8: Probability

Exercise 8.1

1. (i) 6   (ii) H1, H2, H3, T1, T2, T3
2. 8
3. HH, HT, TH, TT
4. (i) 10
(ii) H1, H2, H3, H4, H5, T1, T2, T3, T4, T5
5. 30   **6.** 20
7. (i) 12
(ii) G3, G4, G5, G6, B3, B4, B5, B6, R3, R4, R5, R6
8. 12   **9.** 25
10. 45   **11.** 24
12. HHH, HHT, HTT, HTH, THH, TTH, TTT, THT; 8
13. 24   **14.** 9

Exercise 8.2

1. a = Very Unlikely, b = Unlikely, c = Likely,
d = Very Likely
2. (i) E   (ii) B   (iii) C
(iv) A   (v) D
3. (i) Certain   (ii) Even Chance
(iii) Impossible   (iv) Likely
(v) Likely   (vi) Even Chance
(vii) Unlikely   (viii) Certain
(ix) Even Chance   (x) Unlikely
(xi) Impossible

4. (i) E   (ii) C   (iii) A
(iv) B   (v) D
6. (i) D   (ii) A
(iii) B   (iv) D
7. A = Impossible, B = Very Unlikely, C = $\frac{1}{3}$,
D = 0.5, E = Likely, F = $\frac{5}{6}$, G = Certain
9. (i) 0   (ii) $\frac{1}{2}$ (iii) $\frac{1}{2}$
(iv) $\frac{1}{4}$ (v) $\frac{3}{4}$ (vi) 1
10. (i) Lower   (ii) Higher
(iii) Equally Likely

Exercise 8.3

1. 1, 2, 3, 4, 5, 6;
(i) 2, 3, 4, 5   (ii) 2, 4, 6   (iii) 1, 6
(iv) 4, 5, 6   (v) 3, 5   (vi) 6
2. (i) 4   (ii) 3   (iii) 4
(iv) 1   (v) 3
3. (i) 3   (ii) 5   (iii) 2
(iv) 4   (v) 3   (vi) 3
4. Greater than 6
5. (i) Equally Likely   (ii) No
(iii) Equally Likely   (iv) No
6. (i) B   (ii) C   (iii) B   (iv) 3
7. (i) B   (ii) C   (iii) C
(iv) A   (v) B   (vi) C
8. (i) 6   (ii) 4   (iii) 2
(iv) 4   (v) 4

Exercise 8.4

1. (I) $\frac{3}{7}$ (II) $\frac{2}{7}$ (iii) $\frac{4}{7}$ (iv) $\frac{5}{7}$
2. (i) $\frac{3}{8}$ (ii) $\frac{1}{4}$ (iii) $\frac{1}{4}$
(iv) $\frac{3}{8}$ (v) $\frac{5}{8}$ (vi) $\frac{5}{8}$
3. (i) $\frac{1}{6}$ (ii) $\frac{1}{2}$ (iii) $\frac{1}{3}$
4. (i) $\frac{1}{5}$ (ii) $\frac{2}{5}$ (iii) $\frac{2}{5}$
5. (i) $\frac{1}{2}$ (ii) $\frac{1}{2}$ (iii) $\frac{1}{3}$
6. (i) Blue   (ii) $\frac{1}{3}$ (iii) $\frac{5}{9}$
(iv) 1 yellow and 2 blue
(v) 1 yellow
7. (i) $\frac{1}{10}$ (ii) $\frac{3}{10}$ (iii) $\frac{1}{2}$ (iv) $\frac{2}{5}$
(v) $\frac{4}{5}$ (vi) $\frac{1}{5}$ (vii) $\frac{4}{5}$ (viii) $\frac{1}{10}$
8. (i) $\frac{1}{4}$ (ii) $\frac{1}{3}$ (iii) $\frac{2}{3}$ (iv) $\frac{1}{2}$
(v) $\frac{1}{4}$ (vi) $\frac{1}{4}$ (vii) $\frac{5}{12}$ (viii) $\frac{1}{4}$
9. (i) $\frac{1}{4}$ (ii) $\frac{3}{8}$ (iii) $\frac{1}{4}$ (iv) $\frac{5}{8}$
10. (i) $\frac{1}{2}$ (ii) $\frac{1}{4}$ (iii) $\frac{1}{13}$ (iv) $\frac{1}{26}$
11. (i) $\frac{1}{2}$ (ii) $\frac{3}{10}$ (iii) $\frac{1}{2}$ (iv) $\frac{7}{10}$

12. (i) $\frac{1}{6}$ (ii) $\frac{1}{2}$ (iii) $\frac{1}{3}$ (iv) $\frac{2}{3}$

13. (i) $\frac{1}{9}$ (ii) $\frac{1}{3}$ (iii) $\frac{2}{9}$ (iv) $\frac{4}{9}$

14. (i) $\frac{1}{7}$ (ii) $\frac{3}{7}$ (iii) $\frac{4}{7}$

15. (i) 4   (ii) 5   (iii) $\frac{2}{5}$

16. (i) $\frac{7}{15}$ (ii) $\frac{2}{15}$ (iii) $\frac{3}{5}$ (iv) $\frac{3}{5}$

17. (i) $\frac{1}{6}$ (ii) $\frac{1}{3}$ (iii) $\frac{1}{3}$ (iv) $\frac{1}{6}$
    (v) $\frac{5}{12}$

18. (i) 3   (ii) 1   (iii) 5   (iv) $\frac{1}{2}$;
    (a) F   (b) T   (c) T

20. (i) $\frac{1}{4}$ (ii) $\frac{3}{8}$ (iii) $\frac{1}{4}$ (iv) $\frac{1}{8}$
    (v) $\frac{3}{8}$

21. (ii) $P(6) = \frac{1}{2} \Rightarrow$ Estimate of 50

Test yourself 8

1. (i) Impossible   (ii) Likely
    (iii) Evens   (iv) Certain
    (v) Unlikely

2. (i) A   (ii) B   (iii) E   (iv) G
    (v) C   (vi) D   (vii) F

3. 20, 25, 30, 35; Yes

4. (i) $\frac{1}{8}$ (ii) $\frac{1}{4}$ (iii) $\frac{5}{8}$ (iv) $\frac{7}{8}$
    (v) $\frac{3}{4}$

5. (i) 10   (ii) $\frac{1}{2}$ (iii) $\frac{2}{5}$ (iv) $\frac{2}{5}$
    (v) $\frac{1}{5}$ (vi) $\frac{3}{5}$

6. (i) $\frac{3}{20}$ (ii) $\frac{3}{5}$ (iii) $\frac{1}{5}$ (iv) $\frac{4}{5}$

7. (i) $A = \frac{5}{9}, B = \frac{3}{5}, C = \frac{2}{3}$
    (ii) $A = \frac{4}{9}, B = \frac{2}{5}, C = \frac{1}{3}$

8. It doesn't matter; $\frac{3}{5} = \frac{6}{10}$

9. (i) $\frac{2}{11}$ (ii) $\frac{4}{11}$ (iii) $\frac{9}{11}$

For the problem solver... (8)

1. 6   **2.** D (4)   **3.** 56
4. 1   **5.** 85
6. (i) 3   (ii) 5
7. 1st January (today); 31st December (birthday)
8. E

Chapter 9: Perimeter and Area

Exercise 9.1

1. (i) 8 cm 4 mm   (ii) 12 cm 6 mm
    (iii) 11 cm

2. (i) 28.5 cm   (ii) 28 cm
    (iii) 7.6 cm   (iv) 150 cm

3. (i) 300 cm   (ii) 360 cm
    (iii) 70 cm   (iv) 53 cm

4. (i) 50 mm   (ii) 4.5 cm
    (iii) 65 mm   (iv) 28 cm
    (v) 240 cm   (vi) 75 cm

5. (i) 25 cm   (ii) 90 mm   (iii) 0.25 m

7. (i) 12 cm   (ii) 14 cm   (iii) 16 cm

8. (i) 32 cm   (ii) 88 cm   (iii) 41 m

9. (i) 20 cm   (ii) 22 cm   (iii) 21 m
    (iv) 22 cm

10. (i) 36 cm   (ii) 32 cm   (iii) 24 cm

11. (i) 44 cm   (ii) 60 cm   (iii) 34 cm

12. (i) 50 cm   (ii) 56 cm   (iii) 176 m

13. (i) 182 cm
    (ii) (36 cm + 55 cm) $\times$ 2 = 182 cm

14. (i) 54 cm   (ii) 44 cm   (iii) 38 cm

15. (i) 46 cm   (ii) 72 cm

16. (i) 6 m   (ii) 7 cm

17. (i) 8 cm   (ii) 64 cm

Exercise 9.2

1. (i) 5 cm²   (ii) 7 cm²   (iii) 12 cm²
    (iv) 7 cm²   (v) 4.5 cm²   (vi) 9 cm²

2. 16.8 km²

3. (i) 63 cm²   (ii) 468 cm²   (iii) 102 m²

4. (i) 112 cm²   (ii) 105 cm²   (iii) 198 cm²

5. (i) 49 m²   (ii) 225 cm²   (iii) 484 mm²

6. (i) 5 m   (ii) 20 m

7. (i) 9 cm   (ii) 12 cm   (iii) 20 m

8. (i) 8 cm   (ii) 20 m   (iii) 12 mm

9. (i) 24 cm   (ii) 22 cm²

10. (i) 124 cm²   (ii) 96 cm²   (iii) 1436 m²

11. (i) 36 m²   (ii) 27 m²

12. (i) 20 cm²   (ii) 15 cm²   (iii) 30 cm²
    (iv) 48 cm²   (v) 156 cm²   (vi) 36 cm²

13. (i) 42 cm²   (ii) 31.5 cm²   (iii) 120 cm²

14. A = 8 cm², B = 9 cm², C = 10 cm², D = 12 cm²

15. (i) 4   (ii) 10   (iii) 6

16. (i) 100 cm²   (ii) 182 cm²   (iii) 270 cm²

17. (i) 4.2 m²   (ii) 4.5 m²

18. 2100 cm²

19. (i) 1050 cm²   (ii) 352 m²

20. 50 cm²

21. (i) 252 cm²   (ii) 264 m²

22. (i) 13.5 m²   (ii) 9 m²

23. 10 m²   **24.** €84   **25.** €780

Test yourself 9

1. (i) 60 cm   (ii) 72 cm
    (iii) 39 cm   (iv) 92 cm

2. (i) 216 cm²   (ii) 260 cm²
    (iii) 67.5 cm²   (iv) 529 cm²

4. (i) 69 cm²   (ii) 90 m²   (iii) 165 mm²
5. X = 8 cm², Y = 6 cm², Z = 10 cm²
6. (i) 100 cm²   (ii) 182 cm²
   (iii) 270 cm²
7. (i) 106 m²   (ii) 117 m²
8. 5 cm
9. (i) 25 cm   (ii) 32 cm²
10. (ii) It is a square   (iii) 625 m²

For the problem solver... (9)

1. E
2. 16 cm
3. E (4 cm)
4. 4.5 cm²
5. 90 cm
6. 400 cm²
7. The explanation is based on the fact that the diagonal of a rectangle bisects its area.
8. 270 cm²
9. A
10. 27 sq units
11. D (36 cm²)
12. D

Chapter 10: Geometry 1:
Points – Angles – Lines

Exercise 10.1

3. (i) Line AB   (ii) Line segment [AB]
   (iii) Ray [AB   (iv) Ray [BA
5. (i) 4 cm   (ii) 4.5 cm
   (iii) 4.5 cm   (iv) 4.9 cm
6. (i) [AD]   (ii) [CB]   (iii) [AC]
7. (i) 2.8 cm   (ii) 44.8 m

Exercise 10.2

1. ∠ADC, ∠ABC, ∠NLM, ∠NML
2. ∠D, ∠B, ∠L, ∠M
3. River NILE
4. ∠ABC
5. HOW ARE YOU?
6. (i) Acute   (ii) Right
   (iii) Obtuse   (iv) Acute
7. A: acute, B: obtuse, C: acute, D: obtuse, E: reflex, F: acute
8. 360°, 180°, 90°, 120°, 60°, 30°
9. (i) $\frac{1}{4}$ (ii) $\frac{1}{2}$ (iii) $\frac{1}{12}$ (iv) $\frac{2}{3}$
10. (i) 90°   (ii) 180°   (iii) 30°   (iv) 240°
11. (i) 120°   (ii) 60°   (iii) 180°   (iv) 90°
   (v) 120°   (vi) 120°   (vii) 210°   (viii) 240°
12. (i) 120°   (ii) 75°   (iii) 135°   (iv) 105°

Exercise 10.3

1. (i) 110°   (ii) 150°   (iii) 80°   (iv) 20°
2. A = 117°, B = 143°, C = 73°, D = 85°, E = 112°, F = 45°

3. (i) 14°   (ii) 33°   (iii) 62°
4. A = 140°, B = 130°, C = 100°, D = 70°, E = 215°, F = 23°
5. (i) 30°   (ii) 40°   (iii) 18°
6. A = 70°, B = 110°, C = 100°, D = 80°, E = 110°, F = 70°
7. a = 150°, b = 30°, c = 40°, d = 140°, e = 140°, f = 40°, g = 140°
8. (i) 30°   (ii) 65°   (iii) 35°
9. (i) 120°   (ii) 40°   (iii) 30°
10. A = 58°, B = 137°
12. A = 71°, B = 98°, C = 72°
13. a = 100°, b = 80°, c = 80°, d = 138°, e = 42°, f = 42°, g = 70°, h = 110°, i = 110°, j = 52°, k = 128°, l = 128°
14. (i) (a) 100°   (b) 80°
   (ii) B is true

Exercise 10.4

1. (i) 5   (ii) 4   (iii) 7
   (iv) 7   (v) 6   (vi) 4
2. A = 140°, B = 50°, C = 130°, D = 65°, E = 65°
3. (i) 7   (ii) 6   (iii) 4
4. (i) (1, 3), (2, 4), (6, 7), (5, 8)
   (ii) (1, 7), (2, 5) etc.
   (iii) (3, 7), (4, 5)
5. A = 40°, B = 140°, C = 60°, D = 120°, E = 120°, F = 60°, G = 120°
6. a = 110°, b = 70°, c = 50°, d = 50°, e = 36°, f = 72°, g = 72°
7. x = 104°, y = 104°
8. A = 110°, B = 70°, C = 50°, D = 130°, E = 134°
9. (i) (c) is true
   (ii) |∠A| must be greater or equal to 135°
10. (i) d   (ii) g   (iii) c
   (iv) d   (v) f   (vi) d
   (vii) e   (viii) e   (ix) e
   (x) e
11. V = 58°, W = 60°, X = 62°, Y = 60°, Z = 60°
12. a = 50°, b = 50°, c = 42°, d = 44°

Exercise 10.5

1. (i) 90°   (ii) AC
2. (i) PQ   (ii) SP and RQ
   (iii) PS
3. (i) [PC] and [HG]   (ii) [DH] and [CG]
   (iii) 3   (iv) [BC], [FG], [EF] etc
4. (i) T   (ii) F   (iii) T
   (iv) F   (v) T   (vi) T
8. (i) ∠D and ∠C (ii) [DC]   (iii) ∠A
   (iv) ∠E or ∠B   (v) ED ∥ BC

9. (i) River Road (ii) Church Road
(iii) Lacken Road and River Road
10. (i) 20° (ii) 18° (iii) 30°
11. $x = 90°, y = 20°$

Test yourself 10

1. (i) ∠ABC (ii) ∠FIG
(ii) $x = 130°, y = 60°, z = 86°$
(iii) $a = 110°, b = 70°, c = 140°, d = 55°,$
$e = 125°$
2. (i) AB ∥ DE, AD ∥ BE; AD ⊥ AB, DE ⊥ BE etc
(ii) (a) 60° (b) 150° (c) 105°
(iii) $A = 50°, B = 140°, C = 50°, D = 70°$
3. (i) $a = 40°, b = 80°, c = 48°$
(ii) $a = 70°, b = 110°, c = 70°, d = 108°,$
$e = 72°, f = 108°, g = 84°, h = 96°,$
$i = 84°$
(iii) $A = 125°, B = 44°$
4. (ii) $a = 40°, b = 90°, c = 50°, d = 40°,$
$e = 60°, f = 60°, g = 60°, h = 60°$
(iii) $A = 70°, B = 50°, C = 60°$

For the problem solver... (10)

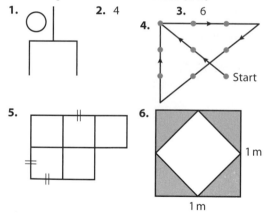

1. **2.** 4 **3.** 6
4.
Start
5. **6.**
1 m
1 m

Chapter 11: Ratio and Proportion
Exercise 11.1

1. (i) $\frac{5}{12}$ (ii) 5 : 7 (iii) 7 : 12
2. (i) 4 : 9 (ii) 1 : 3 (iii) 3 : 10
3. (i) 2 (ii) 8 (iii) 3
(iv) 9 (v) 8
4. (i) 2 : 1 (ii) 3 : 1 (iii) 1 : 5
(iv) 1 : 3 (v) 2 : 3
5. (i) 3 : 2 (ii) 5 : 8 (iii) 3 : 7
(iv) 2 : 5 (v) 5 : 9
6. (i) 15 (ii) 25 ml (iii) 600 g
(iv) 600 ml (v) 15

7. (i) 750 g (ii) 6 eggs (iii) 2000 g
(iv) 10
8. (i) 6 (ii) 6 (iii) 4
(iv) 21 (v) 1 (vi) 3
9. (i) 1 : 5 (ii) 5 : 14 (iii) 1 : 4
(iv) 1 : 5 (v) 1 : 3 (vi) 3 : 1
10. (i) 2 : 3 (ii) 3 : 5
11. (i) 1 : 4 (ii) 1 : 6 (iii) 3 : 1
(iv) 2 : 7
12. (i) 1 : 4 (ii) 2 : 1 (iii) 1 : 3
(iv) 1 : 2 (v) 1 : 2 (vi) 5 : 8
(vii) 6 : 7 (viii) 4 : 5
13. (i) 24 (ii) $2\frac{1}{2}$ (iii) 3

Exercise 11.2

1. (i) $\frac{2}{5}$ (ii) $\frac{3}{5}$
(iii) Anna – €36, Billy – €54
2. Claire – €250, Dara – €150
3. 16
4. Pat – 24; Emer – 12
5. (i) €90, €30 (ii) €306, €408
(iii) €66, €55 (iv) €74.55, €31.95
(v) €480, €384 (vi) 81 mins, 9 mins
6. €800 : €400 : €200
7. 40
8. Beet – 39. barley – 52
9. €231
10. 13
11. 70 cm
12. 288
13. (i) 70 (ii) 90 (iii) 105
14. (i) 40 kg (ii) 10 kg (iii) 18
15. 30 home wins and 5 draws
16. €2880
17. (i) 27 (ii) 36
18. (i) 400 g (ii) 80 g
19. Alan – €3240, Emer – €2160; Alan – €3000,
Emer – €2400
20. (i) 5 : 7 (ii) 25 : 49
21. 3 : 1
22. 195

Exercise 11.3

1. (i) 2 : 3 (ii) $\frac{3}{5}$ (iii) 40%
2. (i) $\frac{7}{10}$ (ii) 30% (iii) 7 : 3
3. (ii) $\frac{3}{4}$ (iii) $\frac{2}{3}$ (iv) $\frac{7}{10}$
(v) $\frac{4}{7}$ (vi) Boys
4. (i) $\frac{1}{6}$ (ii) $\frac{5}{6}$ (iii) 1 : 5
5. (i) and (iii)

6. (i)

x	5	7	9
y	10	14	18

(ii)

x	8	9	11
y	24	27	33

(iii)

x	10	18	30
y	5	9	15

7. €71.10   **8.** €10.12   **9.** €54.95
10. €688   **11.** 250 km   **12.** 270 g
13. (i) €162   (ii) 23 hours
14. (i) 280 km   (ii) 120 km
15. (i) 625 g   (ii) 10
    (iii) 300 g
16. (i) 75 mins   (ii) 176 km
17. (i) €42   (ii) 250 km
18. (i) 5 m   (ii) 3.5 cm
19. (i) 400   (ii) $4\frac{1}{2}$ mins
20. (i) (a) 2.28 l   (b) 2 l   (c) 0.95 l
    (ii) (a) 5.3 pints   (b) 2.65 pints
      (c) 1.6 pints
    (iii) 8.5 l

Exercise 11.4

1. (i) €1.04   (ii) €0.98   (iii) Value pack
2. 80-bag box
3. (i) €1.28   (ii) €1.20   (iii) Large   (iv) Lighter
4. S: €0.90; M: €0.77; L: €0.82; EL: €0.88; Medium
5. Family size   **6.** 1.5 l
7. Large size   **8.** 24, 8
9. (i) 18 days (ii) 6 days   **10.** 9 days
11. (i) 20 days (II) 5 days (iii) 8 days
12. 45   **13.** 16 days
14. (i) 6 days   (ii) 20 days   **15.** (i) 9 days   (ii) 12
16. (i) 6 days   (ii) 9   **17.** (i) 18 days (ii) 45
18. (i) $\frac{1}{12}$ (ii) $\frac{1}{6}$ (iii) $\frac{1}{4}$ (iv) 4 mins

Test yourself 11

1. (i) 1:6   (ii) 2:3   (iii) 2:3
    (iv) 3:4   (v) 3:2
2. (i) $\frac{7}{9}$ (ii) $\frac{2}{9}$
    (iii) Ava – €70, Barry – €20
3. (i) $\frac{4}{9}$ (ii) 4:9   (iii) 81 cm²
4. (i) 500 g   (ii) 125 g   (iii) 10
5. 45 l   **6.** 240 tigers
7. €462   **8.** €83.25
9. (i) L – €2.16, S – €2.28, E – €2.26, T – €3.10
    (ii) L, E, S, T
10. Sarah – €150, Jack – €300, Ciara – €450
11. 9
12. (i) 20%   (ii) 1:4
13. (i) 15   (ii) 7   (iii) 1

14. (i) 75 kg   (ii) 20 kg
15. 275 km   **16.** 80° : 60° : 40°
17. (i) 231 km   (ii) 60 litres
18. 750 g   **19.** €5.76

For the problem solver... (11)

1. 4.20 pm   **2.** 7 mins
3. 24 000 km   **4.** 5 children
5. 2 hours
6. (i) Each bigger one is twice the size of the
        smaller one, i.e. A3 = 2A4 = 4A5
    (ii) Same ratio of length to breadth
7. 70 children   **8.** €2.42
9. 5 days   **10.** E$\left(\frac{7}{8}\right)$

Chapter 12: Collecting Data

Exercise 12.1

1. (i) 15   (ii) 21
2. (i) 13   (ii) 51   (iii) White
3. (i) A = 28, B = 12, C = 23, D = 5, E = 2
    (ii) Walk   (iii) $\frac{1}{14}$ (iv) Car and Bus
4. (ii) 9   (iii) Red   (iv) Blue
5. (i) 10 years   (ii) 10
    (iii) 11   (iv) 8
6. (i) 10   (ii) 6–10   (iii) 17

Exercise 12.2

1. (i) P   (ii) P   (iii) S
    (iv) S   (v) P   (vi) S
2. (i) N   (ii) N   (iii) C
    (iv) C   (v) N
3. (i) C   (II) N
4. (i) D   (ii) D   (iii) C
    (iv) C   (v) D   (vi) D
5. (i) Cost of its postage
    (ii) Weight of the parcel
6. (i) 5-door, €18 000, 40 km/hr
    (ii) discrete, discrete, continuous
7. 5 eggs – discrete; 200 g flour – continuous
8. (i) D   (ii) D   (iii) C
    (iv) C   (v) D
9. (a) Primary   (b) (i) and (ii)   (c) (iii)
10. Categorical, ordinal

Exercise 12.4

3. B more suitable   **5.** (i) Too personal
10. B is better
11. (i) Too personal
    (ii) Leading question
    (iii) Not specific enough considering the time-
         frame of one week

Test yourself 12

1. (i) D   (ii) D   (iii) C   (iv) C
   (v) D   (vi) C   (vii) D
2. (i) C   (ii) N   (iii) C
   (iv) C   (v) N   (vi) C
3. (i) N   (ii) C   (iii) C   (iv) C
4. (i) D   (ii) Colour (or type)
5. (i) P   (ii) S   (iii) P
   (iv) S   (v) P
6. $33\frac{1}{3}\%$ 8. All leading questions
9. As most of the people there would have driven due to the location.

For the problem solver... (12)

1. 6D   2. $29\frac{1}{3}$ sec
3. 5   4. 1122
5. (i) 20 km   (ii) 11 km
   (iii) A → B → G → D → C → E → F → H → I
6. 640

Chapter 13: Coordinates

Exercise 13.1

1. A(3, 9), B(9, 5), C(10, 1), D(11, 3)
2. A(2, 1), B(12, 1), C(12, 5), D(9, 8), E(7, 7), F(5, 3), G(2, 3)
3. A(1, 2), B(2, 8), C(3, 4), D(3, 2), E(6, 1), F(10, 2), G(8, 4), H(5, 5), I(7, 7), J(10, 7), K(6, 9), L(9, 10)
4. a square
5. (i) (a) DOG   (b) HORSE   (c) MONKEY
   (ii) (a) LIFFEY   (b) BOYNE   (c) SLANEY
6. (i) (a) (8, 2)   (b) (7, 5)   (c) (4, 4)
   (ii) (a) Caves   (b) Pool   (c) Pier
   (d) Evergreen tree
7. x-axis
8. (0, 1), (0, 4), (0, −3), (0, −7), etc
9. (i) (a) (2, 7)   (b) (9, 6)   (c) (4, 4)   (d) (0, 5)
   (ii) Telephone box
   (iii) Pub and church
   (iv) Bus stop and telephone box
   (v) (3, 0), (6, 0), (6, 2), (3, 2)

Exercise 13.2

1. A(2, 2), B(3, 3), C(5, 3), D(5, 1), E(3, 1), F(−2, 3), G(−4, 2), H(−3, 1), I(−4, −1), J(−2, −1), K(−3, −2), L(3, −1), M(4, −3), N(1, −2)
3. (i) D(−2, −3)   (ii) S(−1, −2)
4. (i) A(5, 2), B(2, 4)
   (ii) J(−4, −2), G(−2, −3)
   (iii) L(2, −1), H(4, −1)
   (iv) F(−3, 0), I(4, 0)
   (v) C(0, 1), K(0, −2)

5. A –1st, B– 4th, C – 3rd, D – 3rd
6. (i) x-axis   (ii) y-axis   (iii) x-axis
   (iv) y-axis   (v) both axes
7. (ii) (2, 4)
8. (iii) D(−1, 2)
9. (i) (11, 9), (13, 10)
   (ii) (11, 8), (13, 10)
   (iii) (8, −2), (9, −4)
   (iv) (−8, −6), (−10, −9)
10. (i) The x-coordinate and y-coordinate together add up to 8
    (ii) (7, 1), (0, 8), (−2, 10)
11. A(5, −3), B(−3, −3), C(−2, 3), D(3, 0), E(0, −2)
12. A(3, 2), B(7, −3)
13. (2 km WEST, 6 km SOUTH)
14. (i) (6, 4), (9, 6)   (ii) (12, 8)   (iii) (15, 10)

Exercise 13.3

1. (i) A(−4, 3), B(2, 3), C(2, −1), D(−4, −3)
   (ii) (a) (−1, 3)   (b) (2, 1)   (c) (−4, 0)
2. (i) A(−2, 5), B(4, 5), C(4, −3)
   (ii) (a) (1, 5)   (b) (4, 1)
   (iii) D (−2, −3)
3. (i) (4, 3)
   (ii) Add the x-values and divide by two and do likewise with the y-values
4. (i) (3, 2)   (ii) (3, 3)   (iii) (2, 4)
   (iv) (5, 2)   (v) (3, 3)   (vi) (3, 1)
5. (i) $\left(3, \frac{5}{2}\right)$
6. (i) (2, 4)   (ii) (4, 3)   (iii) (2, 1)
   (iv) (2, 5)   (v) (2, 1)   (vi) (3, −3)
7. (1, 0); x-axis
8. (i) (4, 0)   (ii) (1, −1)   (iii) $\left(-\frac{1}{2}, -\frac{1}{2}\right)$
9. (i) (−1, 0)   (ii) Yes it is
10. (0, 2)   11. (5, 4)

Test yourself 13

1. (i) A(3, 10), B(11, 10), C(14, 7), D(12, 7), E(2, 7), F(0, 7), G(2, 1)
   (ii) (3, 1), (3, 6), (6, 6), (6, 1)
2. (i) (a) (2, 1)   (b) (−2, 1)   (c) (−3, −1)
   (d) (0, −1)
   (ii) Post office, bus station, park
3. a quadrilateral (trapezium)
4. A(2, 4), B(3, 2), C(2, −1), D(−1, 3), E(−4, 2), F(−4, −1), G(−2, −3), H(4, −3)
5. (i) A(−3, 4), B(1, 4), C(1, −2)
   (ii) D(−3, −2)
   (iii) (a) (−1, 4)   (b) (1, 1)   (c) (−1, 1)
6. (0, 3), (0, 1), $\left(2, \frac{1}{2}\right)$
7. (i) 3   (ii) −2   (iii) (1, 2)

For the problem-solver... (13)

1. a swan
2. D$(-6, -2)$
3. E$(1, 1)$

Chapter 14: Solving Equations

Exercise 14.1

1. 2	**2.** 7	**3.** 11	**4.** 12
5. 13	**6.** 12	**7.** 12	**8.** 6
9. 6	**10.** 6	**11.** 4	**12.** 35
13. 8	**14.** 24	**15.** 4	**16.** 12 g
17. 8 g	**18.** 9 g	**19.** 8 g	**20.** 5 g
21. 4 g	**22.** 8 g		

Exercise 14.2

1. (i) 12 g (ii) 6 g

2. $x = 6$	**3.** $x = 12$	**4.** $x = 5$
5. $x = 8$	**6.** $x = 11$	**7.** $x = 10$
8. $x = 8$	**9.** $x = 11$	**10.** $x = 8$
11. $x = 4$	**12.** $x = 5$	**13.** $x = 3$
14. $x = 5$	**15.** $x = 5$	**16.** $x = 4$
17. $x = 2$	**18.** $x = 5$	**19.** $x = 2$
20. $x = 4$	**21.** $x = 11$	**22.** $x = 7$
23. $x = 4$	**24.** $x = 4$	**25.** $x = 5$
26. $x = 3$	**27.** $x = 2$	**28.** $x = 3$
29. $x = 7$	**30.** $x = 6$	**31.** $x = 4$
32. $x = 1$	**33.** $x = 4$	**34.** $x = 10$
35. 6	**36.** 6	**37.** 6
38. 8	**39.** 3	

40. (i) $x = 4$ (ii) $x = 6$ (iii) $x = 8$

Exercise 14.3

1. $7x + 4 = 3x + 20; x = 4$

2. $x = 4$	**3.** $x = 5$	**4.** $x = 6$
5. $x = 3$	**6.** $x = 5$	**7.** $x = 1$
8. $x = 6$	**9.** $x = 5$	**10.** $x = 3$
11. $x = 8$	**12.** $x = 6$	**13.** $x = 7$
14. $x = 7$	**15.** $x = 5$	**16.** $x = 9$

17. (i) 3 (ii) 2

18. 7 cm

19. 180°; (i) 35° (ii) 30° (iii) 50°

20. RABBIT

Exercise 14.4

1. $x = 3$	**2.** $x = 4$	**3.** $x = 2$
4. $x = 3$	**5.** $x = 5$	**6.** $x = 6$
7. $x = 2$	**8.** $x = 5$	**9.** $x = 10$
10. $x = 6$	**11.** $x = 1$	**12.** $x = 10$
13. $x = 10$	**14.** $x = 3$	**15.** $x = 3$
16. $x = 4$	**17.** $x = 5$	**18.** $x = 3$
19. 2	**20.** 5	

Exercise 14.5

1. (i) $x + 2$ (ii) $x + 4$ (iii) $x - 3$
   (iv) $x - 10$ (v) $x + 14$ (vi) $2x$
   (vii) $5x$ (viii) $2x + 2$

2. (i) $x + 6 = 12$ (ii) $x - 7 = 10$
   (iii) $2x = 14$ (iv) $2x + 5 = 19$
   (v) $3x - 6 = 15$ (vi) $4(x + 2) = 28$

3. (i) $3n + 7 = 19$ (ii) $4n - 5 = 17$
   (iii) $4(n + 3) = 28$ (iv) $3(n - 2) = 9$

Exercise 14.6

1. 6	**2.** 7	**3.** 8
4. 3	**5.** 4	**6.** 3
7. 27, 32	**8.** 6	**9.** 7, 12

10. (i) 7 (ii) 5 (iii) $\frac{4}{5}$

11. 4	**12.** 7	**13.** 4

14. Mary = 23, Ann = 28

15. (i) 6 (ii) 12 (iii) 23

16. (i) $x = 44°$ (ii) $x = 29°$

17. 16 years old

18. (i) $3(a + 5) + 3(a + 5) + 4(2a + 1) = 76$
   (ii) $a = 3$ (iii) 24 cm

19. (i) $(x - 7)$ years (ii) $(2x - 7)$ years
   (iii) 13 years old

Test yourself 14

1. (i) $x = 2$ (ii) $x = 1$ (iii) $x = 2$

2. 12

3. (i) $x = 4$ (ii) $x = 7$

4. (i) $x = 3$ (ii) $x = 6$ (iii) $x = 5$

5. 9	**6.** 1 cm

7. (i) $x = 6$ (ii) $x = 6$ (iii) $x = 3$

8. 10 cm	**9.** 14

10. (i) $x = 4$ (ii) $x = 0$

11. 3	**12.** 6 cm

13. (i) 11 (ii) 6 **14.** 3

For the problem solver... (14)

1. D	**2.** B	**3.** A	**4.** E
5. $P = 3, Q = 2, R = 6, S = 5$			**6.** C

Chapter 15: Geometry 2 – Triangles

Exercise 15.1

1. (i) 55° (ii) 43° (iii) 82°
   (iv) 5 cm (v) 6 cm (vi) 7 cm

2. 32°

4. $A = 30°, B = 56°, C = 19°, D = 49°$

5. $A = 45°, B = 70°, C = 28°, D = 99°, E = 28°,$
   $F = 72°, G = 58°, H = 19°$

6. $A = 110°$, $B = 101°$, $C = 30°$, $D = 141°$,
   $E = 118°$, $F = 68°$
7. (i) $a = 55°$, $b = 100°$
   (ii) $a = 100°$, $b = 55°$
   (iii) $a = 70°$, $b = 110°$
8. $x = 120°$, $y = 85°$
9. $a = 78°$, $b = 42°$, $c = 60°$, $d = 102°$, $e = 78°$
10. As a reflex angle is greater than 180°

Exercise 15.2

1. 4 and 5; (i) 5 (ii) 4 (iii) 180°
2. $A = 138°$, $B = 64°$, $C = 119°$, $D = 120°$,
   $E = 79°$, $F = 115°$
3. (i) 70°   (ii) 70°   (iii) 54°
4. (i) $x = 50°$, $y = 45°$
   (ii) $x = 65°$, $y = 50°$
   (iii) $x = 45°$, $y = 70°$
5. both 56°
6. $x = 70°$, $y = 68°$

Exercise 15.3

1. △PQT, △QRT, △TRS
2. (i) Isosceles
   (ii) Equilateral
   (iii) △BEC
3. (i) Isosceles
   (ii) Equilateral
   (iii) Right-angled
   (iv) Right-angled isosceles
   (v) Scalene
4. 2 and 3; 5 and 6; 7 and 9; b and c; x and z;
   p and r; d and e; m and n
5. $A = 70°$, $B = 72°$, $C = 55°$, $D = 68°$, $E = 70°$,
   $F = 30°$, $G = 40°$, $H = 112°$, $I = 70°$, $J = 60°$,
   $K = 90°$, $L = 70°$
6. (i) Equilateral   (ii) 60°
   (iii) 92°
7. (i) 140°   (ii) 80°
   (iii) 60°
8. (i) Isosceles   (ii) 74°
   (iii) 60°   (iv) 46°
9. (i) 56°   (ii) 80°   (iii) 62°
10. $c = 64°$, $d = 52°$

Test yourself 15

1. $a = 55°$, $b = 80°$, $c = 37°$, $d = 65°$
2. $A = 50°$, $B = 70°$, $C = 70°$
3. $a = 60°$, $b = 45°$, $c = 105°$, $d = 37.5°$,
   $e = 37.5°$
4. $A = 50°$, $B = 115°$
5. 60°; as each angle is 60°

6. (i) F   (ii) T   (iii) F
   (iv) F   (v) F

For the problem solver... (15)

1.
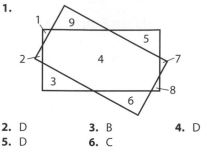

2. D   **3.** B   **4.** D
5. D   **6.** C

Chapter 16: Presenting Data

Exercise 16.1

1. (i) a football match   (ii) 30
   (iii) 6   (iv) 13   (v) 2   (vi) 4
2. (ii) 25   (iii) bus   (iv) 32%
4. (ii) 28   (iii) 11   (iv) 25%

Exercise 16.2

1. (i) 5   (ii) white   (iii) 30
   (iv) $\frac{1}{6}$ (v) 20%
2. (i) Dog   (ii) 36   (iii) 25%
   (iv) fish   (v) $\frac{1}{12}$
3. (i) 16   (ii) 100   (iii) $\frac{2}{25}$
   (iv) 24%   (v) 12
4. (i) 32, 48, 48, 36   (ii) 2nd year
   (iii) 4th year   (v) 1st and 3rd year
   (v) 1st year   (vi) $\frac{3}{8}$
5. (i) 7   (ii) History
   (iii) 3   (iv) 20%
   (v) French and English
7. (i) 60   (ii) 18   (iii) $\frac{1}{5}$
   (iv) 40%   (v) 2
8. (i) 5   (ii) 6   (iii) 20%   (iv) 2
9. (i) Swimming   (ii) 74
10. Can't tell
11. (i) Week B   (ii) Week A   (iii) Week C

Exercise 16.3

1. (i) 20   (ii) 93   (iii) 5
   (iv) 4   (v) 3
2. (i) 7   (ii) 7   (iii) $\frac{1}{5}$
   (iv) 4   (v) 24